Name ______________________

1 NUMBERS 0 THR

How many?

one  1 2	two  1 2
 1 2	 1 2
 1 2	 1 2
 1 2	 1 2

Write the numbers.

1 1 1

2

1

2

Name ______________________________

three	four
(3) 4	3 (4)

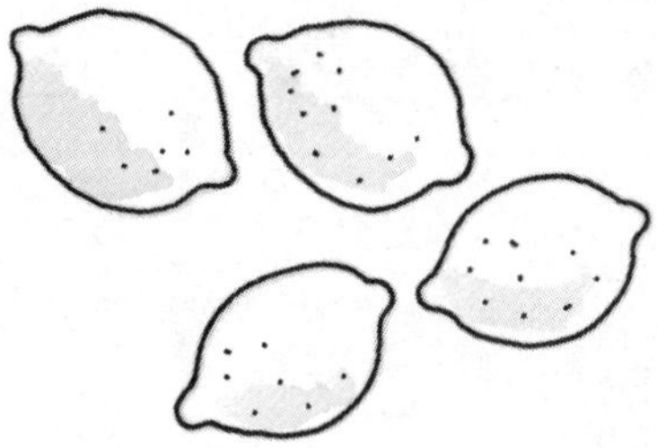

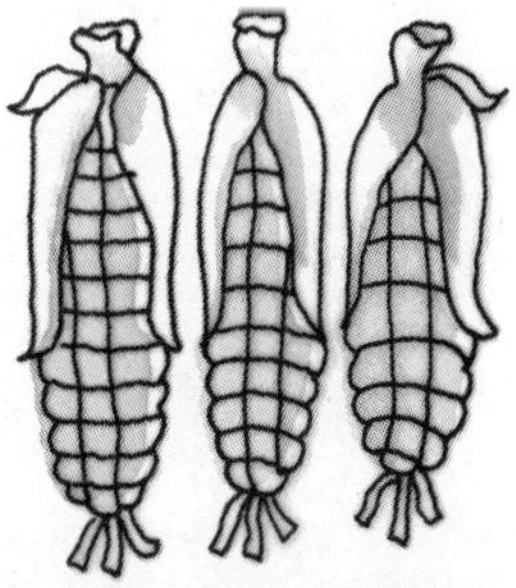

How many?

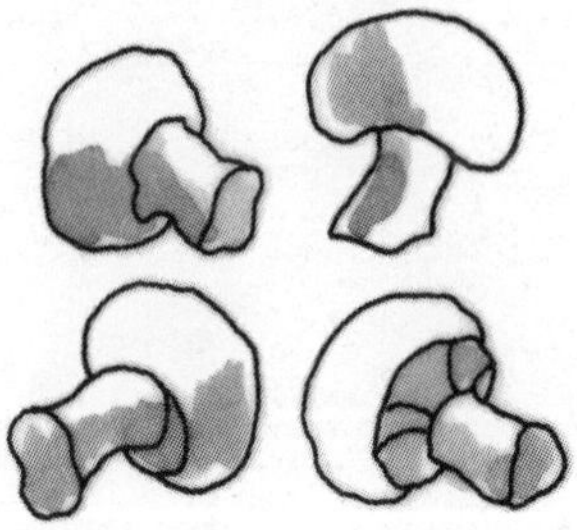

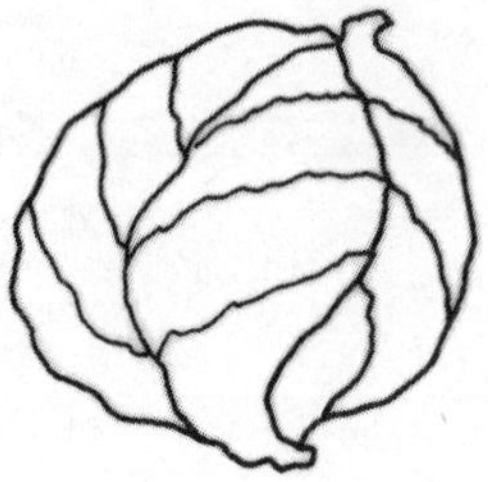

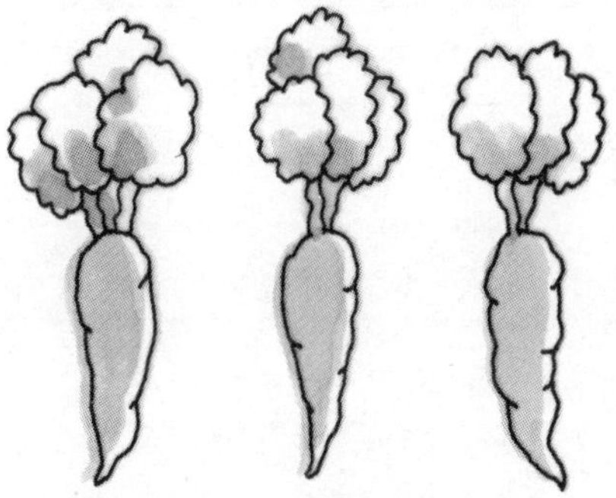

3 4	3 4
3 4	1 2 3
3 4	3 4
1 2 3	2 3 4

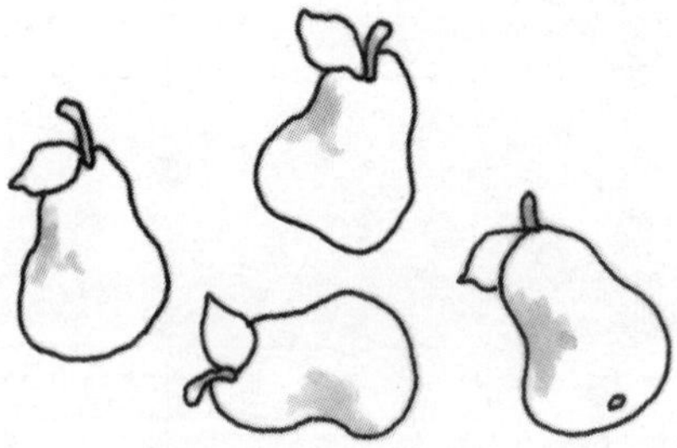

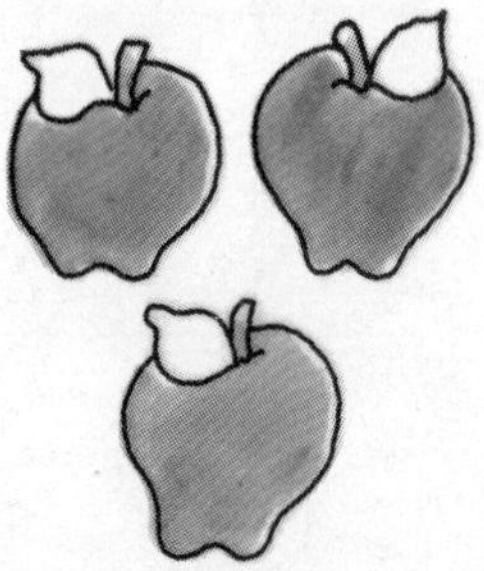

Write the numbers.

3 3 3

4 4 4

3

4

Name ____________________

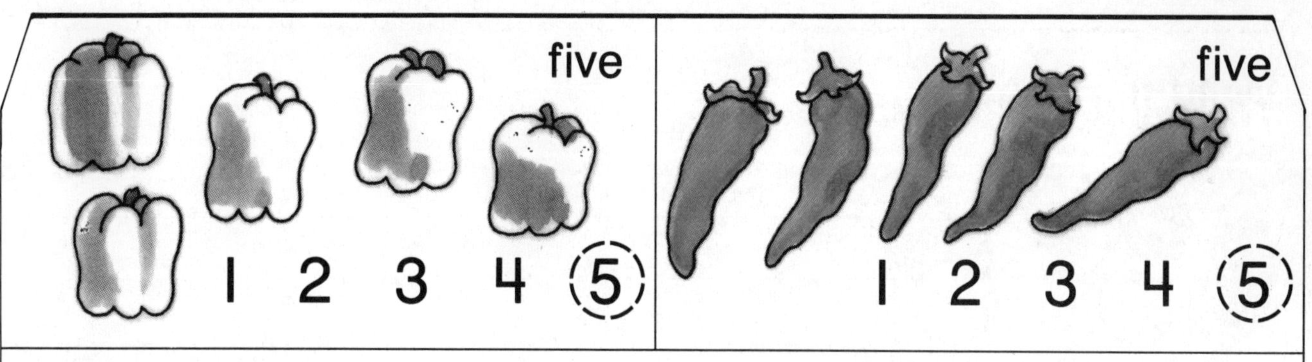

How many?

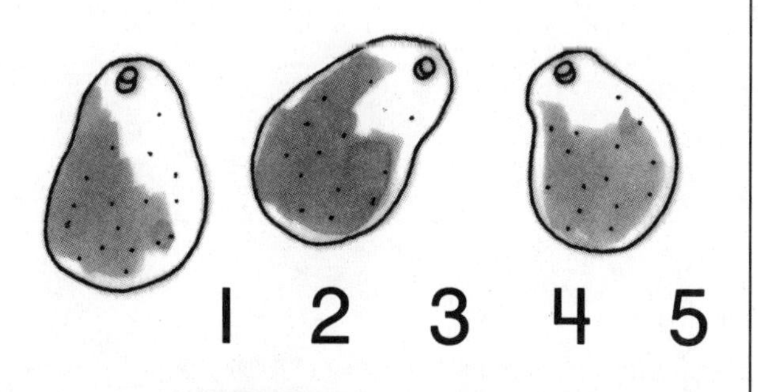

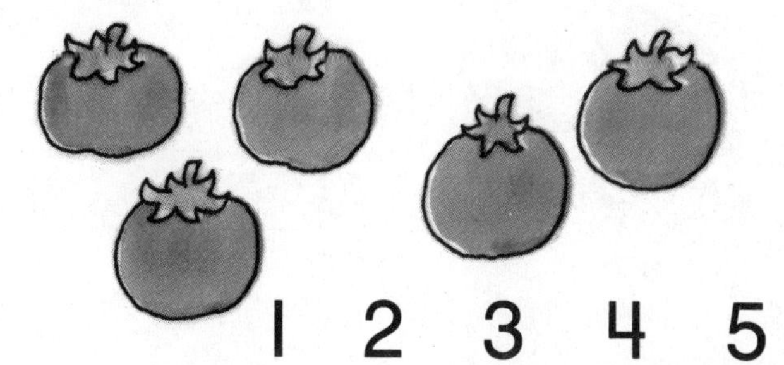

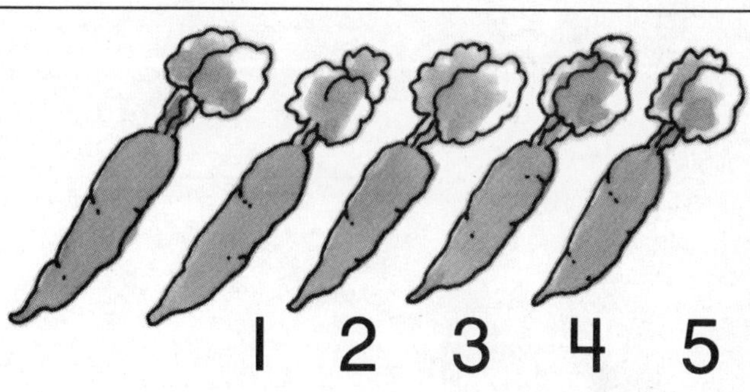

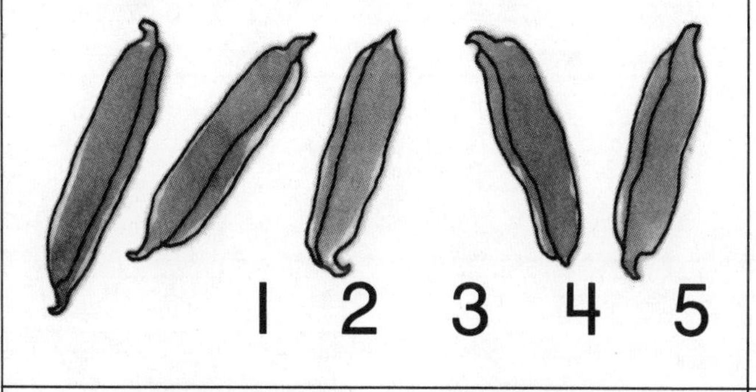

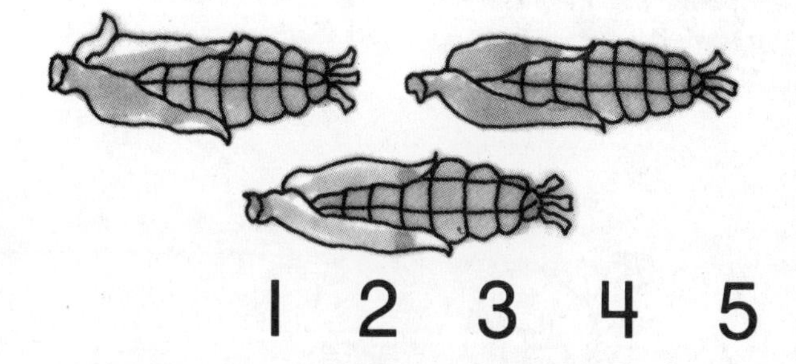

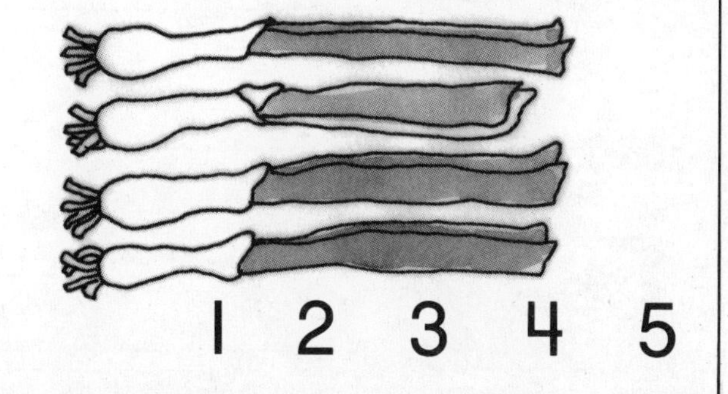

Write the numbers.

5

3

5

4

2

5

Name ______________________________

zero	one	two
(0) 1 2 3	0 (1) 2 3	0 1 (2) 3

How many?

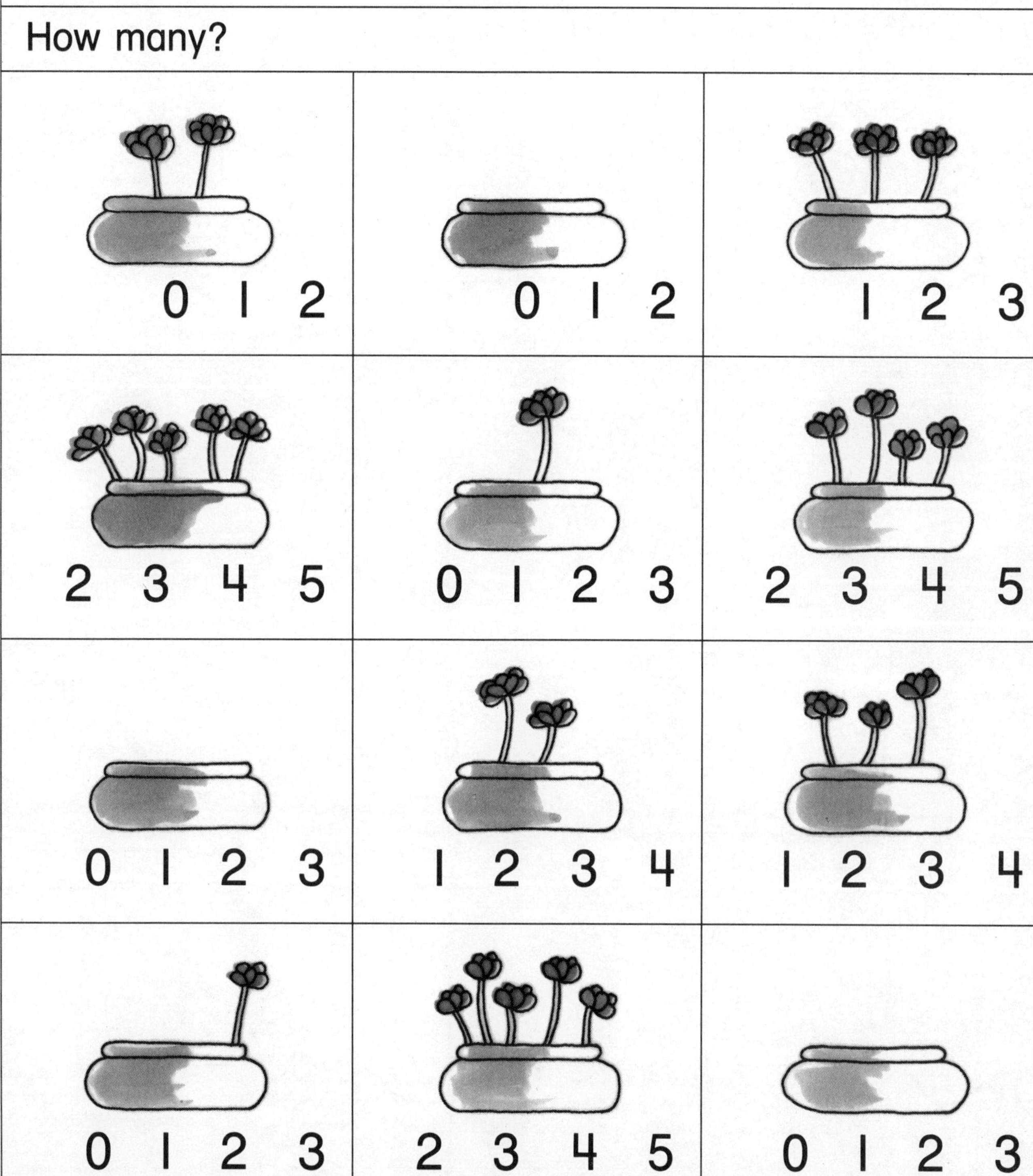

Write the numbers.

3

Name ___

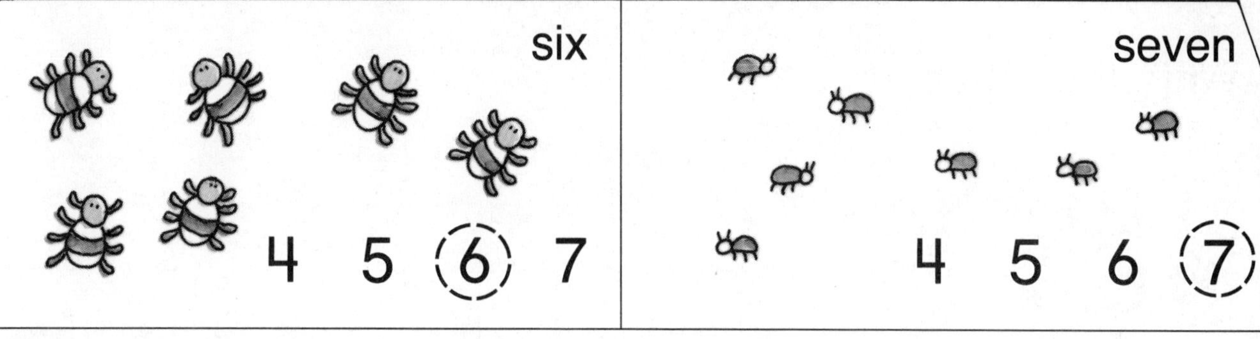

How many?

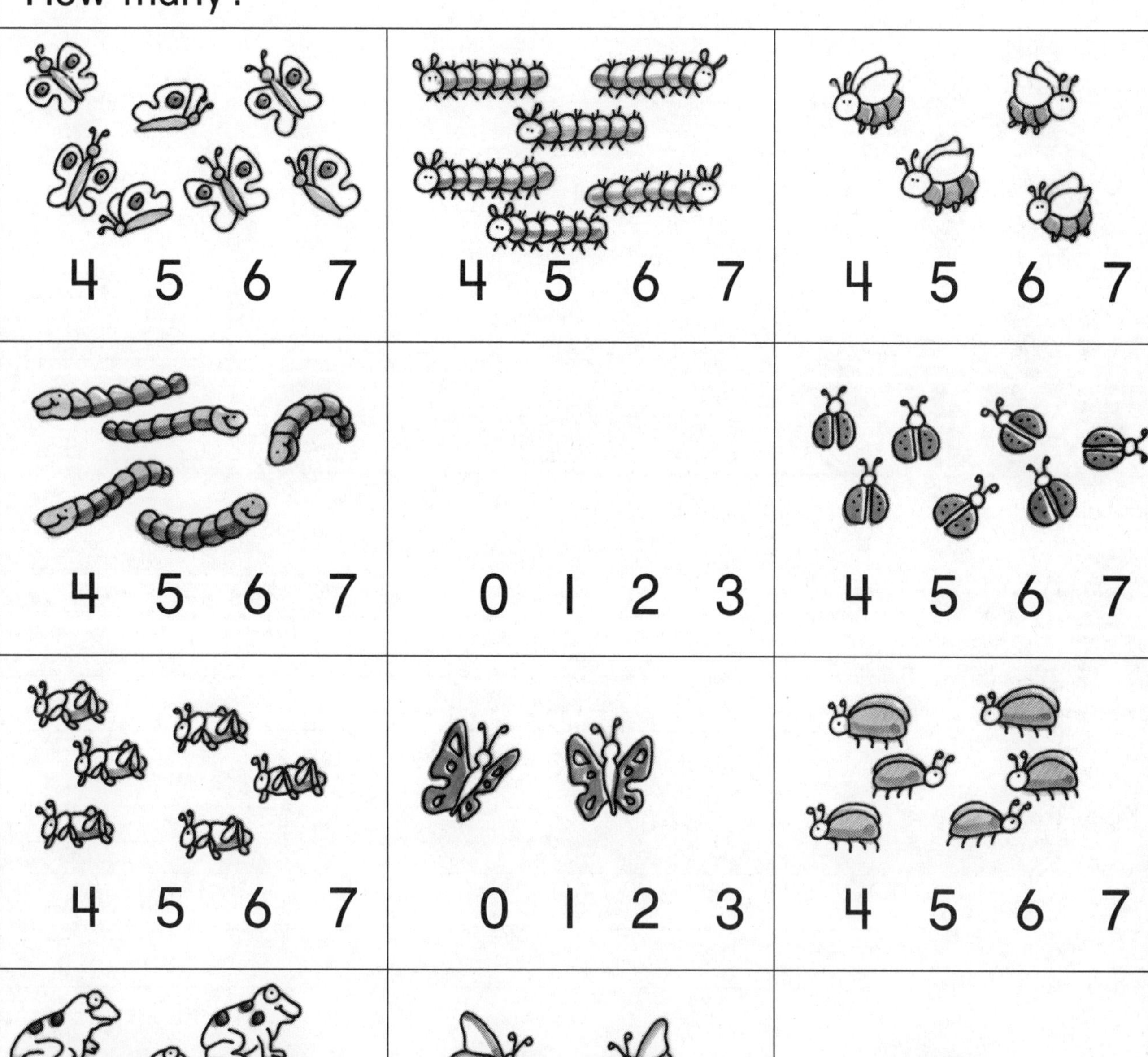

Write the numbers.

6

7

6

7

Name ____________________

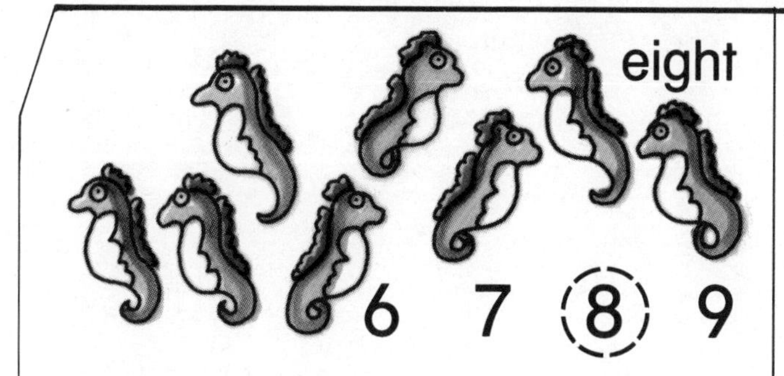

How many?

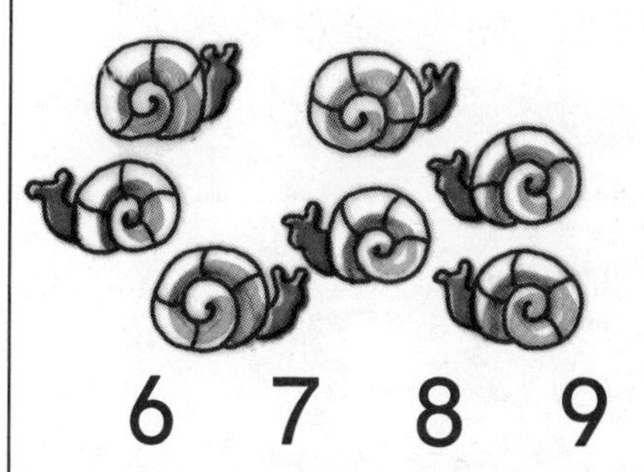

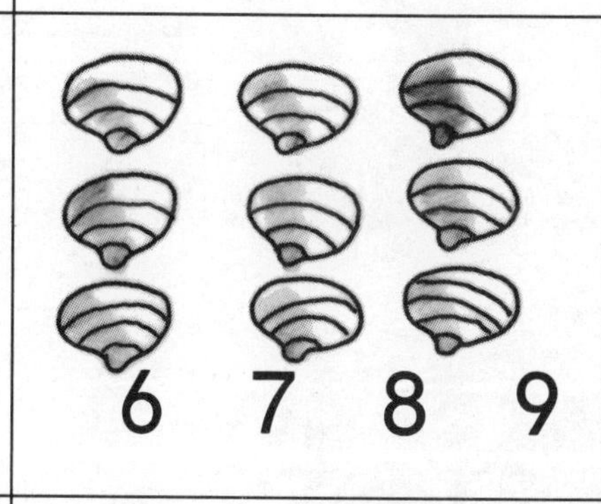

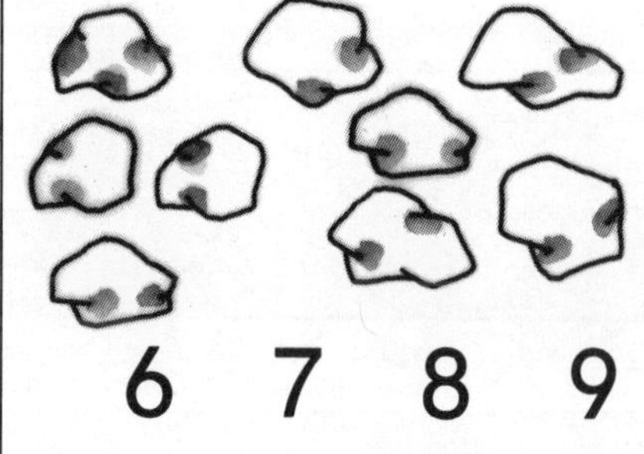

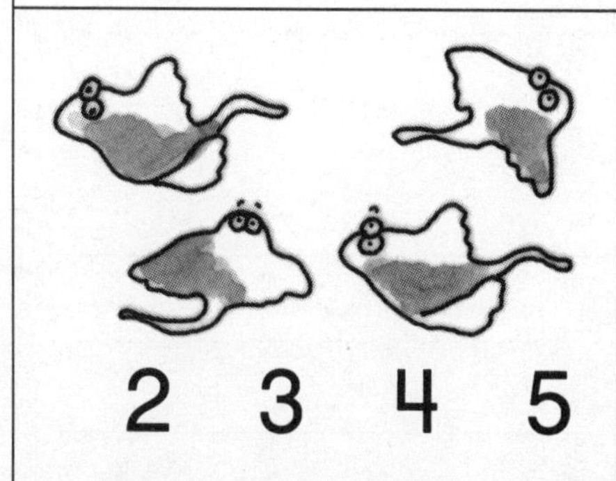

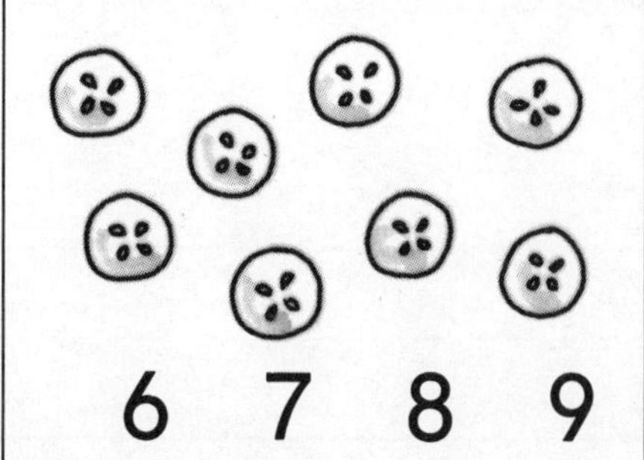

Write the numbers.

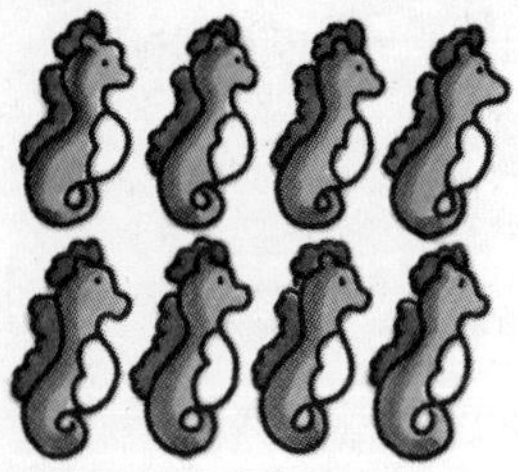

8

9

6

Name ______________________________

How many in all?

1 2 (3) 4	4 5 6 7	4 5 6 7
0 1 2 3	6 7 8 9	0 1 2 3
3 4 5 6	0 1 2 3	6 7 8 9
6 7 8 9	3 4 5 6	0 1 2 3
6 7 8 9	6 7 8 9	6 7 8 9

Write the number in each set.

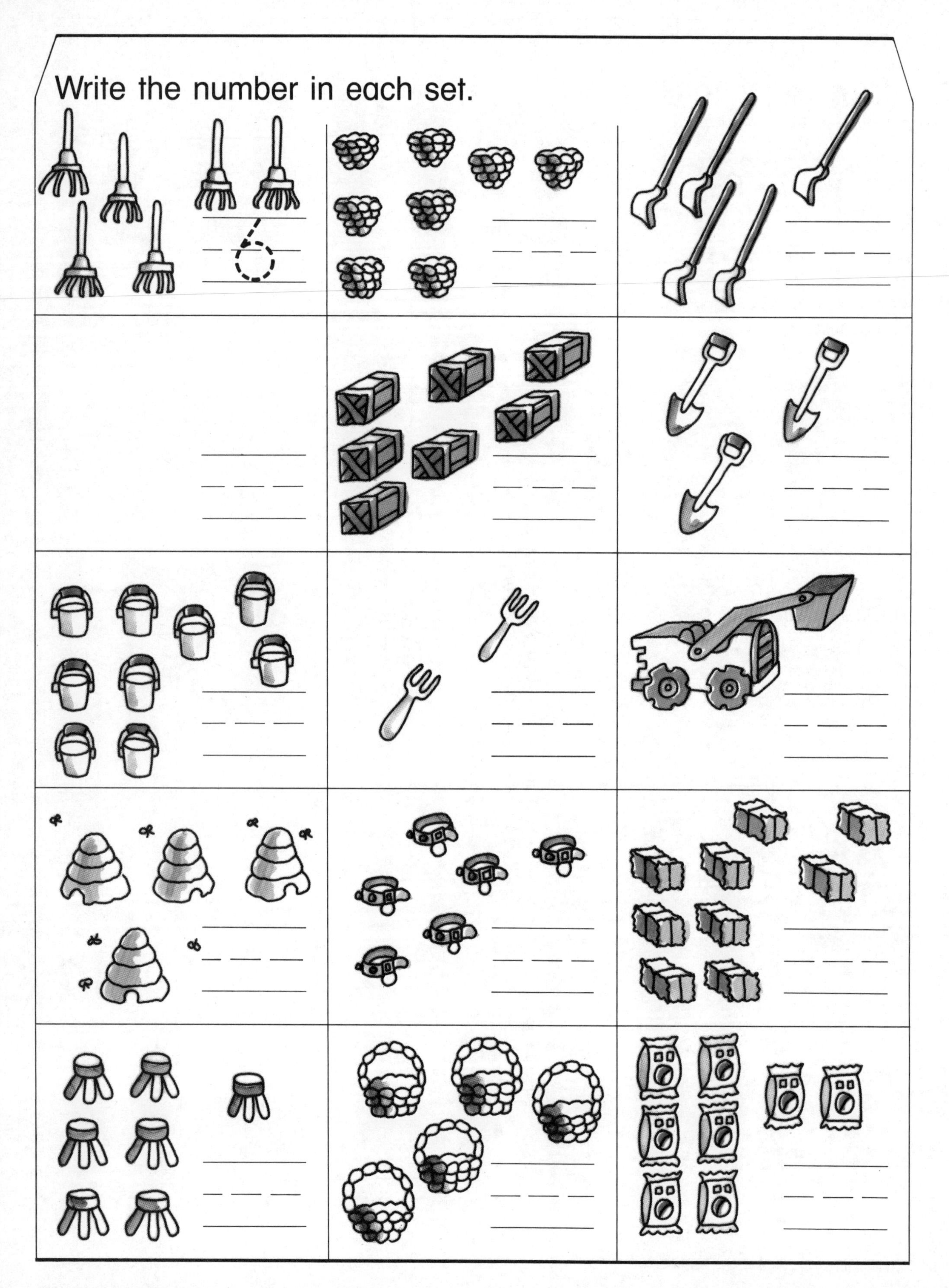

Name ____________________

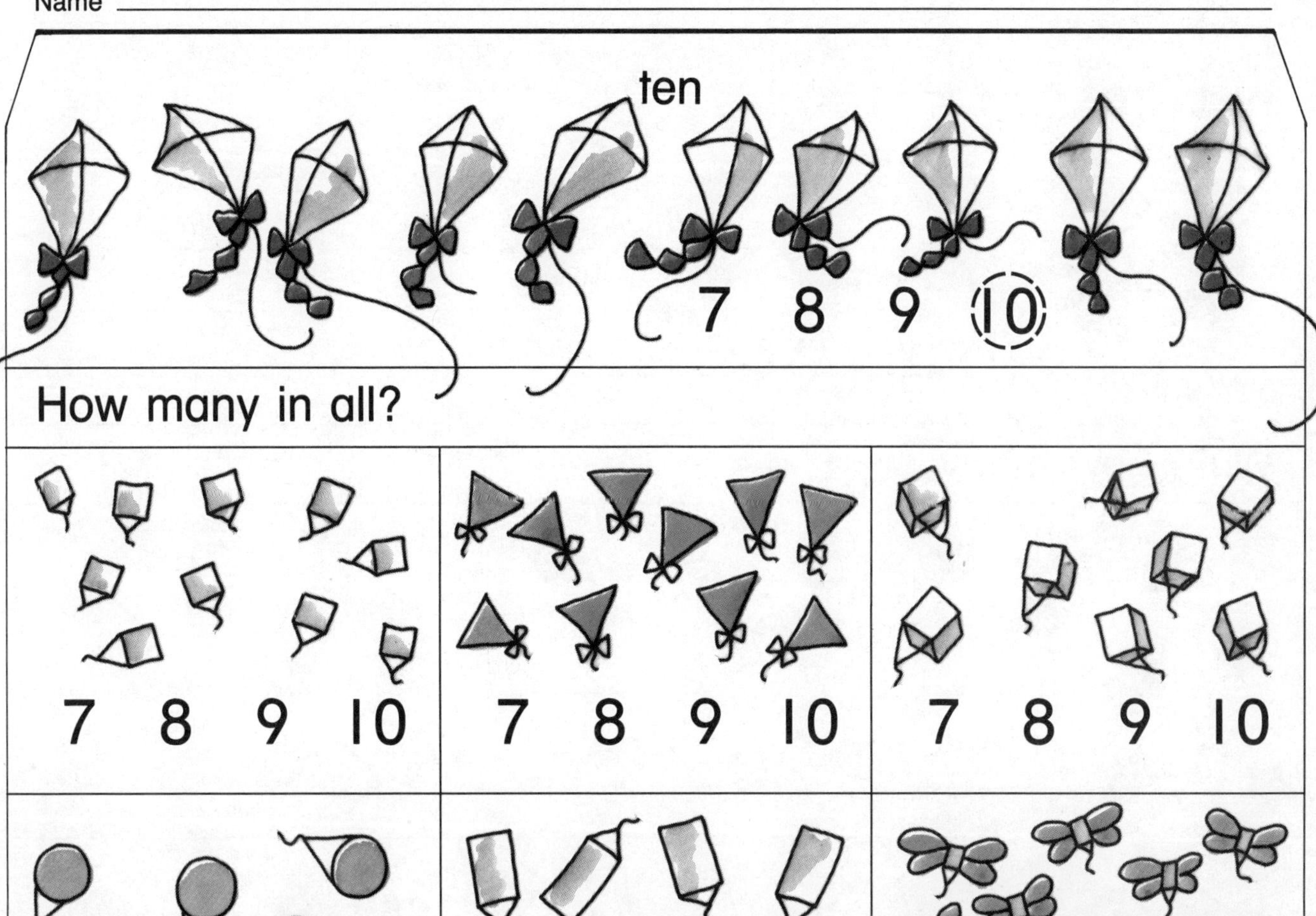

How many in all?

7 8 9 10 | 7 8 9 10 | 7 8 9 10

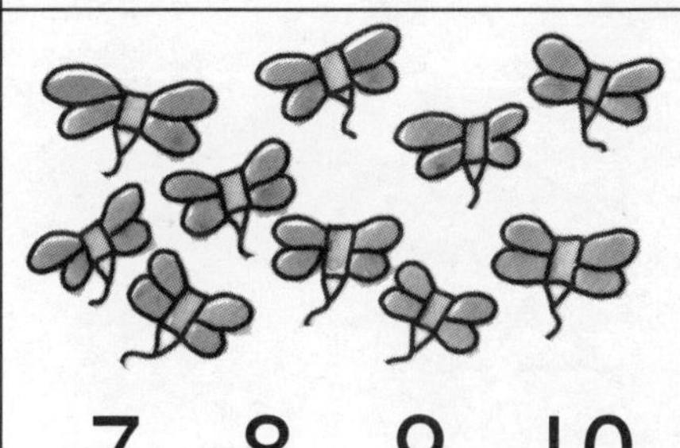

5 6 7 8 | 7 8 9 10 | 7 8 9 10

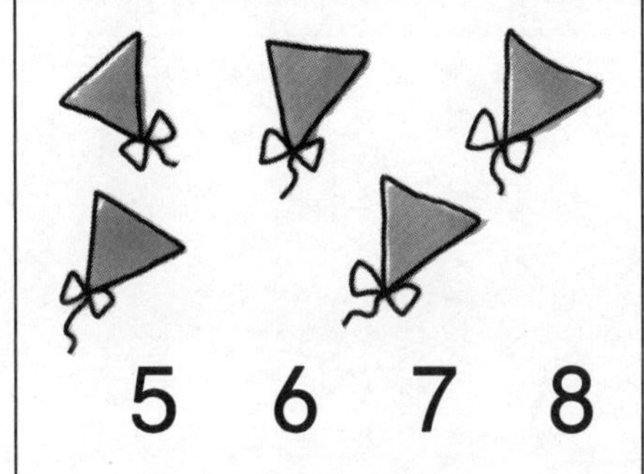

7 8 9 10 | 5 6 7 8 | 7 8 9 10

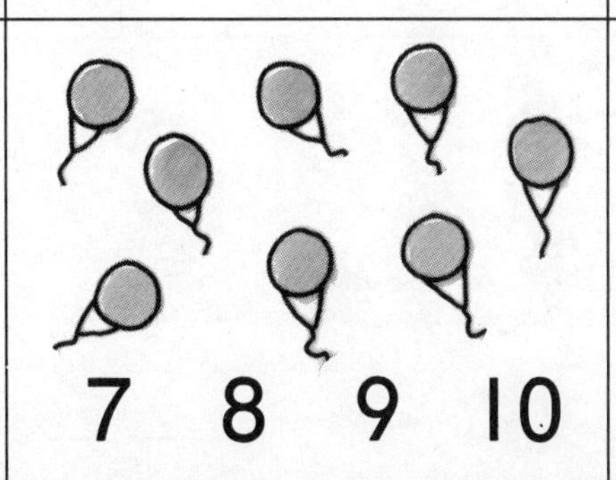

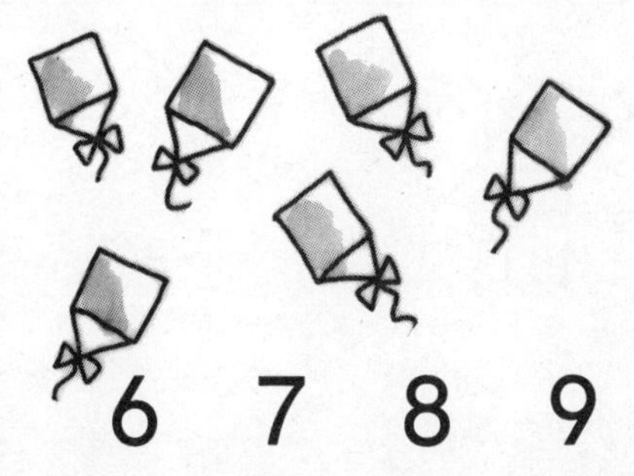

7 8 9 10 | 7 8 9 10 | 6 7 8 9

Write 10.

10 10

Write how many.

Name ______________________

Color the number of blocks.

6
six

7
seven

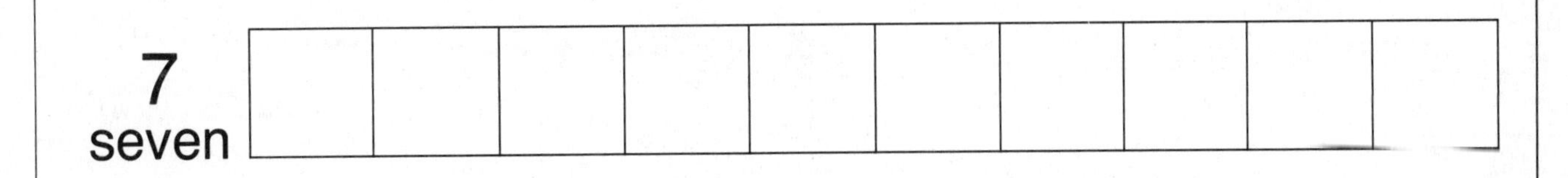

8
eight

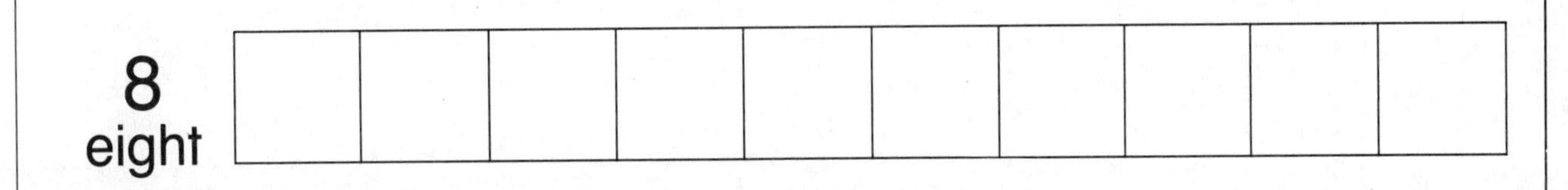

9
nine

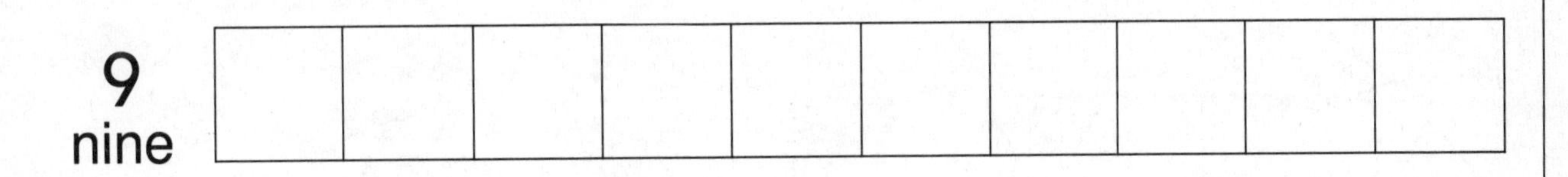

10
ten

Write the missing numbers.

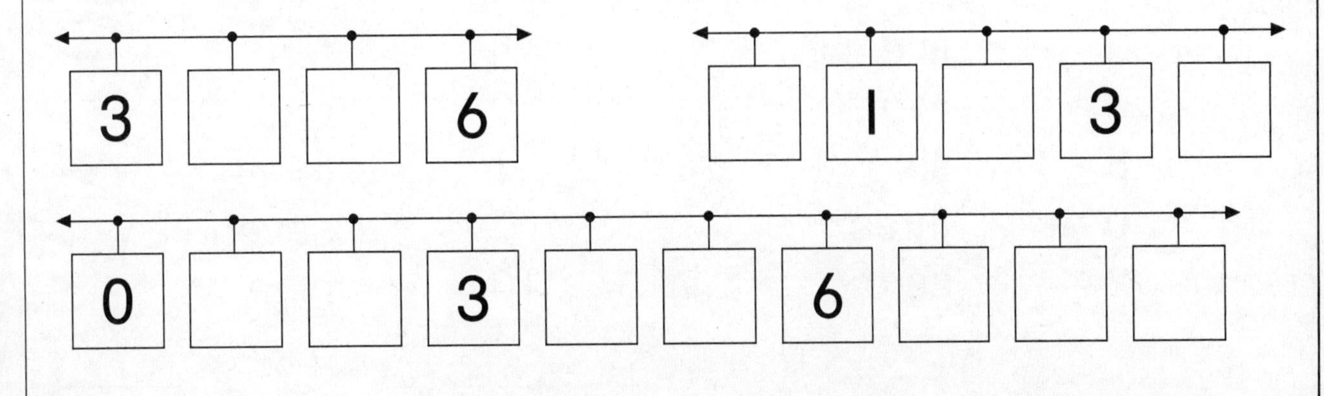

Write the missing numbers.

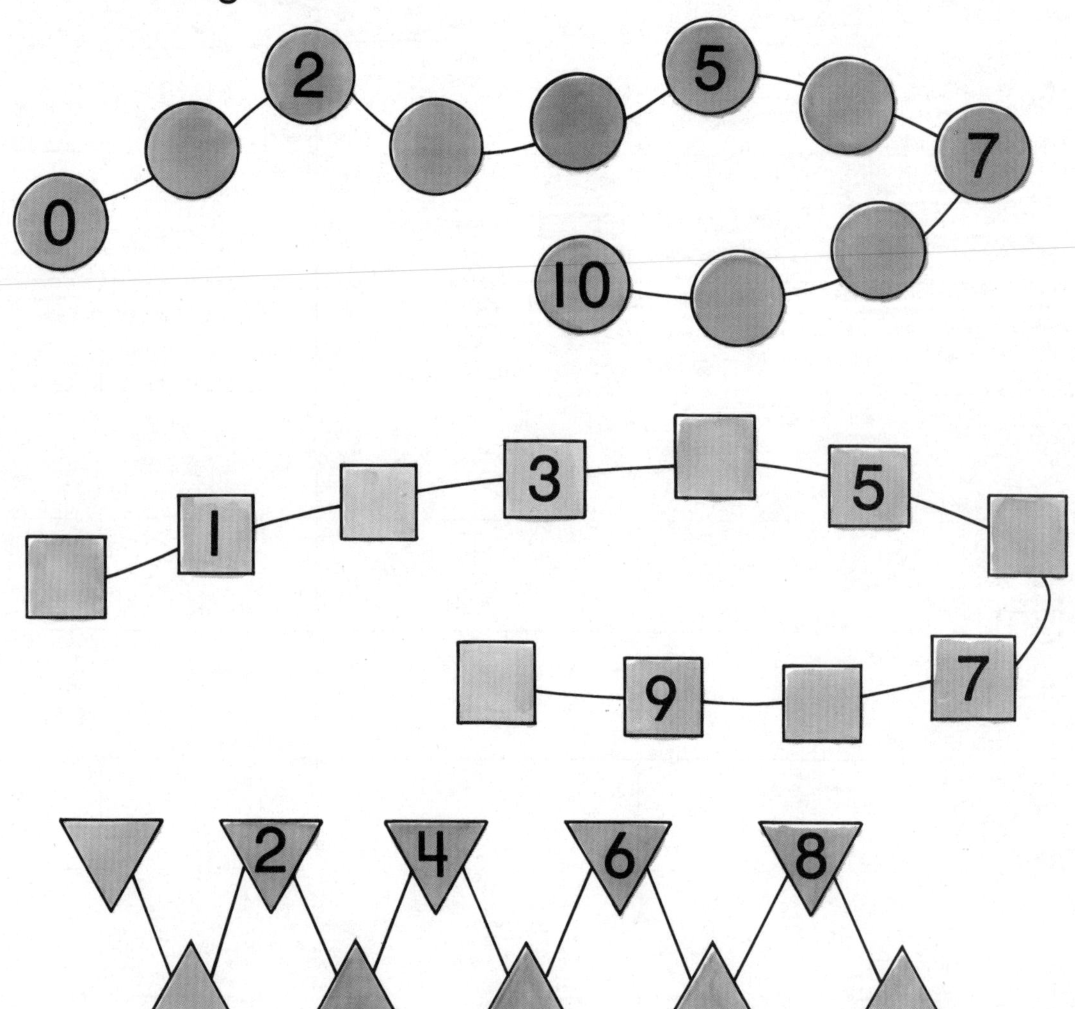

FIELD TRIP

Match each number with its name.

3	five	4	ten
6	two	9	one
5	six	1	four
0	three	7	seven
2	zero	10	nine

Name ____________________

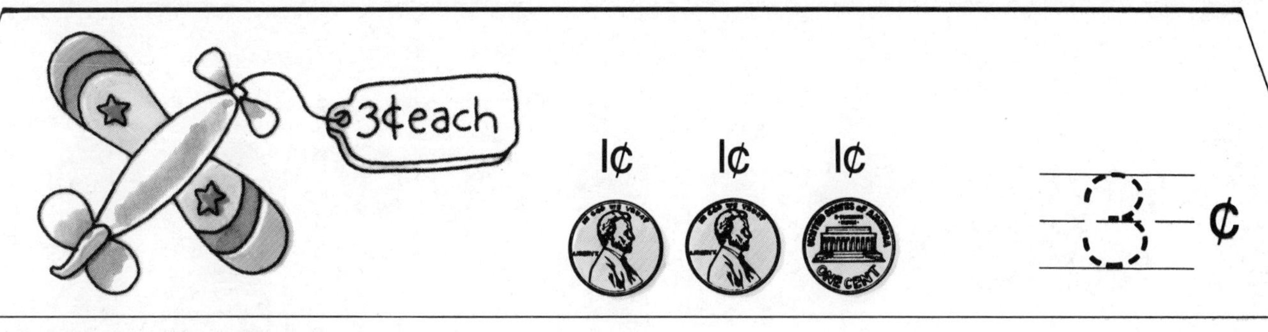

Count the pennies.

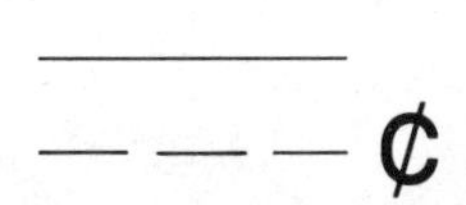

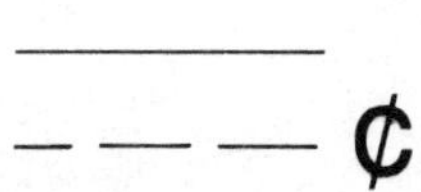

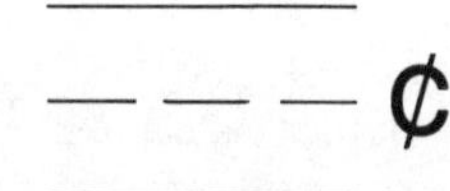

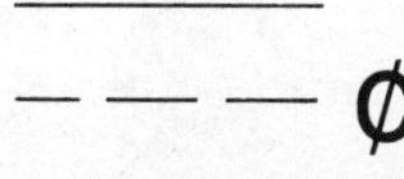

___ ¢

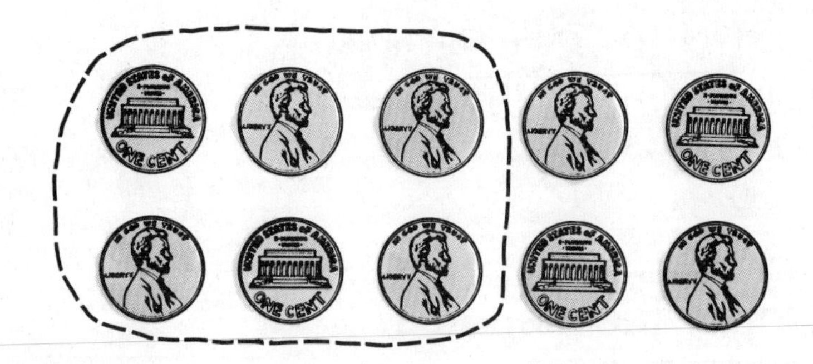

Circle the pennies you need.

Name ______________________

How many in each set?
Circle the number that is greater.

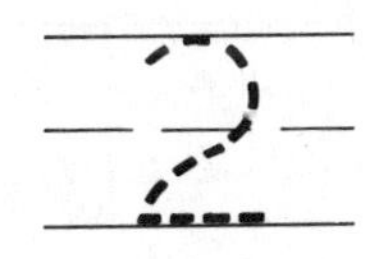
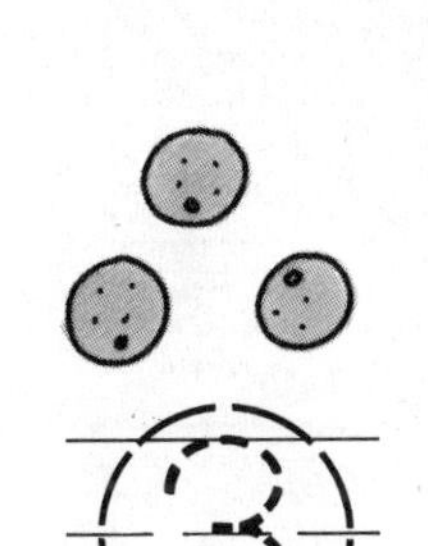

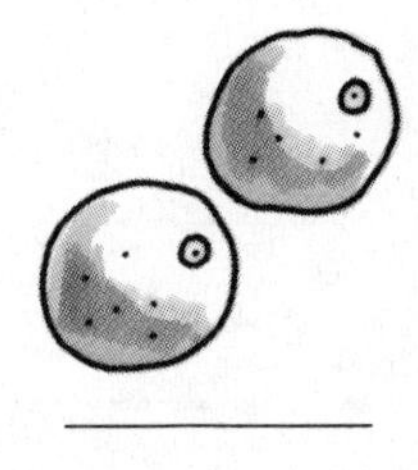

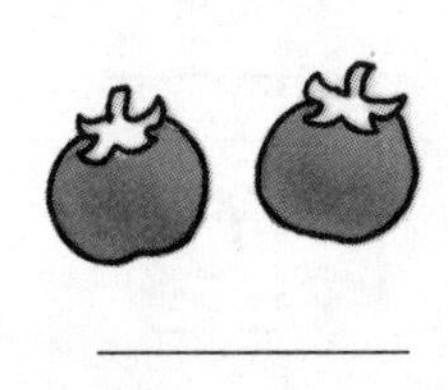

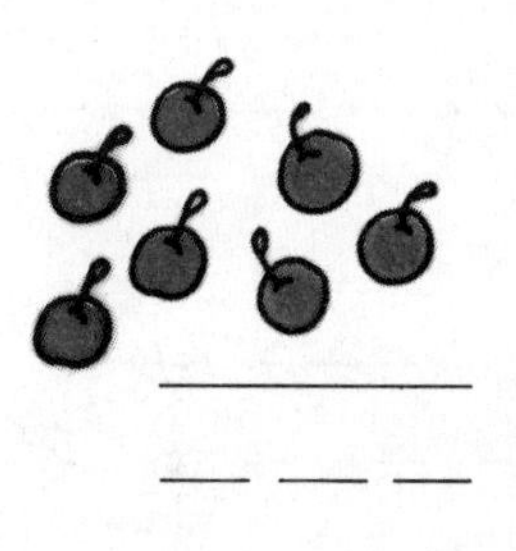

How many in each set?
Circle the number that is less.

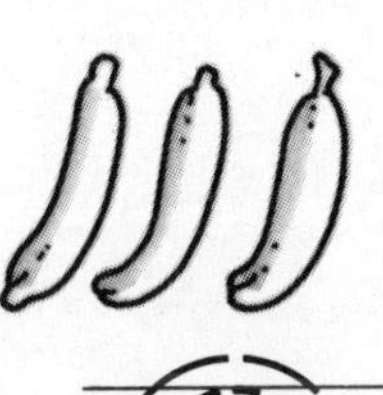
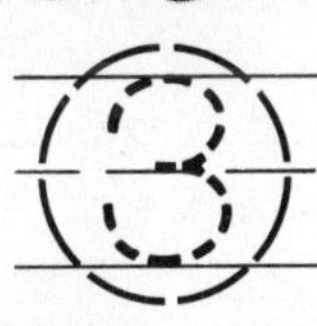
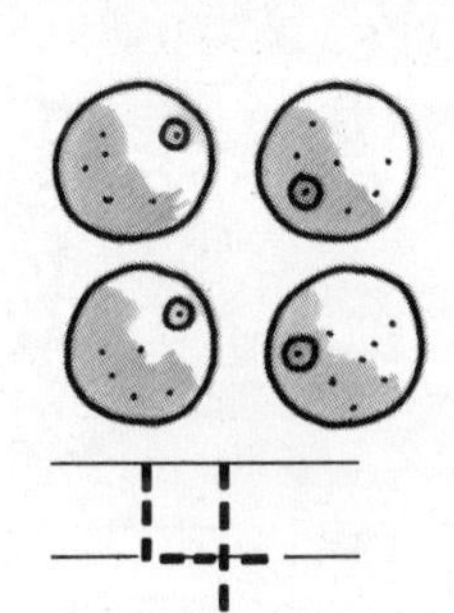

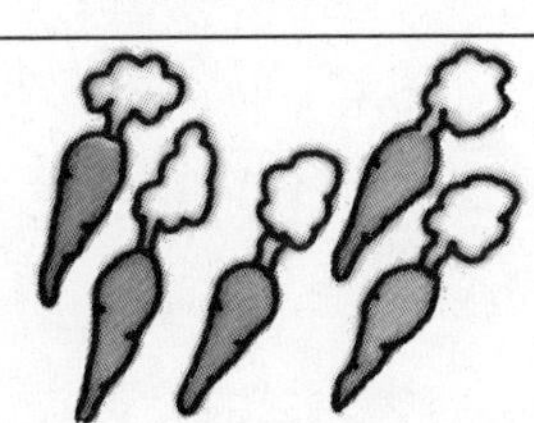

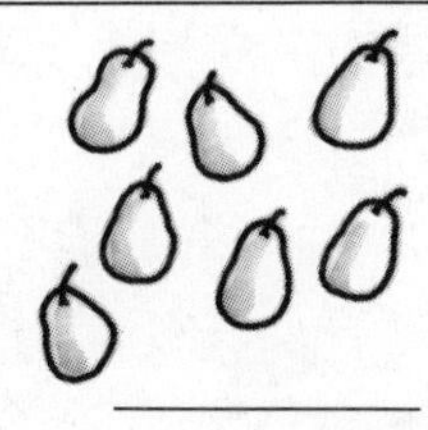

Write the missing numbers.

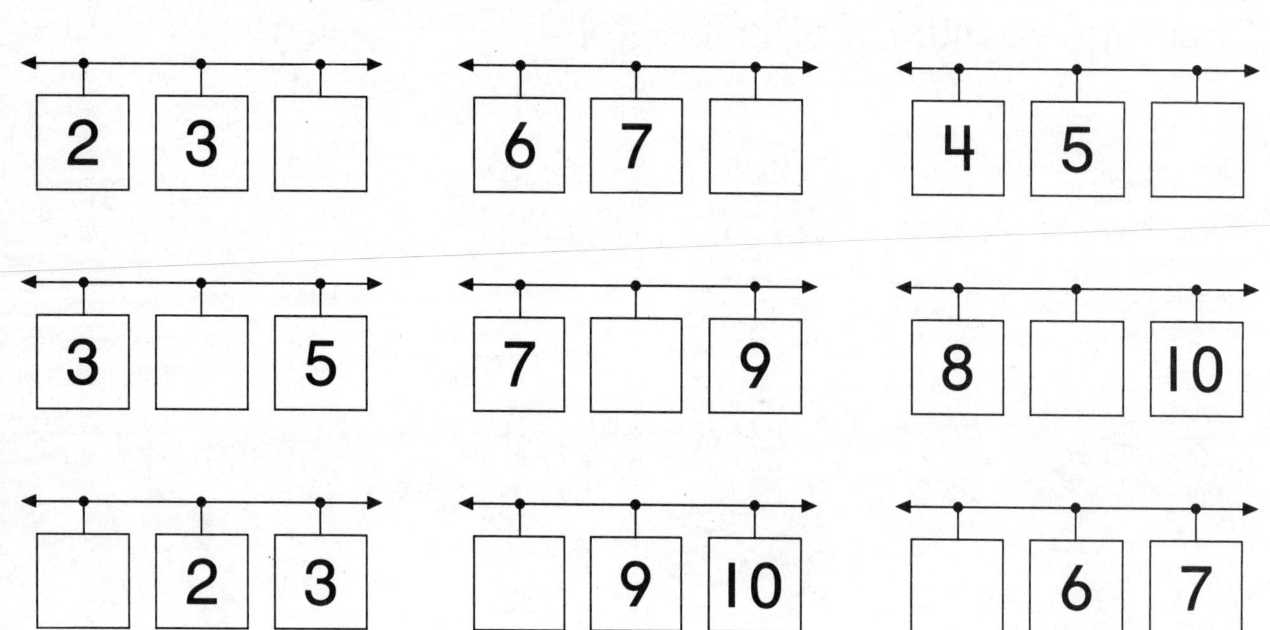

Solve.

Who has more?

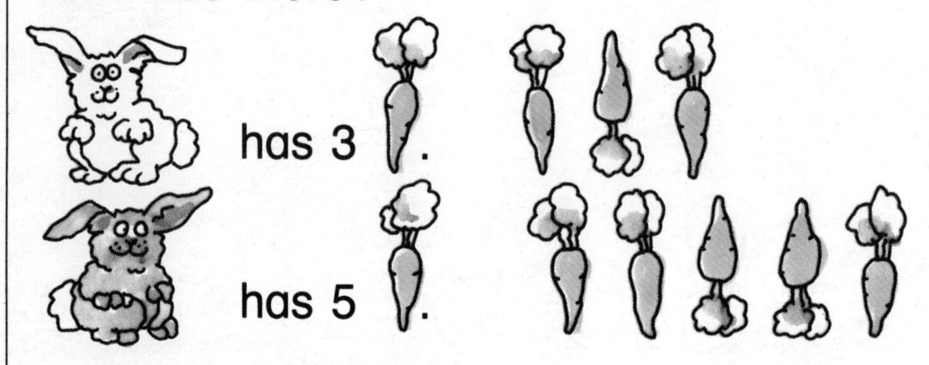

Which dog has more?

has 6 .

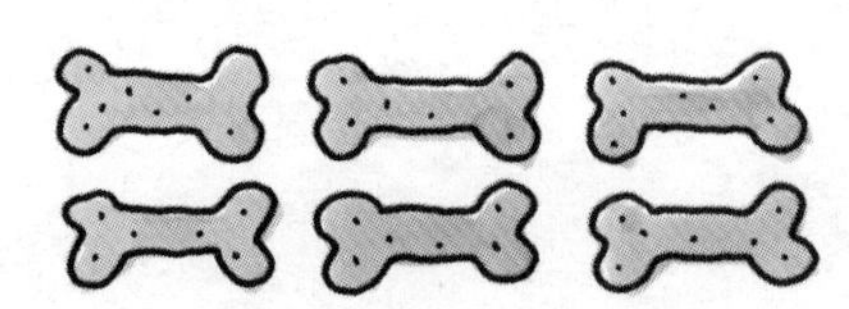

has 3 .

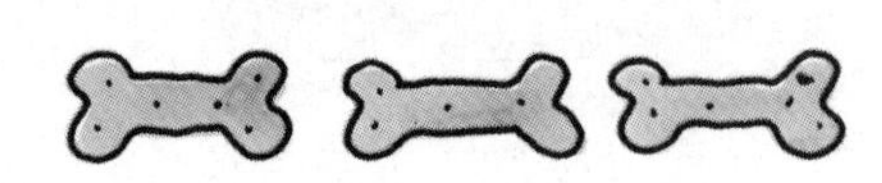

Name ______________________________

CHAPTER CHECKUP

Match the stars to their number.

2

6

4

9

5

10

7

8

Write the number in each set.

Name ______________________________

ADDITION, SUMS THROUGH 10

How many in all?

1 fish

Put in
2 more.

3
in all

3 fish

Put in
1 more.

____ in all

2 fish

Put in
2 more.

____ in all

4 fish

Put in
1 more.

____ in all

2 fish

Put in
3 more.

____ in all

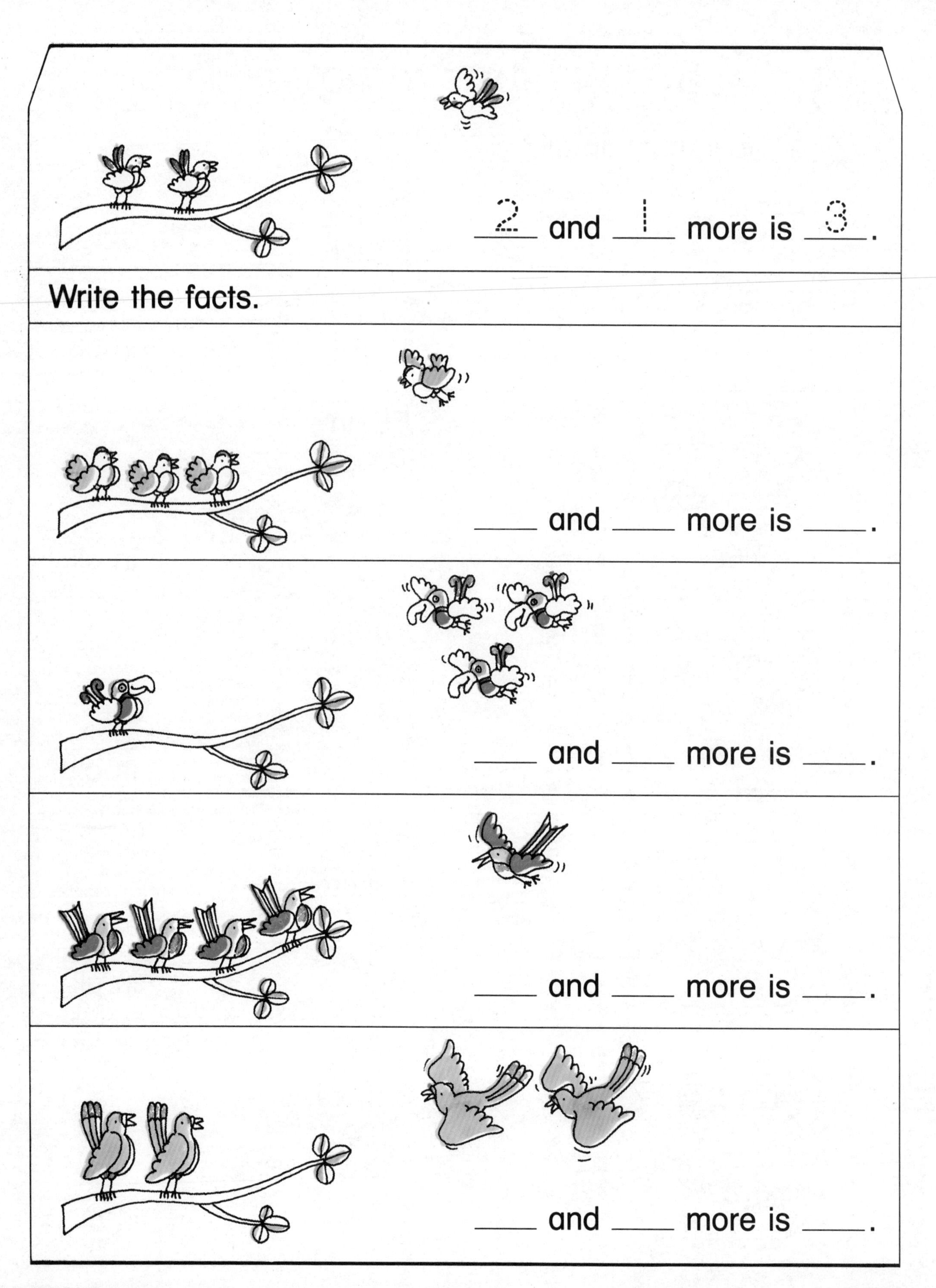

2 and 1 more is 3.

Write the facts.

____ and ____ more is ____.

____ and ____ more is ____.

____ and ____ more is ____.

____ and ____ more is ____.

Name ______________________

2 and 1 more is 3.

$2 + 1 = 3$

How many in all?

$1 + 1 =$ ___

$3 + 1 =$ ___

$2 + 2 =$ ___

$2 + 3 =$ ___

How many in all?

1 + 2 = 3

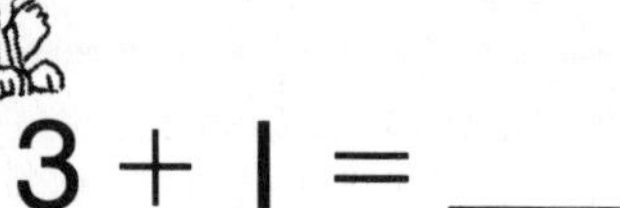

3 + 1 = ___

1 + 1 = ___

2 + 2 = ___

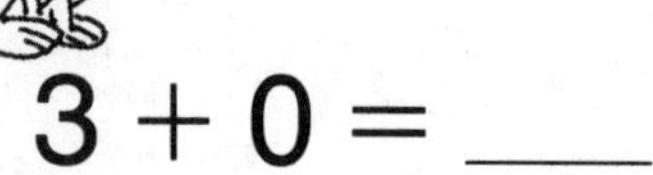

3 + 0 = ___

2 + 3 = ___

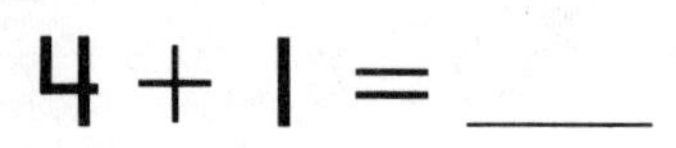

4 + 1 = ___

2 + 1 = ___

1 + 4 = ___

5 + 0 = ___

3 + 2 = ___

0 + 3 = ___

Name ______________________

Complete the facts.

$1 + \underline{0} = 1$

$0 + \underline{1} = 1$

$2 + \underline{0} = 2$

$1 + \underline{1} = 2$

$0 + \underline{2} = 2$

$3 + \underline{0} = 3$

$2 + \underline{\quad} = 3$

$1 + \underline{\quad} = 3$

$0 + \underline{\quad} = 3$

$4 + \underline{0} = 4$

$3 + \underline{\quad} = 4$

$2 + \underline{\quad} = 4$

$1 + \underline{\quad} = 4$

$0 + \underline{\quad} = 4$

Add.

$1 + 0 = \underline{\quad}$ $3 + 1 = \underline{\quad}$ $0 + 2 = \underline{\quad}$

$2 + 1 = \underline{\quad}$ $1 + 1 = \underline{\quad}$ $2 + 2 = \underline{\quad}$

$1 + 3 = \underline{\quad}$ $4 + 0 = \underline{\quad}$ $1 + 2 = \underline{\quad}$

Complete the facts.

5 + 0 = 5   2 + ___ = 5

4 + ___ = 5   1 + ___ = 5

3 + ___ = 5   0 + ___ = 5

Add.

1 + 1 = ___   0 + 0 = ___   4 + 1 = ___

2 + 1 = ___   2 + 2 = ___   1 + 2 = ___

5 + 0 = ___   3 + 2 = ___   2 + 3 = ___

1 + 4 = ___   1 + 3 = ___   3 + 1 = ___

FIELD TRIP

Write the missing number.

1 + 1 = 2   3 + ___ = 5

2 + ___ = 3   2 + ___ = 4

0 + ___ = 4   1 + ___ = 5

Name ____________________

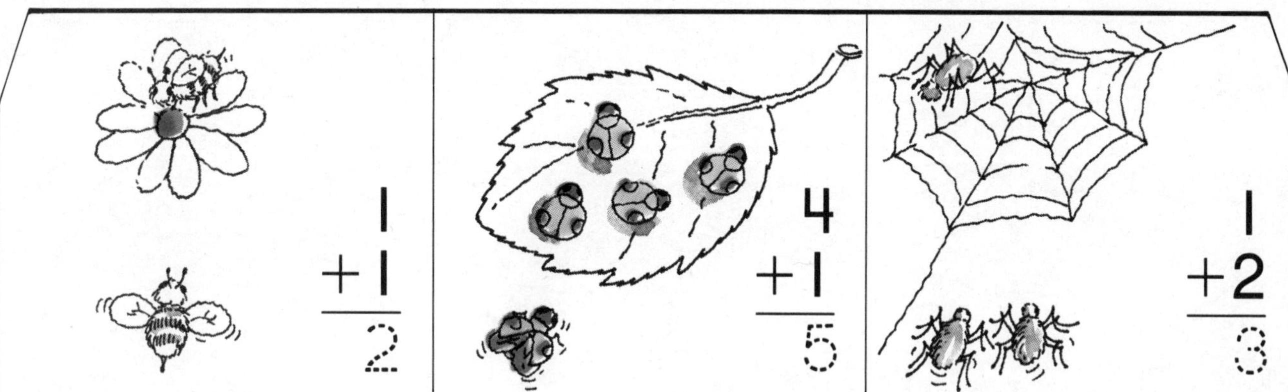

Add.

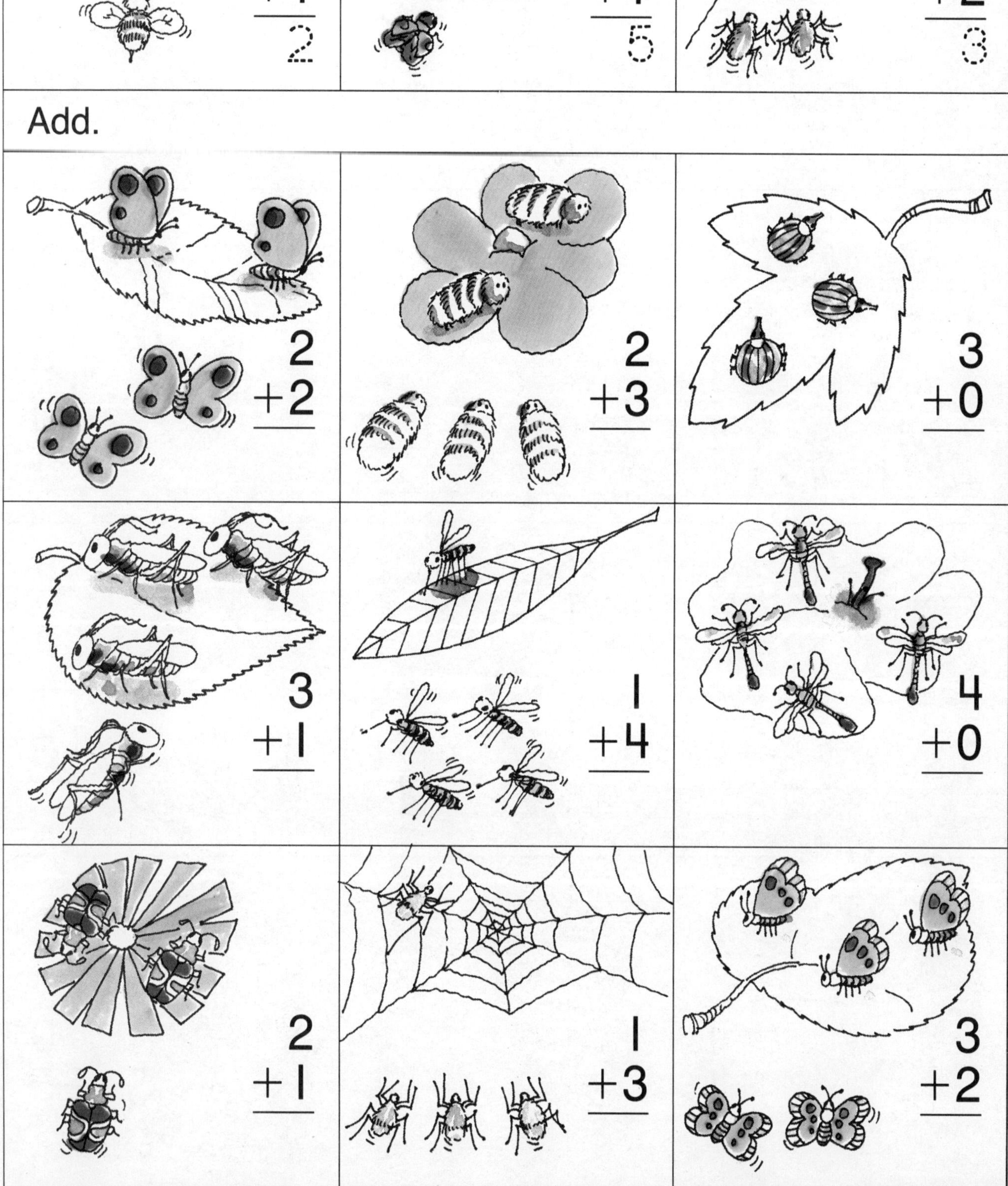

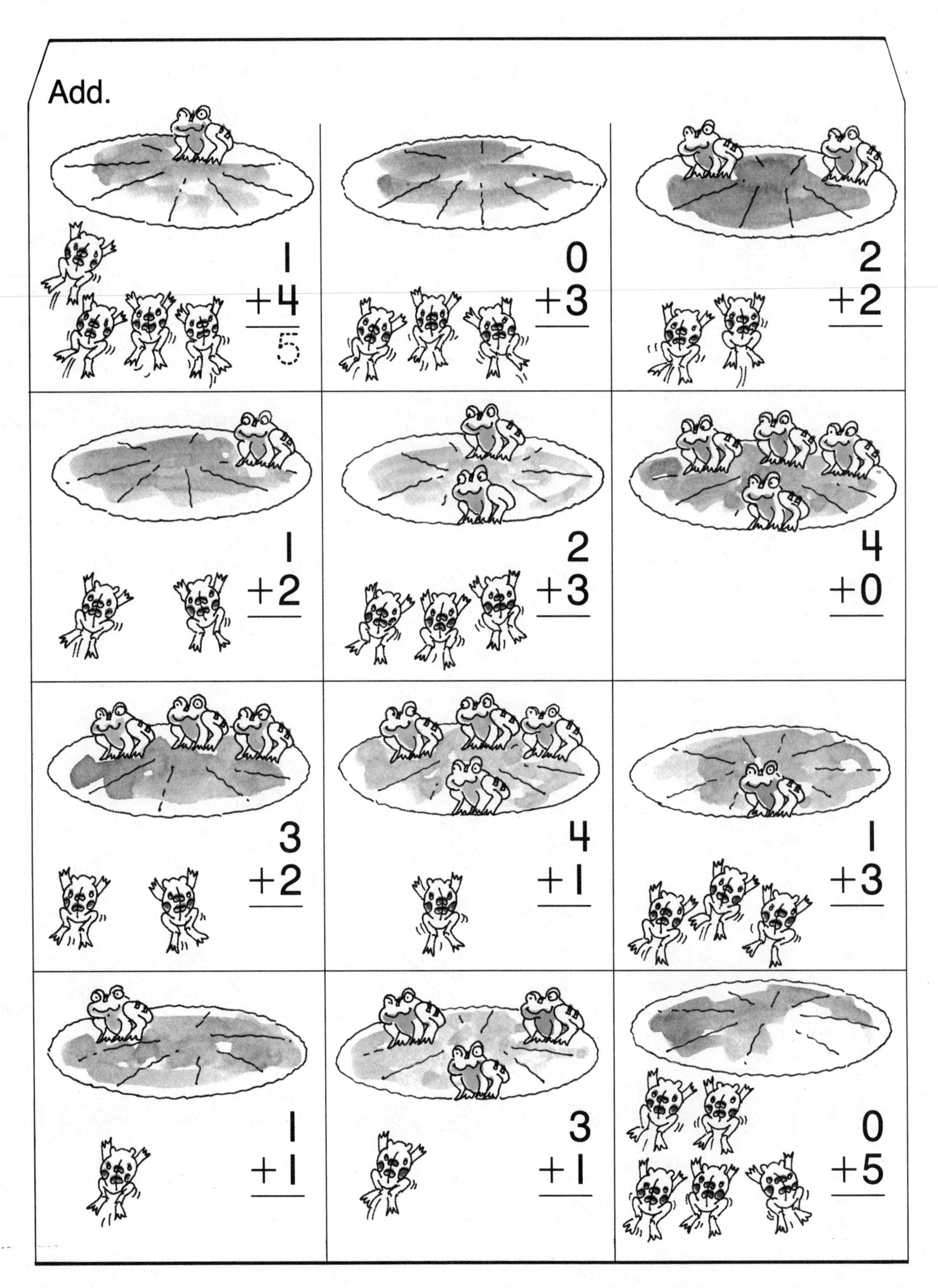
Add.
1
+4
5
0
+3
2
+2
1
+2
2
+3
4
+0
3
+2
4
+1
1
+3
1
+1
3
+1
0
+5

Name ______________________________

Complete the facts.

$3 + \underline{0} = 3$ $\quad$ $4 + \underline{0} = 4$ $\quad$ $5 + \underline{0} = 5$

$2 + \_\_\_ = 3$ $\quad$ $3 + \_\_\_ = 4$ $\quad$ $4 + \_\_\_ = 5$

$1 + \_\_\_ = 3$ $\quad$ $2 + \_\_\_ = 4$ $\quad$ $3 + \_\_\_ = 5$

$0 + \_\_\_ = 3$ $\quad$ $1 + \_\_\_ = 4$ $\quad$ $2 + \_\_\_ = 5$

$0 + \_\_\_ = 4$ $\quad$ $1 + \_\_\_ = 5$

$0 + \_\_\_ = 5$

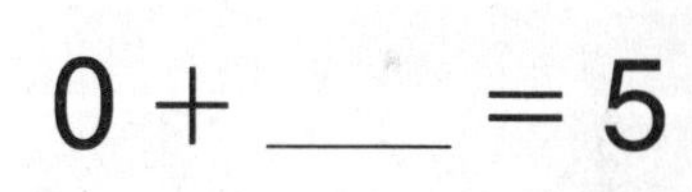

Add.

$2 + 2 = \_\_\_$ $\quad$ $3 + 2 = \_\_\_$ $\quad$ $1 + 1 = \_\_\_$

$1 + 4 = \_\_\_$ $\quad$ $0 + 4 = \_\_\_$ $\quad$ $1 + 2 = \_\_\_$

$5 + 0 = \_\_\_$ $\quad$ $4 + 1 = \_\_\_$ $\quad$ $3 + 1 = \_\_\_$

$2 + 1 = \_\_\_$ $\quad$ $1 + 3 = \_\_\_$ $\quad$ $2 + 3 = \_\_\_$

Add.

$\begin{array}{r} 1 \\ +1 \\ \hline \end{array}$ 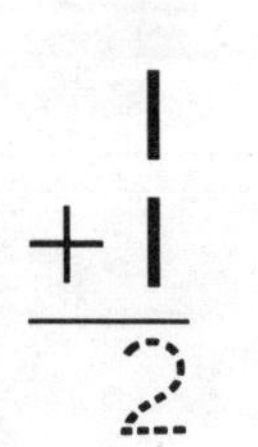	$\begin{array}{r} 2 \\ +3 \\ \hline \end{array}$	$\begin{array}{r} 4 \\ +0 \\ \hline \end{array}$	$\begin{array}{r} 1 \\ +4 \\ \hline \end{array}$	$\begin{array}{r} 2 \\ +0 \\ \hline \end{array}$
$\begin{array}{r} 0 \\ +3 \\ \hline \end{array}$	$\begin{array}{r} 2 \\ +1 \\ \hline \end{array}$	$\begin{array}{r} 1 \\ +0 \\ \hline \end{array}$	$\begin{array}{r} 1 \\ +3 \\ \hline \end{array}$	$\begin{array}{r} 0 \\ +4 \\ \hline \end{array}$
$\begin{array}{r} 4 \\ +1 \\ \hline \end{array}$	$\begin{array}{r} 3 \\ +2 \\ \hline \end{array}$	$\begin{array}{r} 3 \\ +0 \\ \hline \end{array}$	$\begin{array}{r} 1 \\ +2 \\ \hline \end{array}$	$\begin{array}{r} 0 \\ +1 \\ \hline \end{array}$
$\begin{array}{r} 0 \\ +2 \\ \hline \end{array}$	$\begin{array}{r} 5 \\ +0 \\ \hline \end{array}$	$\begin{array}{r} 3 \\ +1 \\ \hline \end{array}$	$\begin{array}{r} 2 \\ +2 \\ \hline \end{array}$	$\begin{array}{r} 0 \\ +5 \\ \hline \end{array}$

Name ______________________________

Complete the facts.

6 + 0 = 6	7 + 0 = 7
5 + ___ = 6	6 + ___ = 7
4 + ___ = 6	5 + ___ = 7
3 + ___ = 6	4 + ___ = 7
2 + ___ = 6	3 + ___ = 7
1 + ___ = 6	2 + ___ = 7
0 + ___ = 6	1 + ___ = 7
	0 + ___ = 7

Add.

2 + 4 = ___	3 + 3 = ___
4 + 3 = ___	6 + 1 = ___
5 + 2 = ___	2 + 4 = ___

Add.

$\begin{array}{r} 5 \\ +0 \\ \hline 5 \end{array}$ $\begin{array}{r} 6 \\ +1 \\ \hline \end{array}$ $\begin{array}{r} 2 \\ +3 \\ \hline \end{array}$ $\begin{array}{r} 0 \\ +6 \\ \hline \end{array}$ $\begin{array}{r} 3 \\ +3 \\ \hline \end{array}$

$\begin{array}{r} 7 \\ +0 \\ \hline \end{array}$ $\begin{array}{r} 5 \\ +1 \\ \hline \end{array}$ $\begin{array}{r} 4 \\ +1 \\ \hline \end{array}$ $\begin{array}{r} 1 \\ +5 \\ \hline \end{array}$ $\begin{array}{r} 1 \\ +4 \\ \hline \end{array}$

$\begin{array}{r} 4 \\ +2 \\ \hline \end{array}$ $\begin{array}{r} 5 \\ +2 \\ \hline \end{array}$ $\begin{array}{r} 4 \\ +3 \\ \hline \end{array}$ $\begin{array}{r} 2 \\ +4 \\ \hline \end{array}$ $\begin{array}{r} 1 \\ +6 \\ \hline \end{array}$

$\begin{array}{r} 3 \\ +2 \\ \hline \end{array}$ $\begin{array}{r} 2 \\ +5 \\ \hline \end{array}$ $\begin{array}{r} 0 \\ +5 \\ \hline \end{array}$ $\begin{array}{r} 3 \\ +4 \\ \hline \end{array}$ $\begin{array}{r} 0 \\ +7 \\ \hline \end{array}$

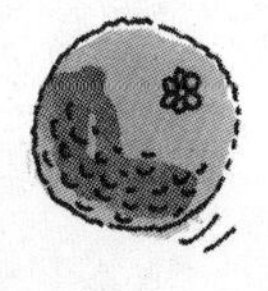

 Adding vertically, sums 5 through 7

Name ______________________________

Complete the facts.

8 + 0 = 8	9 + 0 = 9
7 + ___ = 8	8 + ___ = 9
6 + ___ = 8	7 + ___ = 9
5 + ___ = 8	6 + ___ = 9
4 + ___ = 8	5 + ___ = 9
3 + ___ = 8	4 + ___ = 9
2 + ___ = 8	3 + ___ = 9
1 + ___ = 8	2 + ___ = 9
0 + ___ = 8	1 + ___ = 9
	0 + ___ = 9

Add.

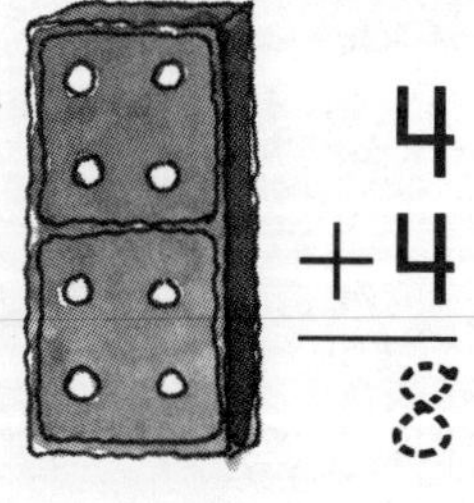

4
+4
8

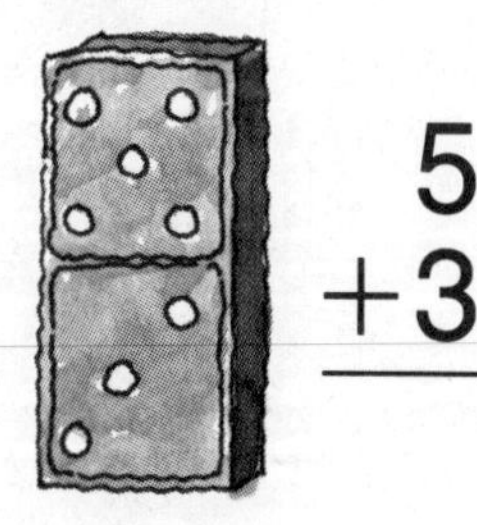

5
+3

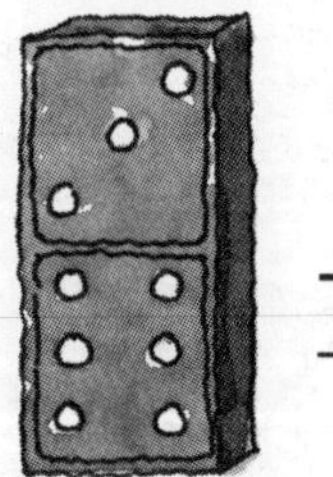
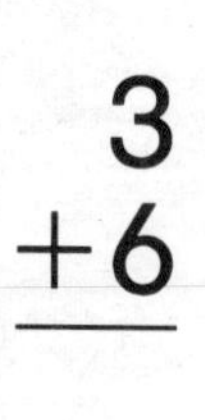

3
+6

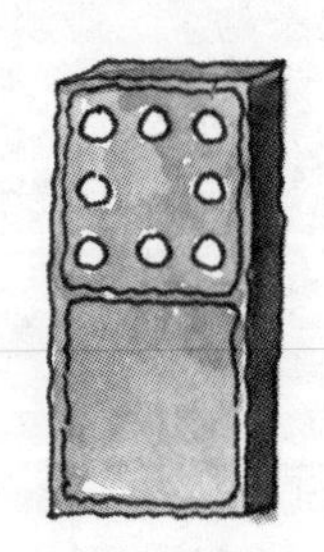

8
+0

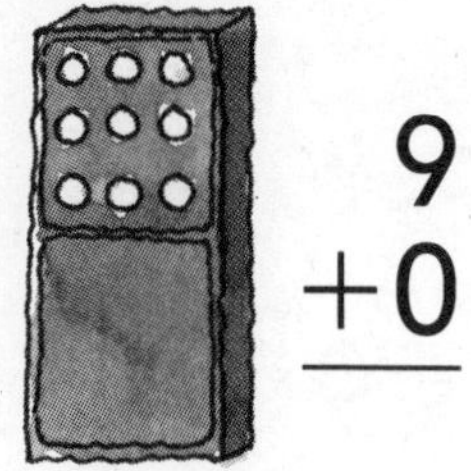

9
+0

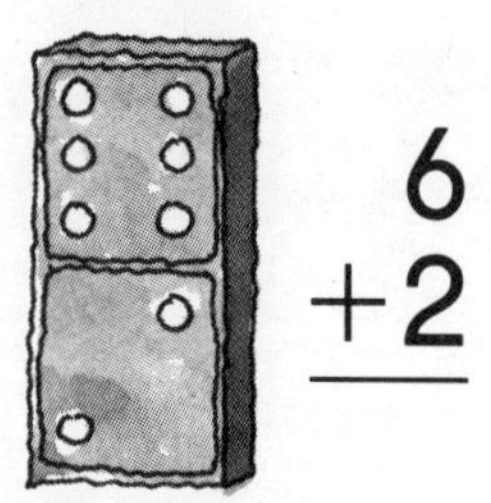

6
+2

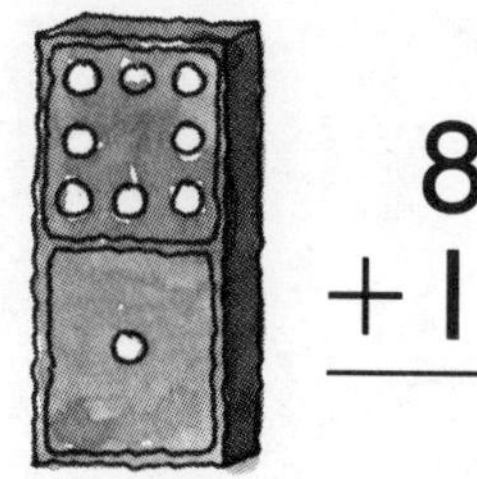

8
+1

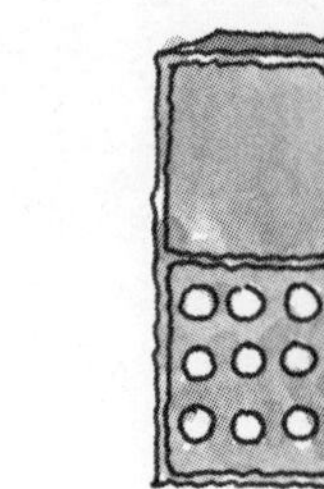

0
+9

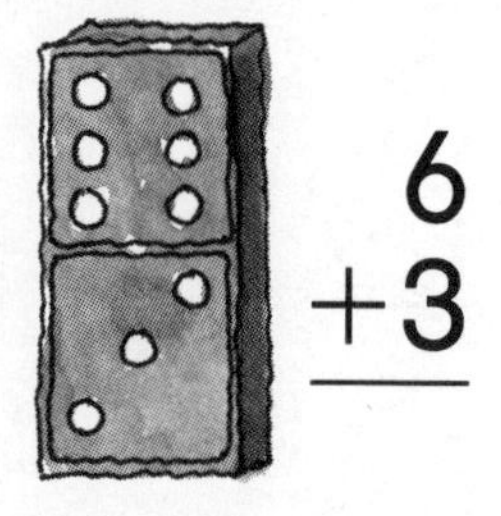

6
+3

1
+7

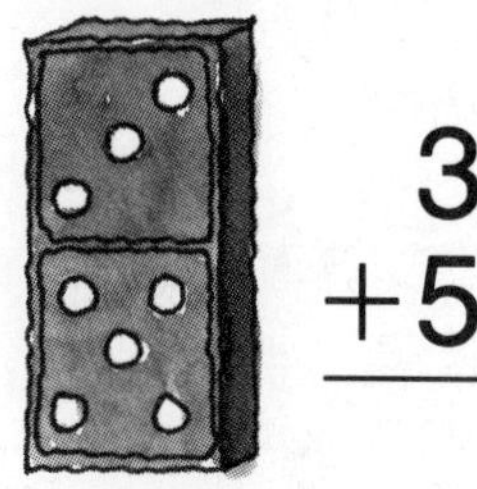

3
+5

7
+2

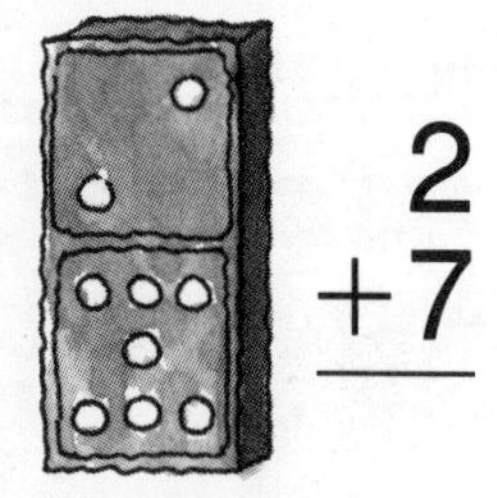

2
+7

0
+8

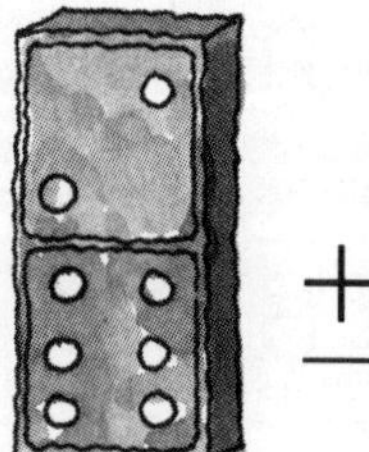
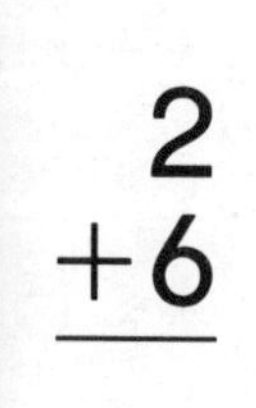

2
+6

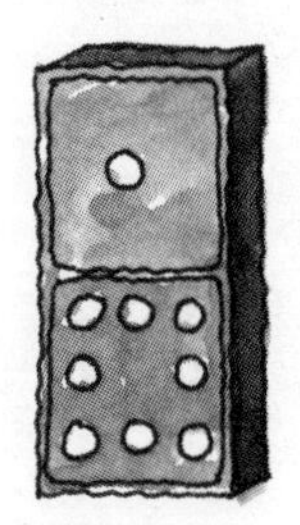

1
+8

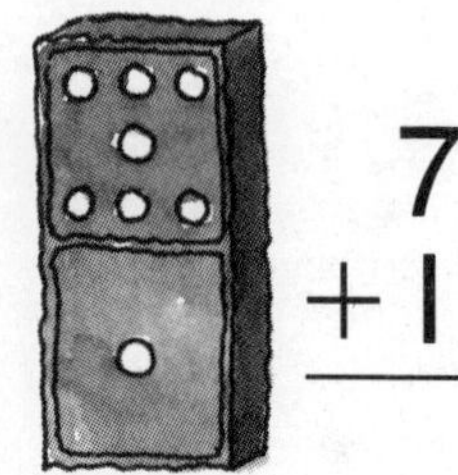

7
+1

5
+4

6
+3

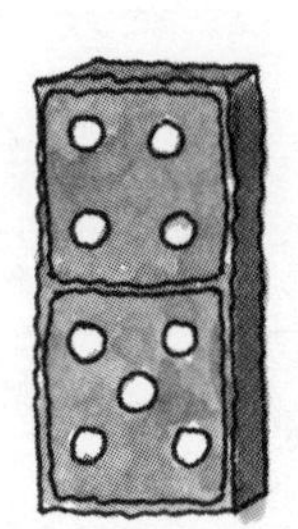

4
+5

Name ____________________

Write the facts.

$10 + \underline{0} = 10$

$9 + \_\_\_ = 10$

$8 + \_\_\_ = 10$

$7 + \_\_\_ = 10$

$6 + \_\_\_ = 10$

$5 + \_\_\_ = 10$

$4 + \_\_\_ = 10$

$3 + \_\_\_ = 10$

$2 + \_\_\_ = 10$

$1 + \_\_\_ = 10$

$0 + \_\_\_ = 10$

Add.

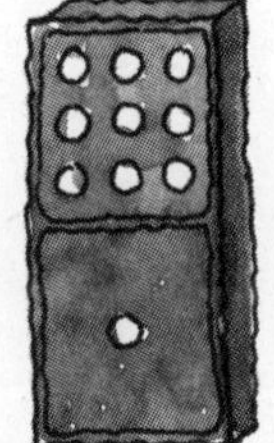

$\begin{array}{r} 9 \\ +1 \\ \hline \end{array}$

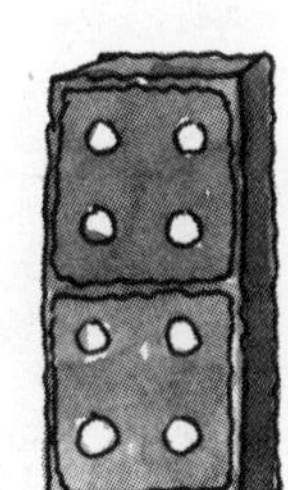

$\begin{array}{r} 4 \\ +4 \\ \hline \end{array}$

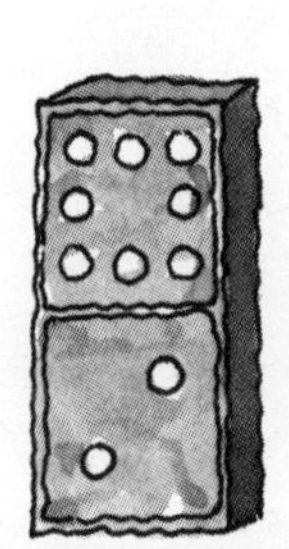

$\begin{array}{r} 8 \\ +2 \\ \hline \end{array}$

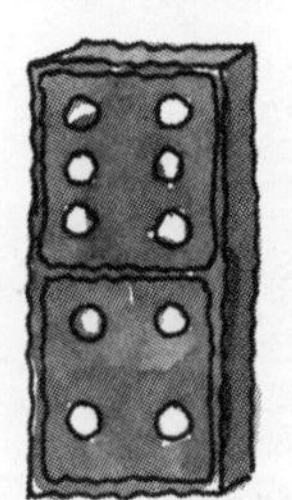

$\begin{array}{r} 6 \\ +4 \\ \hline \end{array}$

$\begin{array}{r} 3 \\ +6 \\ \hline \end{array}$

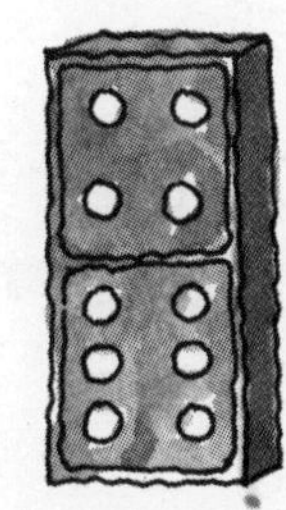

$\begin{array}{r} 4 \\ +6 \\ \hline \end{array}$

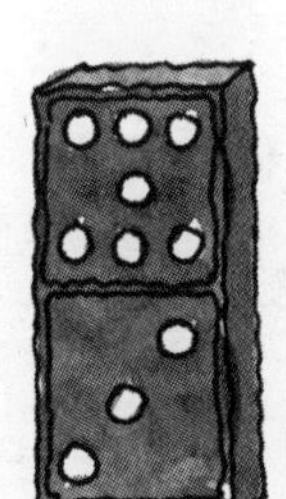

$\begin{array}{r} 7 \\ +3 \\ \hline \end{array}$

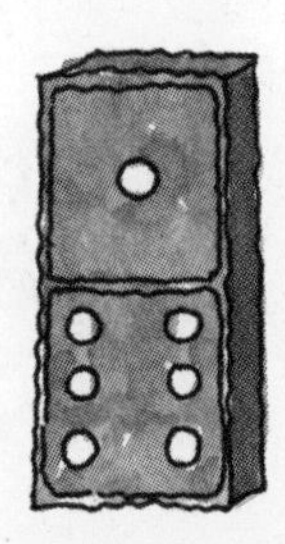

$\begin{array}{r} 1 \\ +6 \\ \hline \end{array}$

Add.

$\begin{array}{r}2\\+2\\\hline 4\end{array}$	$\begin{array}{r}1\\+8\\\hline\end{array}$	$\begin{array}{r}5\\+2\\\hline\end{array}$	$\begin{array}{r}1\\+4\\\hline\end{array}$	$\begin{array}{r}4\\+3\\\hline\end{array}$	$\begin{array}{r}2\\+3\\\hline\end{array}$
$\begin{array}{r}4\\+1\\\hline\end{array}$	$\begin{array}{r}5\\+5\\\hline\end{array}$	$\begin{array}{r}3\\+2\\\hline\end{array}$	$\begin{array}{r}6\\+4\\\hline\end{array}$	$\begin{array}{r}0\\+7\\\hline\end{array}$	$\begin{array}{r}5\\+3\\\hline\end{array}$
$\begin{array}{r}3\\+3\\\hline\end{array}$	$\begin{array}{r}1\\+5\\\hline\end{array}$	$\begin{array}{r}4\\+4\\\hline\end{array}$	$\begin{array}{r}2\\+4\\\hline\end{array}$	$\begin{array}{r}6\\+3\\\hline\end{array}$	$\begin{array}{r}3\\+7\\\hline\end{array}$
$\begin{array}{r}2\\+5\\\hline\end{array}$	$\begin{array}{r}4\\+6\\\hline\end{array}$	$\begin{array}{r}3\\+5\\\hline\end{array}$	$\begin{array}{r}8\\+2\\\hline\end{array}$	$\begin{array}{r}2\\+7\\\hline\end{array}$	$\begin{array}{r}2\\+8\\\hline\end{array}$
$\begin{array}{r}3\\+6\\\hline\end{array}$	$\begin{array}{r}1\\+9\\\hline\end{array}$	$\begin{array}{r}5\\+4\\\hline\end{array}$	$\begin{array}{r}1\\+7\\\hline\end{array}$	$\begin{array}{r}4\\+5\\\hline\end{array}$	$\begin{array}{r}7\\+3\\\hline\end{array}$

Name ___

Add.

$5 + 1 =$ ___ $6 + 2 =$ ___ $4 + 2 =$ ___

$7 + 2 =$ ___ $0 + 7 =$ ___ $2 + 6 =$ ___

$1 + 2 =$ ___ $8 + 1 =$ ___ $3 + 4 =$ ___

$3 + 4 =$ ___ $3 + 2 =$ ___ $2 + 8 =$ ___

$9 + 1 =$ ___ $6 + 1 =$ ___

Add.

9	4	3	0	3	1
+1	+4	+1	+0	+6	+4

6	4	2	8	1	4
+0	+1	+1	+0	+9	+5

0	5	1	8	2	3
+5	+4	+6	+1	+6	+7

Add.

$7 + 2 =$ ___	$3 + 2 =$ ___	$2 + 3 =$ ___
$6 + 4 =$ ___	$7 + 1 =$ ___	$3 + 0 =$ ___
$2 + 5 =$ ___	$4 + 2 =$ ___	$3 + 4 =$ ___
$1 + 2 =$ ___	$1 + 1 =$ ___	$5 + 1 =$ ___
$5 + 2 =$ ___	$6 + 1 =$ ___	

$$\begin{array}{r}1\\+5\\\hline\end{array}\quad\begin{array}{r}7\\+3\\\hline\end{array}\quad\begin{array}{r}1\\+3\\\hline\end{array}\quad\begin{array}{r}5\\+5\\\hline\end{array}\quad\begin{array}{r}4\\+0\\\hline\end{array}\quad\begin{array}{r}2\\+7\\\hline\end{array}$$

$$\begin{array}{r}4\\+3\\\hline\end{array}\quad\begin{array}{r}3\\+5\\\hline\end{array}\quad\begin{array}{r}8\\+2\\\hline\end{array}\quad\begin{array}{r}2\\+2\\\hline\end{array}\quad\begin{array}{r}6\\+3\\\hline\end{array}\quad\begin{array}{r}3\\+1\\\hline\end{array}$$

$$\begin{array}{r}4\\+6\\\hline\end{array}\quad\begin{array}{r}7\\+0\\\hline\end{array}\quad\begin{array}{r}0\\+9\\\hline\end{array}\quad\begin{array}{r}5\\+3\\\hline\end{array}\quad\begin{array}{r}0\\+3\\\hline\end{array}\quad\begin{array}{r}1\\+8\\\hline\end{array}$$

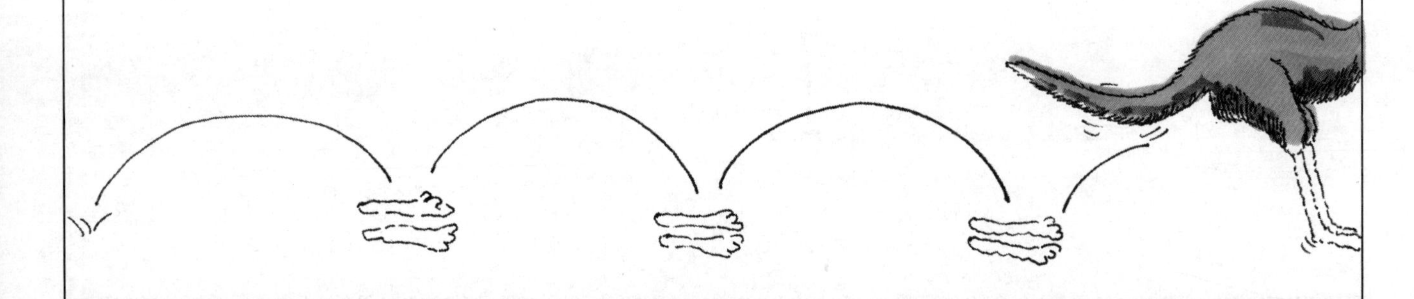

Name ______________________

Have 5¢. Count 2¢ more.

...5,6,7

5 ¢ + 2 ¢ = 7 ¢

Add by counting on.

Have 4¢. Count 2¢ more.

4 ¢ + 2 ¢ = ___ ¢

Have 8¢. Count 2¢ more.

8 ¢ + 2 ¢ = ___ ¢

Have 6¢. Count 3¢ more.

6 ¢ + 3 ¢ = ___ ¢

Have 4¢. Count 4¢ more.

4 ¢ + 4 ¢ = ___ ¢

Have 5¢. Count 2¢ more.

5 ¢ + 2 ¢ = ___ ¢

Have 7¢. Count 3¢ more.

7 ¢ + 3 ¢ = ___ ¢

Have 4¢. Count 3¢ more.

4 ¢ + 3 ¢ = ___ ¢

Have 5¢. Count 5¢ more.

5 ¢ + 5 ¢ = ___ ¢

Have 8¢.

8¢
+1¢
9¢

Add 1¢ more.

Have 6¢.

6¢
+2¢
8¢

Add 2¢ more.

Add.

5¢
+3¢
¢

4¢
+6¢
¢

3¢
+5¢
¢

6¢
+2¢
¢

2¢
+7¢
¢

4¢
+5¢
¢

6¢
+4¢
¢

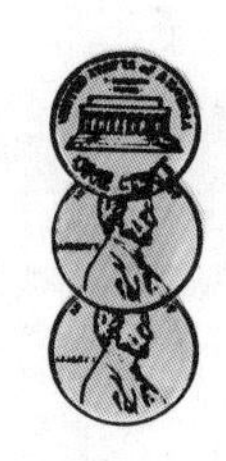

3¢
+7¢
¢

Name ______________________________

Add.

$$\begin{array}{r} 5 \\ 0 \\ +\ 4 \\ \hline 9 \end{array} \quad (5 + 0 = 5)$$

Add.

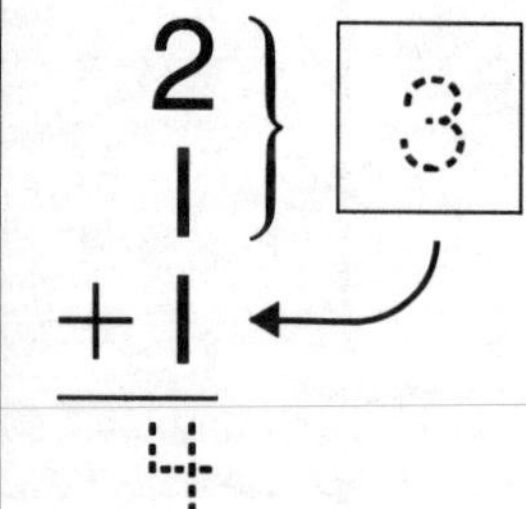

2 1 +1 4 (box: 3)	3 1 +2	1 0 +2	1 3 +1
1 6 +2	1 3 +4	4 4 +2	2 2 +5
3 4 +2	4 1 +1	3 6 +1	4 3 +2
5 1 +2	7 1 +2	5 3 +2	8 0 +1
9 1 +0	4 0 +3	6 1 +1	3 2 +5

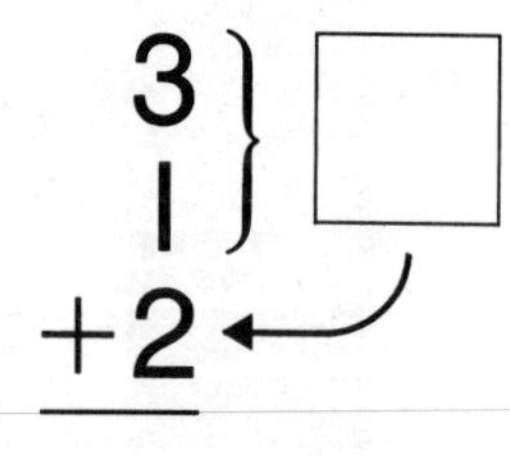

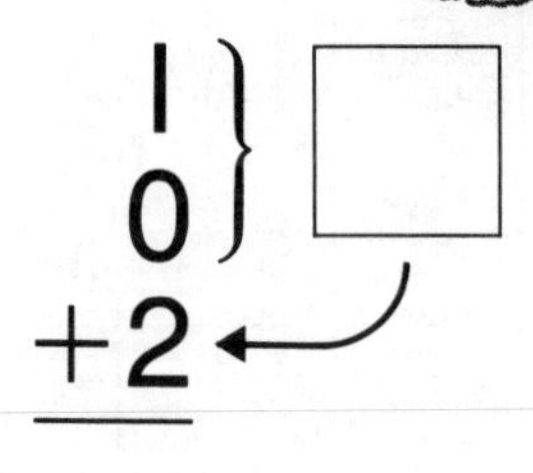

Name ______________________________

CHAPTER CHECKUP

Add.

$4 + 1 =$ ___ $3 + 5 =$ ___ $6 + 4 =$ ___

$2 + 7 =$ ___ $8 + 2 =$ ___ $2 + 5 =$ ___

$2 + 4 =$ ___ $3 + 3 =$ ___ $1 + 3 =$ ___

$\begin{array}{r} 4 \\ +5 \\ \hline \end{array}$ $\begin{array}{r} 7 \\ +3 \\ \hline \end{array}$ $\begin{array}{r} 3 \\ +2 \\ \hline \end{array}$ $\begin{array}{r} 2 \\ +2 \\ \hline \end{array}$ $\begin{array}{r} 3 \\ +6 \\ \hline \end{array}$ $\begin{array}{r} 5 \\ +5 \\ \hline \end{array}$

Solve.

Have 5¢.

Add 3¢ more.

5 ¢ + 3 ¢ = ___ ¢

$\begin{array}{r} 6¢ \\ +4¢ \\ \hline ¢ \end{array}$

Add.

$\begin{array}{r} 3 \\ 4 \\ +1 \\ \hline \end{array}$ $\begin{array}{r} 2 \\ 0 \\ +3 \\ \hline \end{array}$ $\begin{array}{r} 1 \\ 2 \\ +3 \\ \hline \end{array}$ $\begin{array}{r} 2 \\ 4 \\ +4 \\ \hline \end{array}$

ROUNDUP REVIEW

Write the missing numbers.

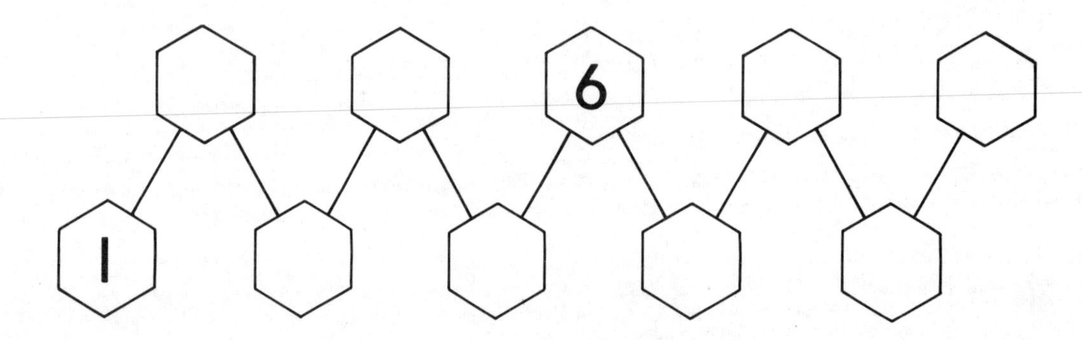

How many?

Add.

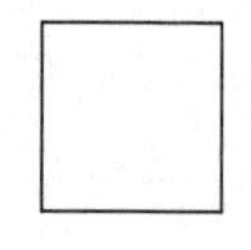

$$\begin{array}{r} 6¢ \\ +3¢ \\ \hline ¢ \end{array}$$

Add.

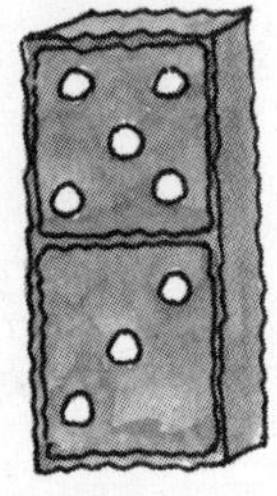

$$\begin{array}{r} 5 \\ +3 \\ \hline \end{array}$$

$4 + 2 =$ ____

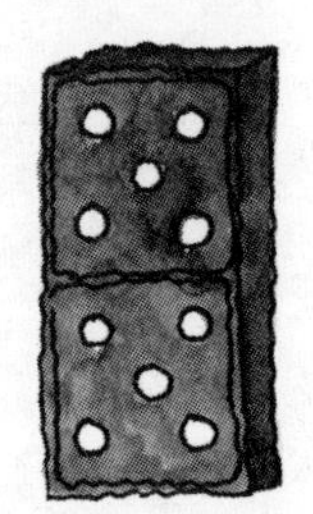

$$\begin{array}{r} 5 \\ +5 \\ \hline \end{array}$$

Add.

$$\begin{array}{r} 3 \\ +3 \\ \hline \end{array} \quad \begin{array}{r} 5 \\ +4 \\ \hline \end{array} \quad \begin{array}{r} 4 \\ +4 \\ \hline \end{array} \quad \begin{array}{r} 7 \\ +3 \\ \hline \end{array} \quad \begin{array}{r} 1 \\ 3 \\ +5 \\ \hline \end{array} \quad \begin{array}{r} 2 \\ 3 \\ +2 \\ \hline \end{array}$$

Name ____________________

3 SUBTRACTION, MINUENDS THROUGH 10

Fill in the blanks.

 3 How many in all?	 1 Subtract.	2 How many left?
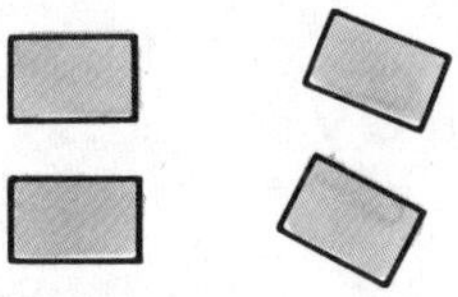 ___ How many in all?	 ___ Subtract.	___ How many left?
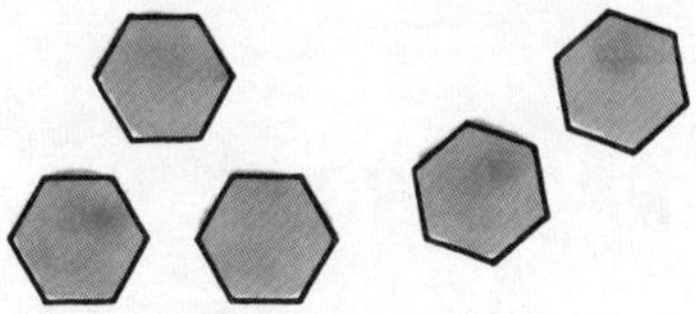 ___ How many in all?	 ___ Subtract.	___ How many left?
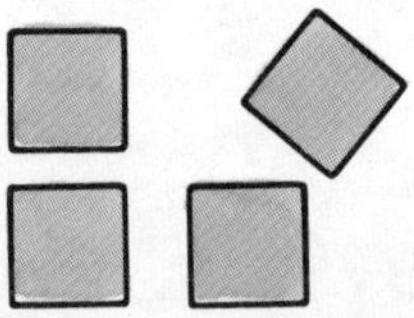 ___ How many in all?	 ___ Subtract.	___ How many left?
 ___ How many in all?	 ___ Subtract.	___ How many left?

How many in all? 4

How many flew away? 2

How many are left? 2

How many?

How many in all? ____

How many ran away? ____

How many are left? ____

How many in all? ____

How many hopped away? ____

How many are left? ____

How many in all? ____

How many ran away? ____

How many are left? ____

How many in all? ____

How many ran away? ____

How many are left? ____

Name ________________

How many hamsters in all?	How many ran away?	How many are left?
5	1	4

$5 - 1 = 4$

Write the facts.

How many dogs in all? How many ran away? How many are left?

____ – ____ = ____

How many birds in all? How many flew away? How many are left?

____ – ____ = ____

How many bunnies in all? How many hopped away? How many are left?

____ – ____ = ____

How many cats in all? How many ran away? How many are left?

____ – ____ = ____

$3 - 1 = \underline{2}$

$5 - 1 = \underline{4}$

Subtract.

$5 - 3 = \underline{\quad}$

$4 - 2 = \underline{\quad}$

$2 - 1 = \underline{\quad}$

$3 - 2 = \underline{\quad}$

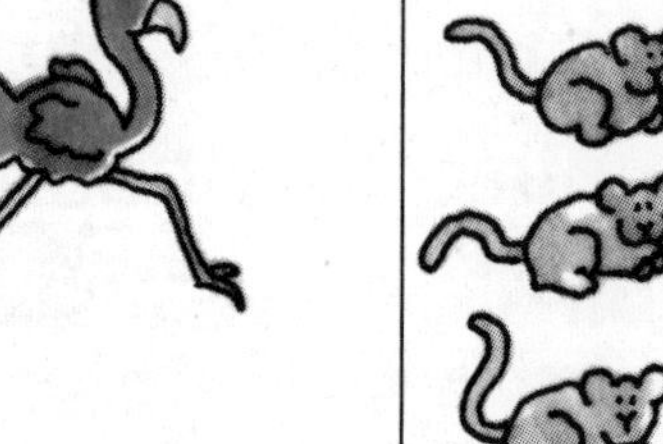

$3 - 1 = \underline{\quad}$

$5 - 2 = \underline{\quad}$

$4 - 3 = \underline{\quad}$

$5 - 4 = \underline{\quad}$

Name ______

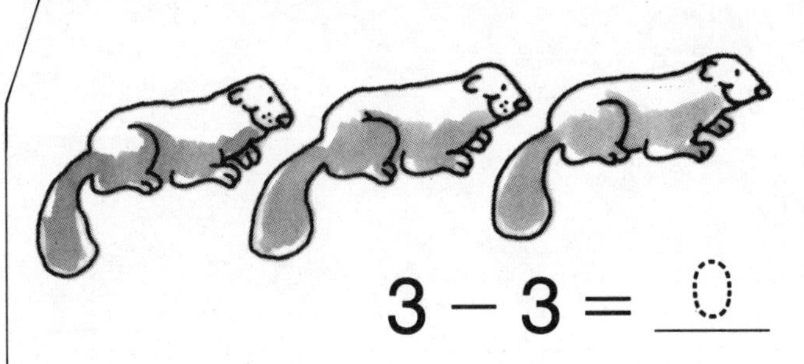

$3 - 3 =$ 0

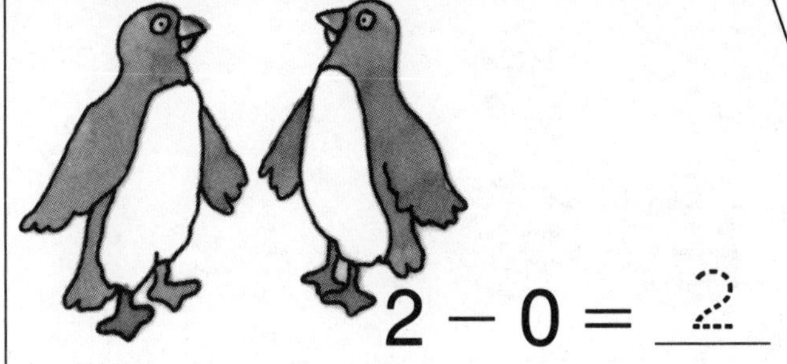

$2 - 0 =$ 2

Subtract.

$3 - 0 =$ ___

$1 - 1 =$ ___

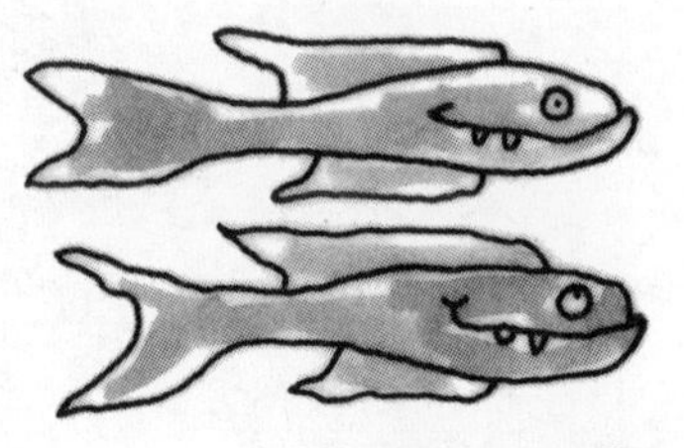

$2 - 2 =$ ___

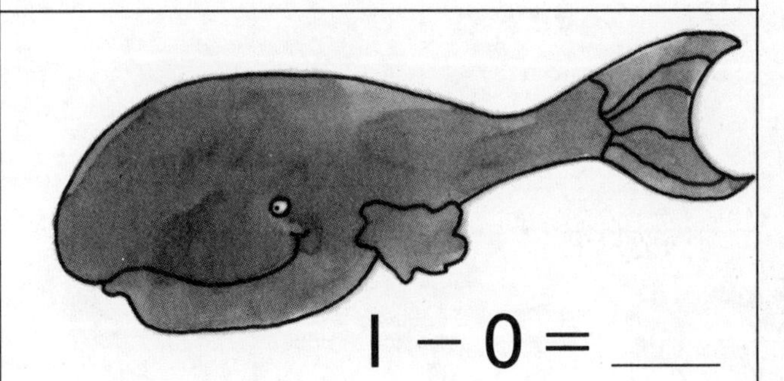

$1 - 0 =$ ___

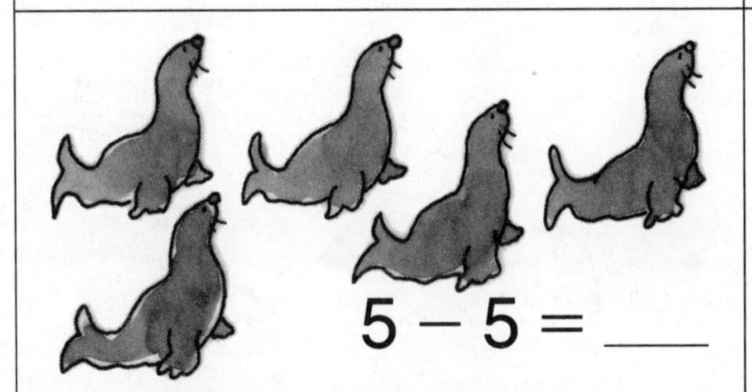

$5 - 5 =$ ___

$5 - 0 =$ ___

$4 - 0 =$ ___

$4 - 4 =$ ___

$4 - 2 =$ 2

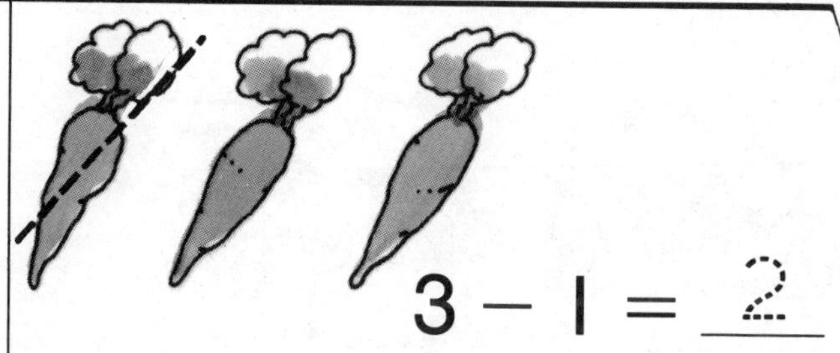

$3 - 1 =$ 2

Cross out and subtract.

$3 - 3 =$ ___

$2 - 0 =$ ___

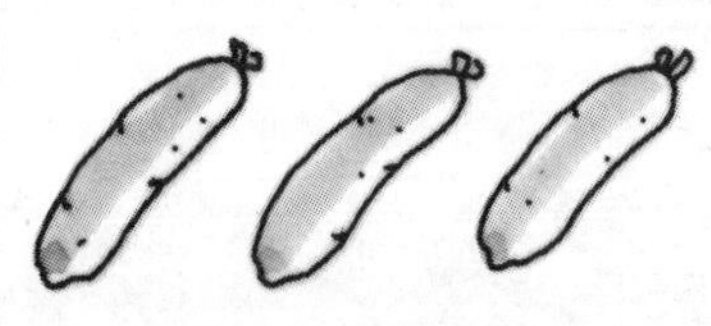

$3 - 2 =$ ___

$4 - 3 =$ ___

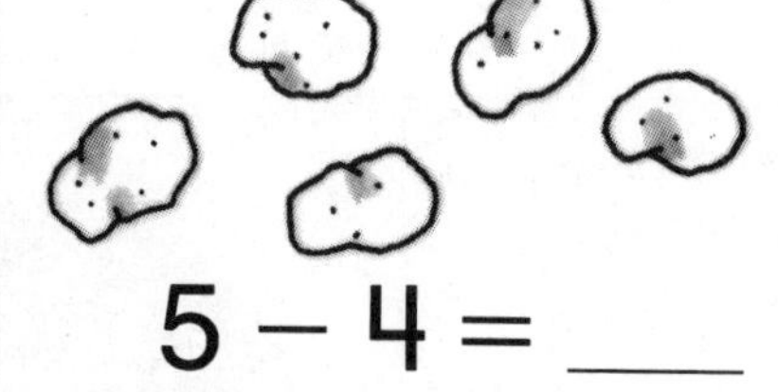

$5 - 4 =$ ___

$5 - 5 =$ ___

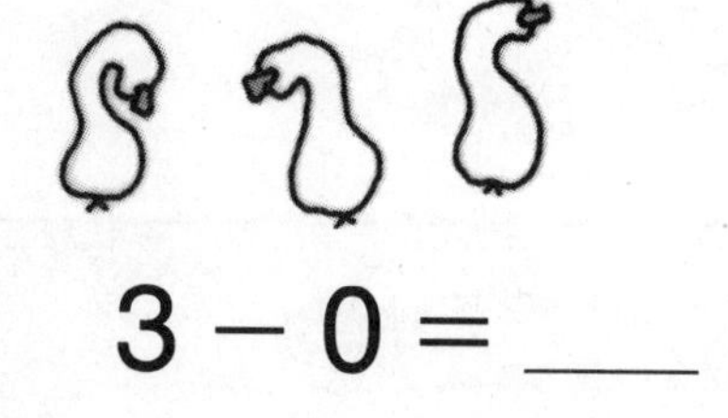

$3 - 0 =$ ___

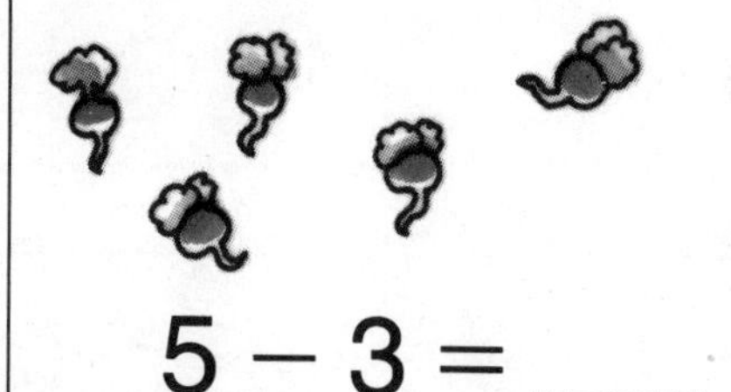

$5 - 3 =$ ___

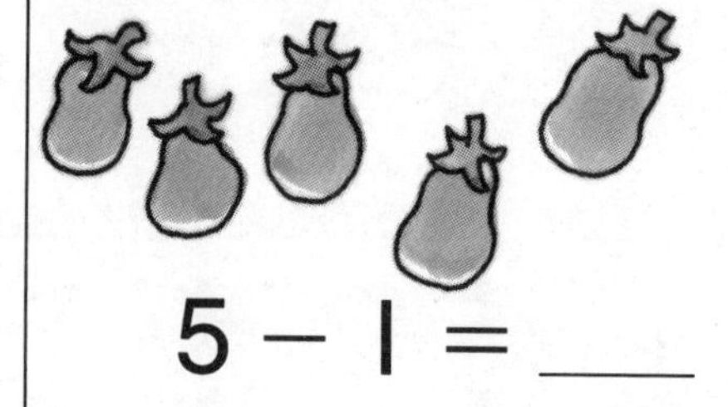

$5 - 1 =$ ___

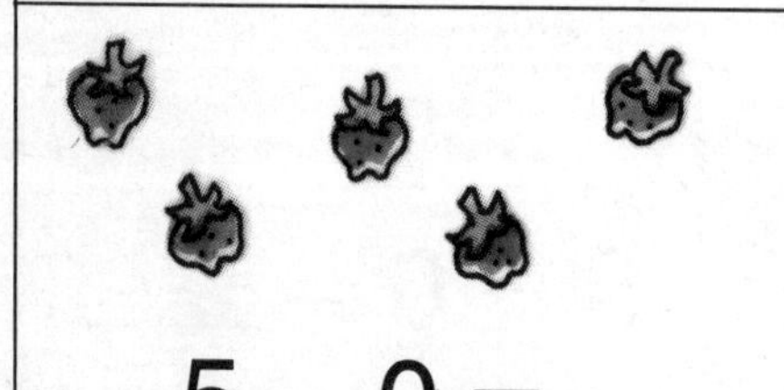

$5 - 0 =$ ___

$4 - 4 =$ ___

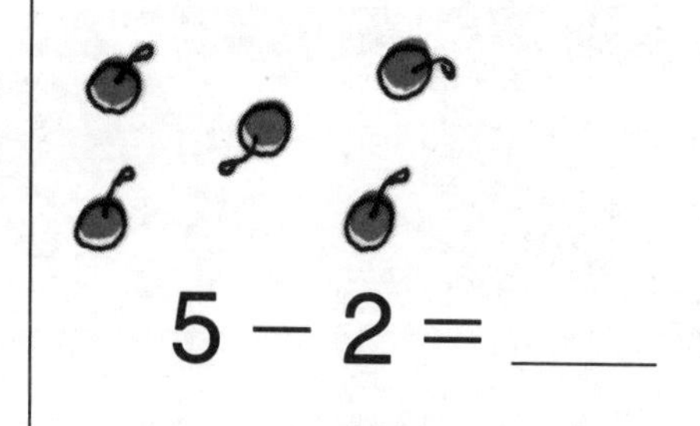

$5 - 2 =$ ___

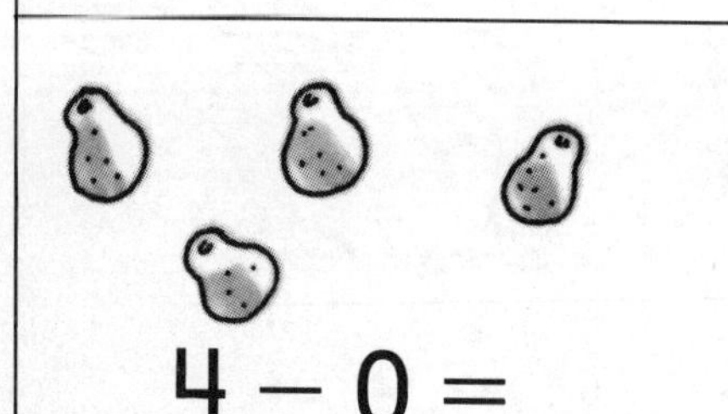

$4 - 0 =$ ___

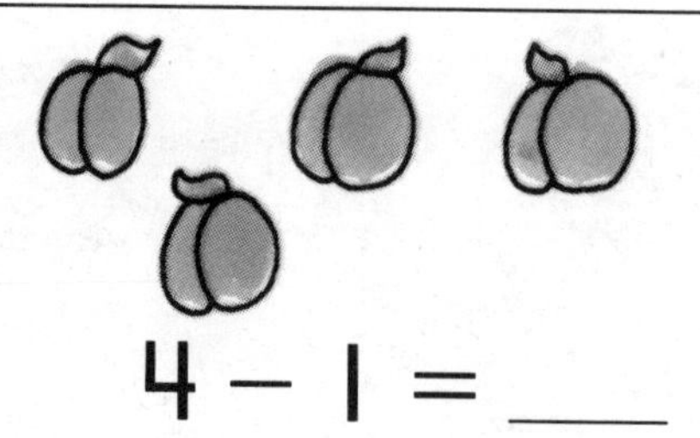

$4 - 1 =$ ___

$2 - 2 =$ ___

Name ____________________

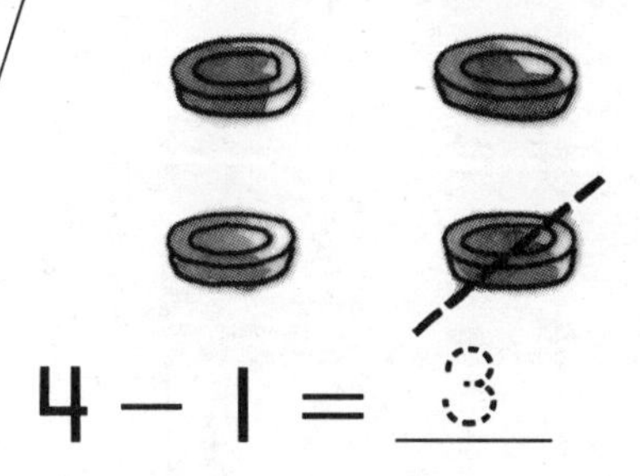

$4 - 1 = $ 3

$$\begin{array}{r} 4 \\ -1 \\ \hline 3 \end{array}$$

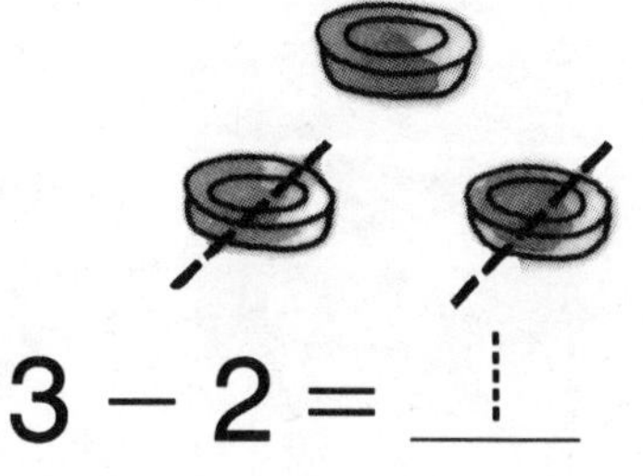

$3 - 2 = $ 1

$$\begin{array}{r} 3 \\ -2 \\ \hline 1 \end{array}$$

Cross out and subtract.

$$\begin{array}{r} 5 \\ -2 \\ \hline \end{array}$$

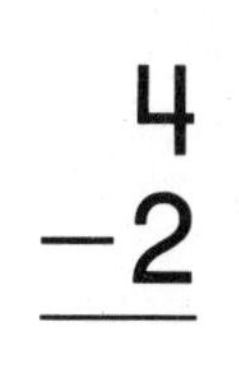

$$\begin{array}{r} 4 \\ -2 \\ \hline \end{array}$$

$$\begin{array}{r} 3 \\ -3 \\ \hline \end{array}$$

$$\begin{array}{r} 4 \\ -3 \\ \hline \end{array}$$

$$\begin{array}{r} 2 \\ -1 \\ \hline \end{array}$$

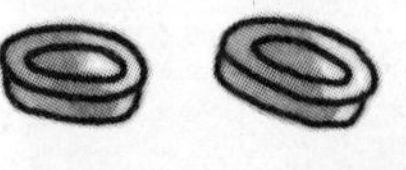

$$\begin{array}{r} 5 \\ -3 \\ \hline \end{array}$$

$$\begin{array}{r} 2 \\ -0 \\ \hline \end{array}$$

$$\begin{array}{r} 3 \\ -1 \\ \hline \end{array}$$

$$\begin{array}{r} 5 \\ -1 \\ \hline \end{array}$$

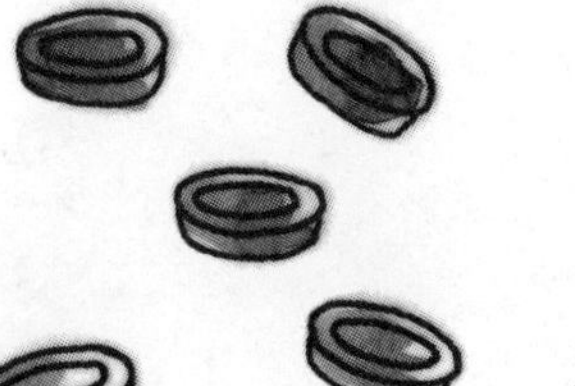

$$\begin{array}{r} 5 \\ -4 \\ \hline \end{array}$$

$$\begin{array}{r} 4 \\ -4 \\ \hline \end{array}$$

$$\begin{array}{r} 1 \\ -0 \\ \hline \end{array}$$

Subtract.

3	5	2	4	5
−1	−2	−0	−1	−4
2				

4	5	5	3	1
−3	−0	−3	−0	−1

5	2	4	3	4
−5	−1	−0	−2	−2

3	5	4	1	2
−3	−1	−4	−0	−2

Name ______________________________

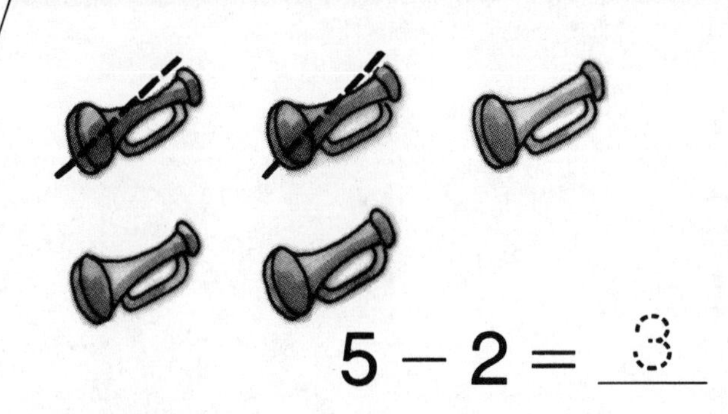

$5 - 2 = \underline{3}$

$3 - 1 = \underline{2}$

Subtract.

$1 - 0 =$ ___	$4 - 1 =$ ___	$2 - 1 =$ ___
$5 - 5 =$ ___	$3 - 2 =$ ___	$5 - 0 =$ ___
$4 - 0 =$ ___	$4 - 3 =$ ___	$4 - 4 =$ ___
$4 - 2 =$ ___	$5 - 1 =$ ___	$3 - 0 =$ ___
$2 - 2 =$ ___	$1 - 1 =$ ___	$5 - 4 =$ ___
$5 - 3 =$ ___	$3 - 3 =$ ___	$2 - 0 =$ ___

Subtract.

4 − 1	5 − 3	2 − 1	4 − 3	3 − 0
5 − 0	3 − 1	5 − 5	1 − 0	5 − 1
2 − 2	4 − 0	1 − 1	5 − 2	3 − 3
4 − 4	3 − 2	4 − 2	2 − 0	5 − 4

Name ____________________

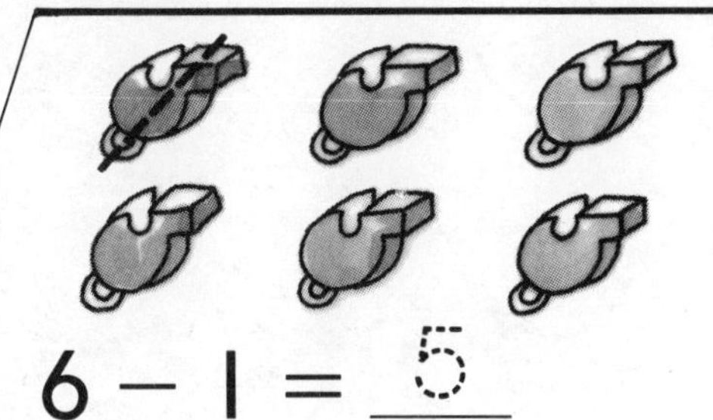

$6 - 1 = \underline{5}$

$$\begin{array}{r} 6 \\ -1 \\ \hline 5 \end{array}$$

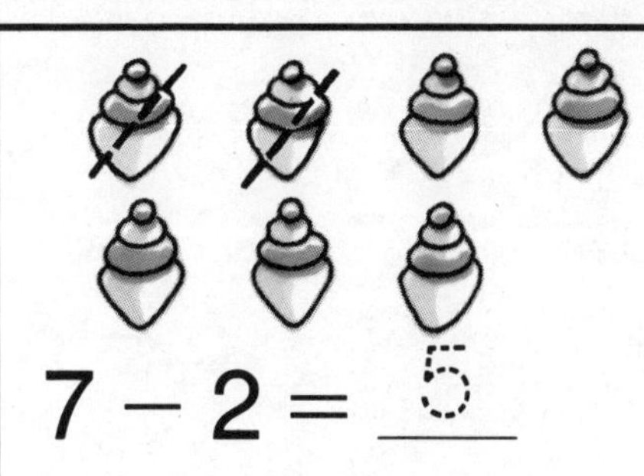

$7 - 2 = \underline{5}$

$$\begin{array}{r} 7 \\ -2 \\ \hline 5 \end{array}$$

How many are left?

$7 - 3 =$ ____

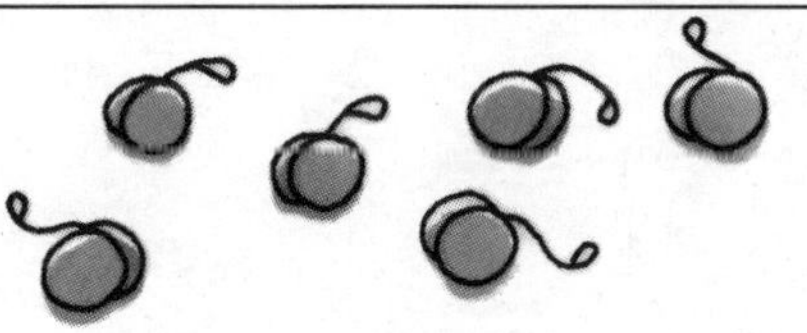

$6 - 2 =$ ____

$6 - 5 =$ ____

$7 - 7 =$ ____

$6 - 0 =$ ____

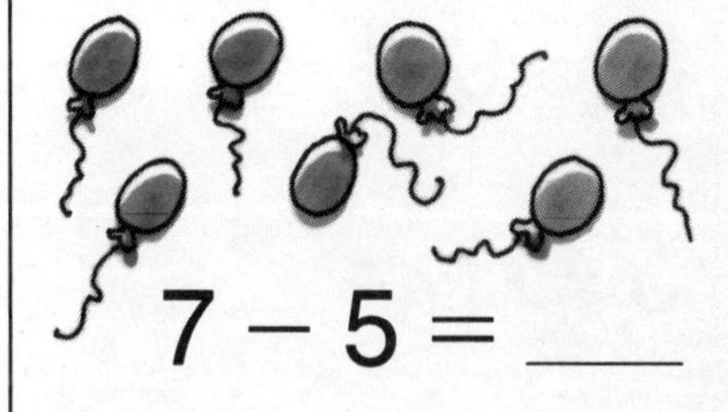

$7 - 5 =$ ____

$$\begin{array}{r} 6 \\ -3 \\ \hline \end{array} \quad \begin{array}{r} 7 \\ -1 \\ \hline \end{array} \quad \begin{array}{r} 6 \\ -4 \\ \hline \end{array} \quad \begin{array}{r} 6 \\ -6 \\ \hline \end{array} \quad \begin{array}{r} 7 \\ -4 \\ \hline \end{array}$$

$$\begin{array}{r} 7 \\ -6 \\ \hline \end{array} \quad \begin{array}{r} 6 \\ -0 \\ \hline \end{array} \quad \begin{array}{r} 6 \\ -2 \\ \hline \end{array} \quad \begin{array}{r} 7 \\ -5 \\ \hline \end{array} \quad \begin{array}{r} 6 \\ -5 \\ \hline \end{array}$$

$$\begin{array}{r} 7 \\ -5 \\ \hline \end{array} \quad \begin{array}{r} 7 \\ -0 \\ \hline \end{array} \quad \begin{array}{r} 6 \\ -1 \\ \hline \end{array} \quad \begin{array}{r} 6 \\ -0 \\ \hline \end{array} \quad \begin{array}{r} 7 \\ -7 \\ \hline \end{array}$$

Subtract.

$7 - 3 =$ ___ $6 - 6 =$ ___ $6 - 2 =$ ___

$3 - 0 =$ ___ $7 - 4 =$ ___ $7 - 0 =$ ___

$6 - 4 =$ ___ $4 - 2 =$ ___ $4 - 3 =$ ___

$7 - 1 =$ ___ $7 - 7 =$ ___ $7 - 2 =$ ___

$5 - 3 =$ ___ $6 - 3 =$ ___ $6 - 0 =$ ___

$6 - 1 =$ ___ $5 - 2 =$ ___ $5 - 5 =$ ___

$\begin{array}{r} 5 \\ -2 \\ \hline \end{array}$ $\begin{array}{r} 7 \\ -6 \\ \hline \end{array}$ $\begin{array}{r} 7 \\ -3 \\ \hline \end{array}$ $\begin{array}{r} 6 \\ -5 \\ \hline \end{array}$ $\begin{array}{r} 4 \\ -1 \\ \hline \end{array}$

$\begin{array}{r} 7 \\ -5 \\ \hline \end{array}$ $\begin{array}{r} 3 \\ -2 \\ \hline \end{array}$ $\begin{array}{r} 6 \\ -6 \\ \hline \end{array}$ $\begin{array}{r} 6 \\ -4 \\ \hline \end{array}$ $\begin{array}{r} 7 \\ -7 \\ \hline \end{array}$

$\begin{array}{r} 6 \\ -3 \\ \hline \end{array}$ $\begin{array}{r} 5 \\ -4 \\ \hline \end{array}$ $\begin{array}{r} 3 \\ -0 \\ \hline \end{array}$ $\begin{array}{r} 6 \\ -2 \\ \hline \end{array}$ $\begin{array}{r} 7 \\ -4 \\ \hline \end{array}$

Name ______________________________

$8 - 3 = \underline{5}$

$$\begin{array}{r} 8 \\ -3 \\ \hline 5 \end{array}$$

How many are left?

$\begin{array}{r} 8 \\ -2 \\ \hline \end{array}$ $\begin{array}{r} 8 \\ -4 \\ \hline \end{array}$ $\begin{array}{r} 8 \\ -1 \\ \hline \end{array}$ $\begin{array}{r} 8 \\ -0 \\ \hline \end{array}$

$\begin{array}{r} 8 \\ -6 \\ \hline \end{array}$ $\begin{array}{r} 8 \\ -5 \\ \hline \end{array}$ $\begin{array}{r} 8 \\ -7 \\ \hline \end{array}$ $\begin{array}{r} 8 \\ -8 \\ \hline \end{array}$

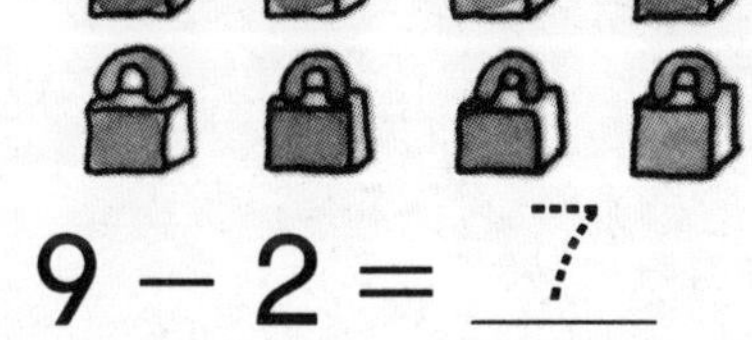

$$\begin{array}{r} 9 \\ -2 \\ \hline 7 \end{array}$$

$9 - 2 = \underline{7}$

$$\begin{array}{r} 9 \\ -5 \\ \hline 4 \end{array}$$

$9 - 5 = \underline{4}$

$\begin{array}{r} 9 \\ -1 \\ \hline \end{array}$ $\begin{array}{r} 9 \\ -4 \\ \hline \end{array}$ $\begin{array}{r} 9 \\ -6 \\ \hline \end{array}$ $\begin{array}{r} 9 \\ -8 \\ \hline \end{array}$

$\begin{array}{r} 9 \\ -0 \\ \hline \end{array}$ $\begin{array}{r} 9 \\ -3 \\ \hline \end{array}$ $\begin{array}{r} 9 \\ -9 \\ \hline \end{array}$ $\begin{array}{r} 9 \\ -7 \\ \hline \end{array}$

Subtract.

$9 - 0 =$ ___ $8 - 7 =$ ___ $8 - 5 =$ ___

$9 - 3 =$ ___ $9 - 4 =$ ___ $9 - 6 =$ ___

$9 - 8 =$ ___ $9 - 7 =$ ___ $8 - 2 =$ ___

$8 - 2 =$ ___ $9 - 5 =$ ___ $8 - 4 =$ ___

$9 - 9 =$ ___ $9 - 3 =$ ___ $9 - 8 =$ ___

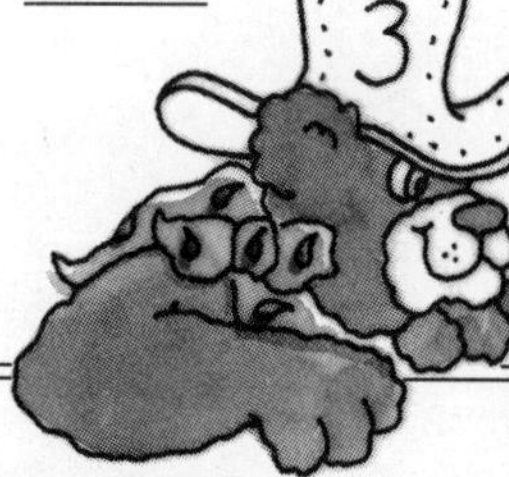

Three numbers can be used to make a number family.

3 2 5

$3 + 2 = 5$ $5 - 2 = 3$

$2 + 3 = 5$ $5 - 3 = 2$

Make number families.

___ + ___ $= 6$ ___ − ___ $= 2$

___ + ___ $= 6$ ___ − ___ $= 4$

4 3 7

___ + ___ $= 7$ ___ − ___ $= 3$

___ + ___ $= 7$ ___ − ___ $= 4$

Name ____________________

Subtract.

7 −1	6 −0	7 −3	7 −5	7 −7
6 −2	7 −6	6 −3	6 −1	7 −4
7 −2	6 −4	7 −0	6 −6	6 −5

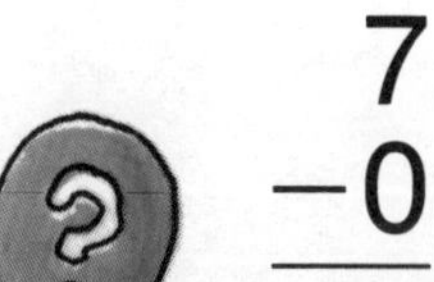
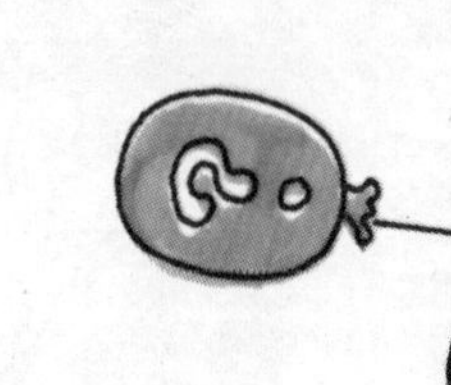
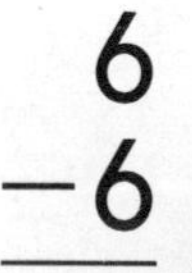
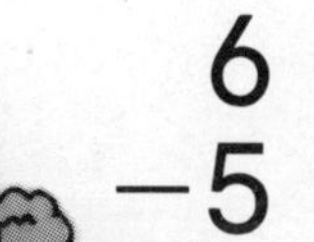

Make a model to show each subtraction.

6
−3
3

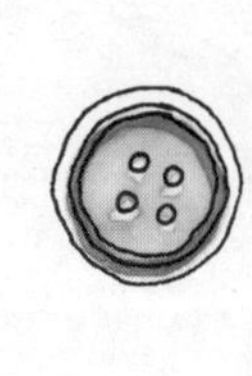

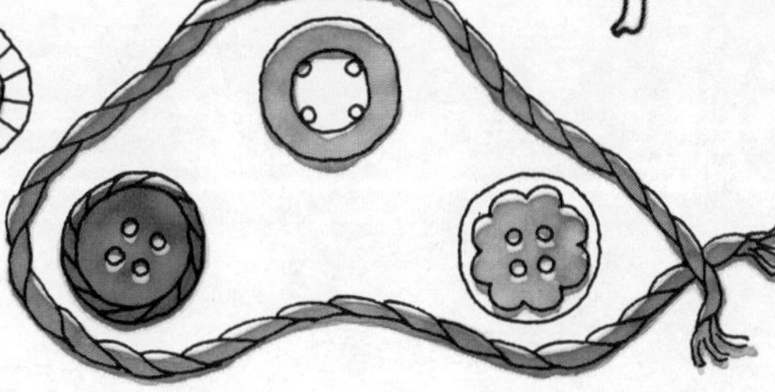

9 −8	8 −5	9 −4

Subtract.

$9 - 2 =$ ___ $9 - 6 =$ ___ $8 - 6 =$ ___

$8 - 4 =$ ___ $8 - 7 =$ ___ $9 - 4 =$ ___

$9 - 4 =$ ___ $8 - 5 =$ ___ $8 - 3 =$ ___

$9 - 1 =$ ___ $9 - 7 =$ ___ $9 - 9 =$ ___

$8 - 0 =$ ___ $9 - 5 =$ ___ $9 - 8 =$ ___

Write a fact for each model.

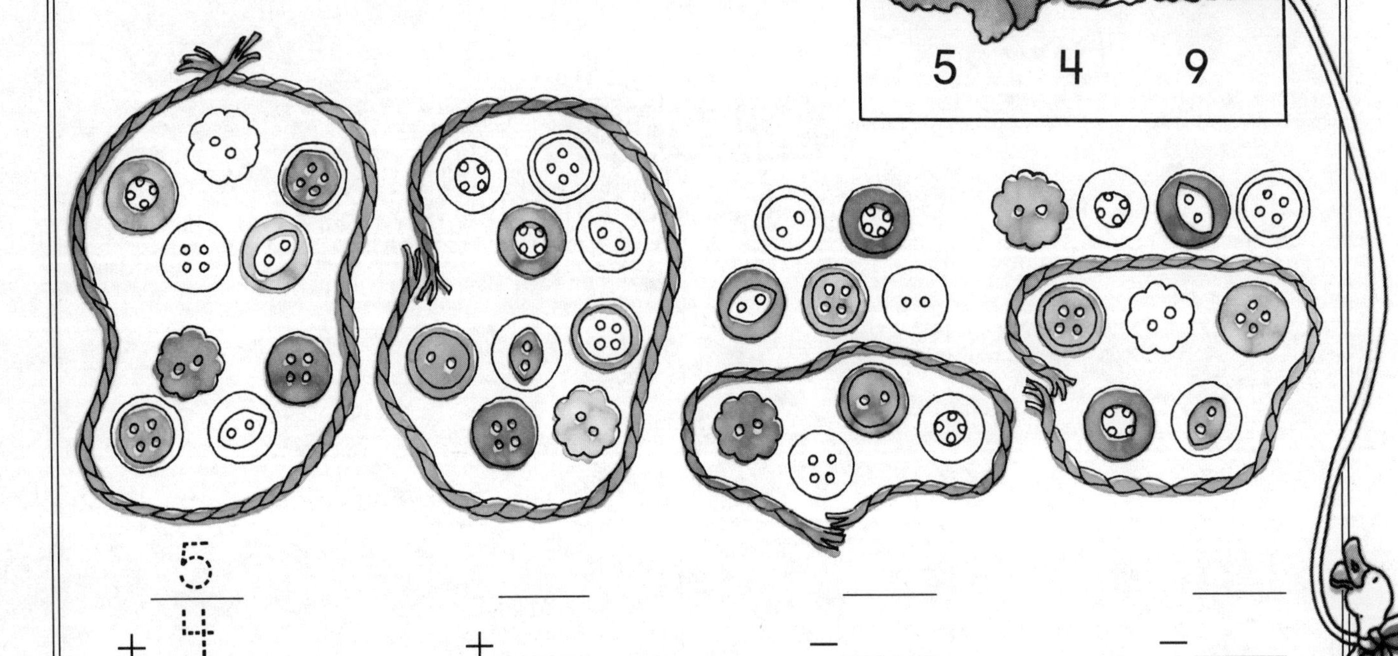

5	___	___	___
+ 4	+ ___	− ___	− ___
9	___	___	___

Name ______________________________

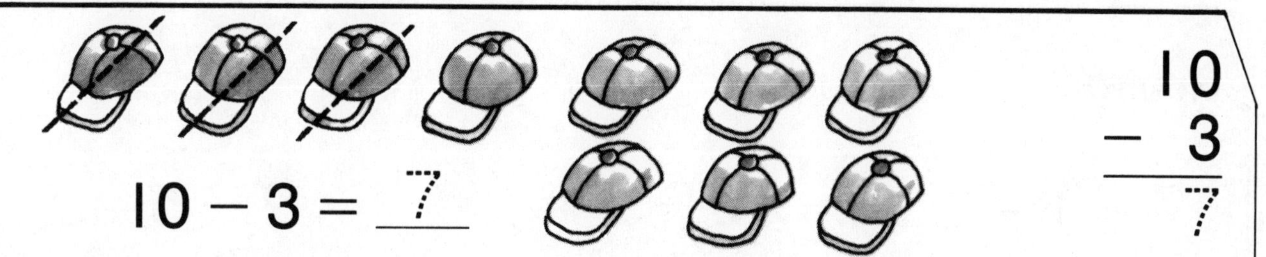

$10 - 3 = \underline{7}$

$$\begin{array}{r} 10 \\ -\ 3 \\ \hline 7 \end{array}$$

Cross out and subtract.

$$\begin{array}{r} 10 \\ -\ 2 \\ \hline \end{array}$$

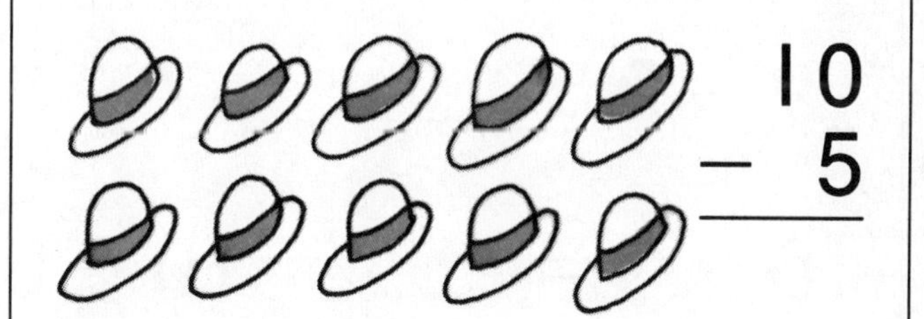

$$\begin{array}{r} 10 \\ -\ 5 \\ \hline \end{array}$$

$$\begin{array}{r} 10 \\ -\ 6 \\ \hline \end{array}$$

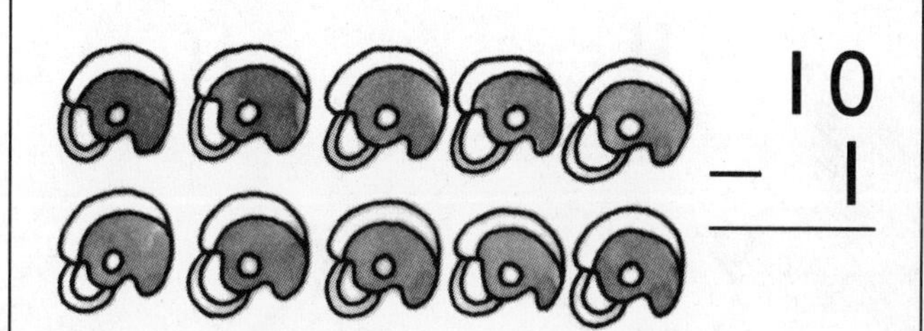

$$\begin{array}{r} 10 \\ -\ 1 \\ \hline \end{array}$$

$$\begin{array}{r} 10 \\ -\ 8 \\ \hline \end{array}$$

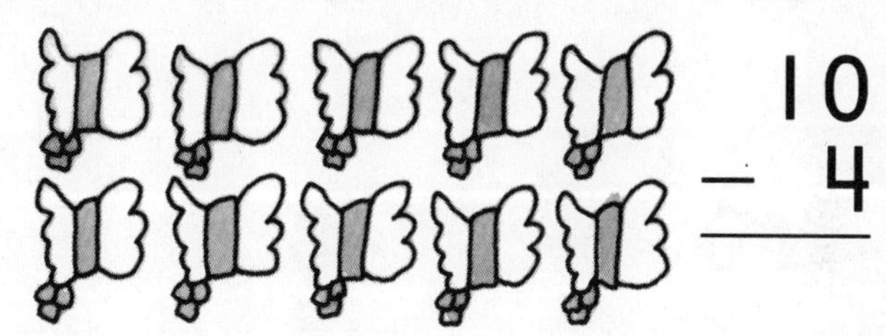

$$\begin{array}{r} 10 \\ -\ 4 \\ \hline \end{array}$$

$$\begin{array}{r} 10 \\ -\ 7 \\ \hline \end{array}$$

$$\begin{array}{r} 10 \\ -\ 9 \\ \hline \end{array}$$

$$\begin{array}{r} 10 \\ -\ 2 \\ \hline \end{array} \qquad \begin{array}{r} 10 \\ -\ 5 \\ \hline \end{array} \qquad \begin{array}{r} 10 \\ -\ 1 \\ \hline \end{array} \qquad \begin{array}{r} 10 \\ -\ 3 \\ \hline \end{array} \qquad \begin{array}{r} 10 \\ -\ 7 \\ \hline \end{array}$$

Subtract.

$7 - 1 =$ ___ $10 - 2 =$ ___ $9 - 5 =$ ___

$8 - 2 =$ ___ $9 - 4 =$ ___ $8 - 6 =$ ___

$9 - 2 =$ ___ $7 - 3 =$ ___ $10 - 8 =$ ___

$10 - 3 =$ ___ $10 - 0 =$ ___ $7 - 5 =$ ___

$7 - 4 =$ ___ $10 - 6 =$ ___ $9 - 6 =$ ___

$\begin{array}{r} 9 \\ -8 \\ \hline \end{array}$ $\begin{array}{r} 7 \\ -2 \\ \hline \end{array}$ $\begin{array}{r} 9 \\ -0 \\ \hline \end{array}$ $\begin{array}{r} 10 \\ -\ 1 \\ \hline \end{array}$ $\begin{array}{r} 10 \\ -\ 4 \\ \hline \end{array}$

$\begin{array}{r} 10 \\ -\ 7 \\ \hline \end{array}$ $\begin{array}{r} 8 \\ -3 \\ \hline \end{array}$ $\begin{array}{r} 9 \\ -7 \\ \hline \end{array}$ $\begin{array}{r} 7 \\ -6 \\ \hline \end{array}$ $\begin{array}{r} 8 \\ -4 \\ \hline \end{array}$

$\begin{array}{r} 8 \\ -7 \\ \hline \end{array}$ $\begin{array}{r} 10 \\ -\ 5 \\ \hline \end{array}$ $\begin{array}{r} 8 \\ -5 \\ \hline \end{array}$ $\begin{array}{r} 7 \\ -0 \\ \hline \end{array}$ $\begin{array}{r} 10 \\ -\ 9 \\ \hline \end{array}$

Name ______________________

How many in all? 5 ¢

Have	5 ¢
Cost of car	−3 ¢
Money left?	2 ¢

Count and subtract.

How many in all? ____ ¢

$$\begin{array}{r} 6¢ \\ -5¢ \\ \hline ¢ \end{array}$$

How many in all? ____ ¢

$$\begin{array}{r} 9¢ \\ -4¢ \\ \hline ¢ \end{array}$$

How many in all? ____ ¢

$$\begin{array}{r} 8¢ \\ -5¢ \\ \hline ¢ \end{array}$$

2¢

How many in all? ____ ¢

$$\begin{array}{r} 7¢ \\ -2¢ \\ \hline ¢ \end{array}$$

How many in all? ____ ¢

$$\begin{array}{r} 10¢ \\ -\ 5¢ \\ \hline ¢ \end{array}$$

How many in all? ____ ¢

$$\begin{array}{r} 10¢ \\ -\ 7¢ \\ \hline ¢ \end{array}$$

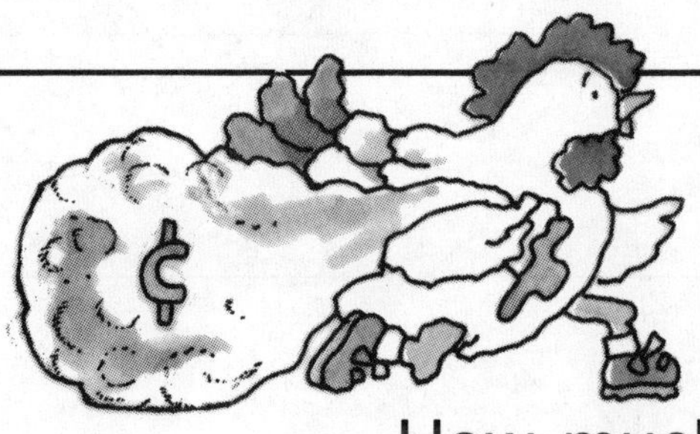

Have	9 ¢
Spent	−5 ¢
How much left?	4 ¢

Subtract.

6 ¢
−2 ¢
¢

Spent 2¢.

7 ¢
−4 ¢
¢

Spent 4¢.

9 ¢	8 ¢	7 ¢	5 ¢	7 ¢
−2 ¢	−5 ¢	−7 ¢	−3 ¢	−5 ¢
¢	¢	¢	¢	¢

6 ¢	10 ¢	4 ¢	6 ¢	10 ¢
−3 ¢	− 2 ¢	−1 ¢	−1 ¢	− 5 ¢
¢	¢	¢	¢	¢

7 ¢	9 ¢	10 ¢	5 ¢	10 ¢
−3 ¢	−4 ¢	− 8 ¢	−2 ¢	− 7 ¢
¢	¢	¢	¢	¢

8 ¢	6 ¢	10 ¢	9 ¢	10 ¢
−3 ¢	−4 ¢	− 1 ¢	−7 ¢	− 6 ¢
¢	¢	¢	¢	¢

Name ______________________________

Subtract.

$8 - 2 =$ ___ $10 - 3 =$ ___ $4 - 3 =$ ___

$9 - 5 =$ ___ $7 - 6 =$ ___ $6 - 1 =$ ___

$5 - 2 =$ ___ $9 - 2 =$ ___ $8 - 6 =$ ___

$8 - 7 =$ ___ $3 - 1 =$ ___ $10 - 2 =$ ___

$6 - 0 =$ ___ $7 - 4 =$ ___ $8 - 5 =$ ___

$9 - 6 =$ ___ $4 - 2 =$ ___ $9 - 1 =$ ___

$\begin{array}{r} 7 \\ -5 \\ \hline \end{array}$ $\begin{array}{r} 10 \\ -8 \\ \hline \end{array}$ $\begin{array}{r} 4 \\ -1 \\ \hline \end{array}$ $\begin{array}{r} 7 \\ -3 \\ \hline \end{array}$ $\begin{array}{r} 5 \\ -5 \\ \hline \end{array}$ $\begin{array}{r} 10 \\ -1 \\ \hline \end{array}$

$\begin{array}{r} 8 \\ -1 \\ \hline \end{array}$ $\begin{array}{r} 10 \\ -9 \\ \hline \end{array}$ $\begin{array}{r} 8 \\ -4 \\ \hline \end{array}$ $\begin{array}{r} 10 \\ -4 \\ \hline \end{array}$ $\begin{array}{r} 8 \\ -3 \\ \hline \end{array}$ $\begin{array}{r} 9 \\ -3 \\ \hline \end{array}$

$\begin{array}{r} 10 \\ -5 \\ \hline \end{array}$ $\begin{array}{r} 9 \\ -7 \\ \hline \end{array}$ $\begin{array}{r} 6 \\ -3 \\ \hline \end{array}$ $\begin{array}{r} 10 \\ -7 \\ \hline \end{array}$ $\begin{array}{r} 7 \\ -7 \\ \hline \end{array}$ $\begin{array}{r} 10 \\ -4 \\ \hline \end{array}$

Add.

3 + 3	5 + 5	0 + 7	4 + 6	4 + 4	6 + 1
2 + 8	7 + 2	2 + 5	2 + 4	5 + 3	8 + 1
5 + 4	1 + 9	6 + 2	3 + 4	3 + 7	1 + 7

Subtract.

8 − 3	5 − 1	10 − 5	8 − 6	6 − 3	5 − 5
10 − 6	6 − 5	7 − 2	4 − 2	9 − 1	9 − 7
7 − 7	10 − 3	6 − 1	9 − 5	10 − 9	7 − 3

Name ____________________

CHAPTER CHECKUP

Subtract.

$\begin{array}{r} 8 \\ -4 \\ \hline \end{array}$	$\begin{array}{r} 9 \\ -2 \\ \hline \end{array}$	$\begin{array}{r} 6 \\ -2 \\ \hline \end{array}$	$\begin{array}{r} 8 \\ -7 \\ \hline \end{array}$	$\begin{array}{r} 6 \\ -3 \\ \hline \end{array}$	$\begin{array}{r} 9 \\ -5 \\ \hline \end{array}$
$\begin{array}{r} 4 \\ -2 \\ \hline \end{array}$	$\begin{array}{r} 7 \\ -3 \\ \hline \end{array}$	$\begin{array}{r} 10 \\ -\ 1 \\ \hline \end{array}$	$\begin{array}{r} 9 \\ -8 \\ \hline \end{array}$	$\begin{array}{r} 4 \\ -4 \\ \hline \end{array}$	$\begin{array}{r} 7 \\ -2 \\ \hline \end{array}$
$\begin{array}{r} 6 \\ -5 \\ \hline \end{array}$	$\begin{array}{r} 10 \\ -\ 4 \\ \hline \end{array}$	$\begin{array}{r} 9 \\ -7 \\ \hline \end{array}$	$\begin{array}{r} 10 \\ -\ 7 \\ \hline \end{array}$	$\begin{array}{r} 9 \\ -0 \\ \hline \end{array}$	$\begin{array}{r} 10 \\ -\ 3 \\ \hline \end{array}$
$\begin{array}{r} 5 \\ -2 \\ \hline \end{array}$	$\begin{array}{r} 8 \\ -2 \\ \hline \end{array}$	$\begin{array}{r} 10 \\ -\ 9 \\ \hline \end{array}$	$\begin{array}{r} 9 \\ -3 \\ \hline \end{array}$	$\begin{array}{r} 10 \\ -\ 5 \\ \hline \end{array}$	$\begin{array}{r} 8 \\ -5 \\ \hline \end{array}$

Solve.

$\begin{array}{r} 9¢ \\ -4¢ \\ \hline ¢ \end{array}$

Spent 4¢.

$\begin{array}{r} 10¢ \\ -\ 4¢ \\ \hline ¢ \end{array}$

Spent 4¢.

ROUNDUP REVIEW

Write the missing numbers.

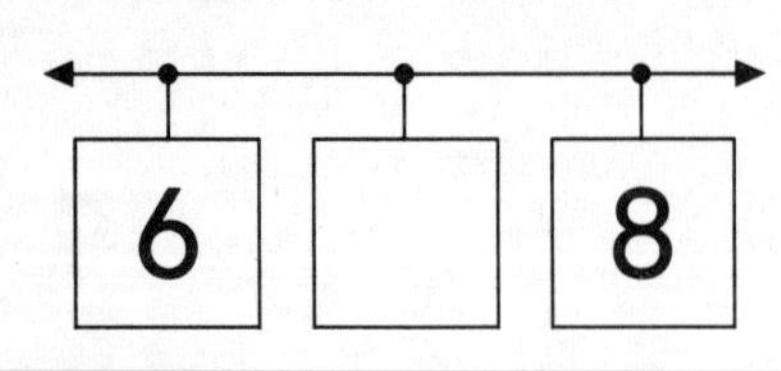

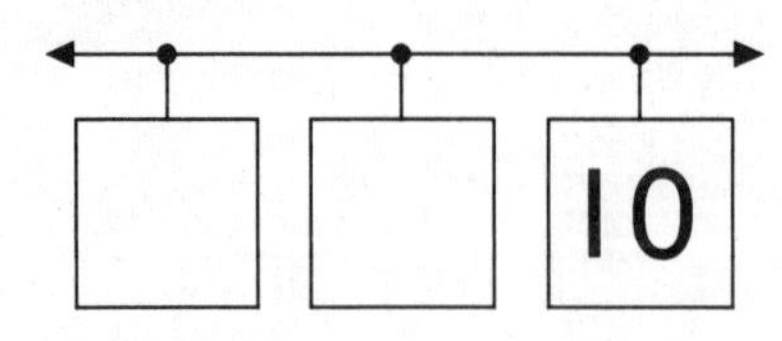

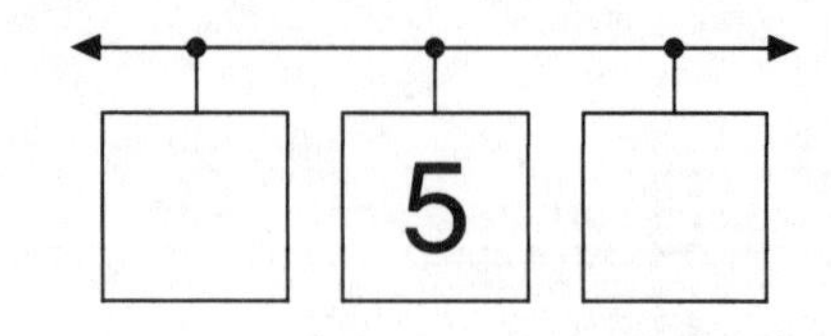

Add.

$\begin{array}{r} 3 \\ +3 \\ \hline \end{array}$	$\begin{array}{r} 6 \\ +2 \\ \hline \end{array}$	$\begin{array}{r} 1 \\ +3 \\ \hline \end{array}$	$\begin{array}{r} 7 \\ +3 \\ \hline \end{array}$	$\begin{array}{r} 2 \\ +1 \\ \hline \end{array}$	$\begin{array}{r} 3 \\ +4 \\ \hline \end{array}$

Subtract.

$10 - 8 =$ ___ $8 - 3 =$ ___ $9 - 6 =$ ___

$7 - 3 =$ ___ $7 - 7 =$ ___ $6 - 4 =$ ___

$10 - 5 =$ ___ $5 - 0 =$ ___ $7 - 4 =$ ___

Solve.

How much money? ___¢

How much money? ___¢

$\begin{array}{r} 6¢ \\ +3¢ \\ \hline ¢ \end{array}$

Spent 4¢.

$\begin{array}{r} 8¢ \\ -4¢ \\ \hline ¢ \end{array}$

Name ______________________________

BASIC FACTS, SUMS THROUGH 10

Add both ways.

$$\begin{array}{r} 4 \\ +2 \\ \hline 6 \end{array} \qquad \begin{array}{r} 2 \\ +4 \\ \hline 6 \end{array}$$

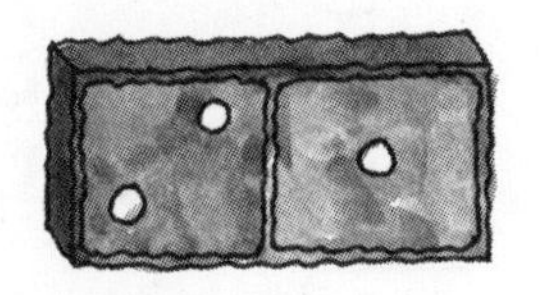

$$\begin{array}{r} 2 \\ +1 \\ \hline \end{array} \qquad \begin{array}{r} 1 \\ +2 \\ \hline \end{array}$$

$$\begin{array}{r} 0 \\ +2 \\ \hline \end{array} \qquad \begin{array}{r} 2 \\ +0 \\ \hline \end{array}$$

$$\begin{array}{r} 3 \\ +2 \\ \hline \end{array} \qquad \begin{array}{r} 2 \\ +3 \\ \hline \end{array}$$

$$\begin{array}{r} 4 \\ +0 \\ \hline \end{array} \qquad \begin{array}{r} 0 \\ +4 \\ \hline \end{array}$$

$$\begin{array}{r} 5 \\ +1 \\ \hline \end{array} \qquad \begin{array}{r} 1 \\ +5 \\ \hline \end{array}$$

$$\begin{array}{r} 1 \\ +0 \\ \hline \end{array} \qquad \begin{array}{r} 0 \\ +1 \\ \hline \end{array}$$

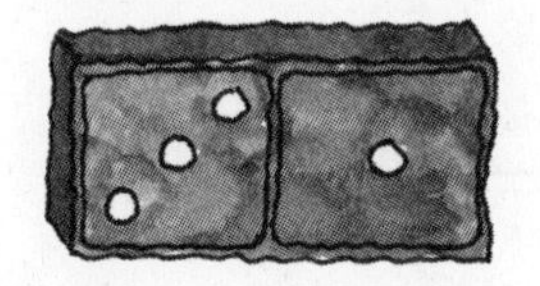

$$\begin{array}{r} 3 \\ +1 \\ \hline \end{array} \qquad \begin{array}{r} 1 \\ +3 \\ \hline \end{array}$$

$$\begin{array}{r} 3 \\ +0 \\ \hline \end{array} \qquad \begin{array}{r} 0 \\ +3 \\ \hline \end{array}$$

$$\begin{array}{r} 4 \\ +1 \\ \hline \end{array} \qquad \begin{array}{r} 1 \\ +4 \\ \hline \end{array}$$

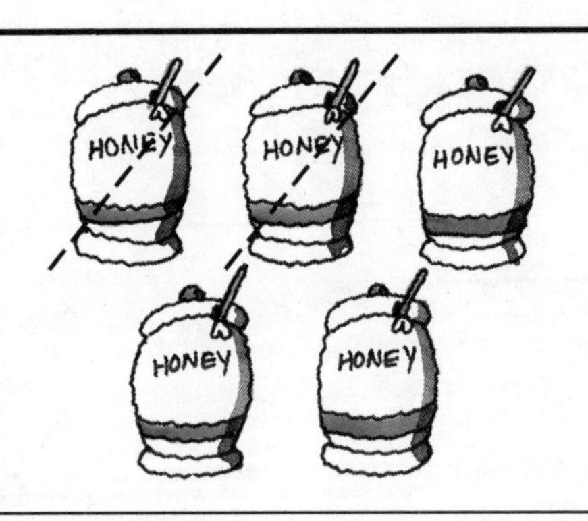

$$\begin{array}{r} 5 \\ -2 \\ \hline 3 \end{array}$$

$$\begin{array}{r} 5 \\ -3 \\ \hline 2 \end{array}$$

Subtract.

$$\begin{array}{r} 3 \\ -1 \\ \hline \end{array} \quad \begin{array}{r} 3 \\ -2 \\ \hline \end{array} \qquad \begin{array}{r} 5 \\ -1 \\ \hline \end{array} \quad \begin{array}{r} 5 \\ -4 \\ \hline \end{array} \qquad \begin{array}{r} 6 \\ -2 \\ \hline \end{array} \quad \begin{array}{r} 6 \\ -4 \\ \hline \end{array}$$

$$\begin{array}{r} 2 \\ -0 \\ \hline \end{array} \quad \begin{array}{r} 2 \\ -2 \\ \hline \end{array} \qquad \begin{array}{r} 4 \\ -1 \\ \hline \end{array} \quad \begin{array}{r} 4 \\ -3 \\ \hline \end{array} \qquad \begin{array}{r} 5 \\ -0 \\ \hline \end{array} \quad \begin{array}{r} 5 \\ -5 \\ \hline \end{array}$$

$$\begin{array}{r} 6 \\ -1 \\ \hline \end{array} \quad \begin{array}{r} 6 \\ -5 \\ \hline \end{array} \qquad \begin{array}{r} 1 \\ -0 \\ \hline \end{array} \quad \begin{array}{r} 1 \\ -1 \\ \hline \end{array} \qquad \begin{array}{r} 3 \\ -0 \\ \hline \end{array} \quad \begin{array}{r} 3 \\ -3 \\ \hline \end{array}$$

$$\begin{array}{r} 2 \\ -1 \\ \hline \end{array} \quad \begin{array}{r} 4 \\ -0 \\ \hline \end{array} \quad \begin{array}{r} 6 \\ -3 \\ \hline \end{array} \quad \begin{array}{r} 4 \\ -2 \\ \hline \end{array} \quad \begin{array}{r} 6 \\ -6 \\ \hline \end{array} \quad \begin{array}{r} 4 \\ -4 \\ \hline \end{array}$$

Name ____________________

$$\begin{array}{r} 6 \\ +4 \\ \hline 10 \end{array} \qquad \begin{array}{r} 4 \\ +6 \\ \hline 10 \end{array}$$

Add both ways.

$$\begin{array}{r} 7 \\ +2 \\ \hline \end{array} \qquad \begin{array}{r} 2 \\ +7 \\ \hline \end{array} \qquad \begin{array}{r} 1 \\ +5 \\ \hline \end{array} \qquad \begin{array}{r} 5 \\ +1 \\ \hline \end{array} \qquad \begin{array}{r} 2 \\ +6 \\ \hline \end{array} \qquad \begin{array}{r} 6 \\ +2 \\ \hline \end{array}$$

$$\begin{array}{r} 9 \\ +1 \\ \hline \end{array} \qquad \begin{array}{r} 1 \\ +9 \\ \hline \end{array} \qquad \begin{array}{r} 5 \\ +3 \\ \hline \end{array} \qquad \begin{array}{r} 3 \\ +5 \\ \hline \end{array} \qquad \begin{array}{r} 6 \\ +3 \\ \hline \end{array} \qquad \begin{array}{r} 3 \\ +6 \\ \hline \end{array}$$

$$\begin{array}{r} 5 \\ +4 \\ \hline \end{array} \qquad \begin{array}{r} 4 \\ +5 \\ \hline \end{array} \qquad \begin{array}{r} 4 \\ +3 \\ \hline \end{array} \qquad \begin{array}{r} 3 \\ +4 \\ \hline \end{array} \qquad \begin{array}{r} 3 \\ +7 \\ \hline \end{array} \qquad \begin{array}{r} 7 \\ +3 \\ \hline \end{array}$$

$$\begin{array}{r} 5 \\ +5 \\ \hline \end{array} \qquad \begin{array}{r} 9 \\ +0 \\ \hline \end{array} \qquad \begin{array}{r} 3 \\ +3 \\ \hline \end{array} \qquad \begin{array}{r} 0 \\ +7 \\ \hline \end{array} \qquad \begin{array}{r} 4 \\ +4 \\ \hline \end{array}$$

$$\begin{array}{r} 10 \\ -\ 3 \\ \hline 7 \end{array}$$

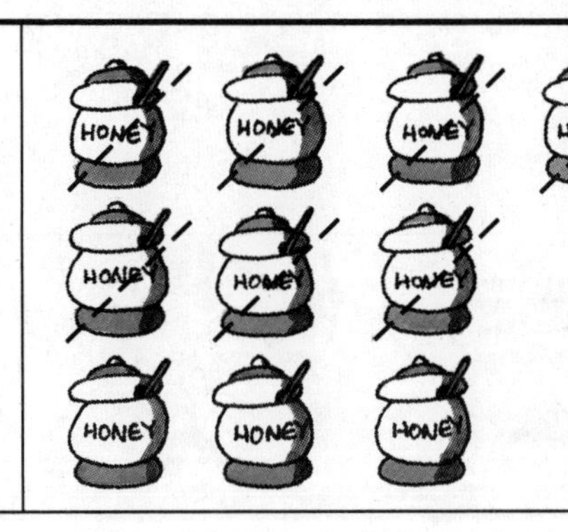

$$\begin{array}{r} 10 \\ -\ 7 \\ \hline 3 \end{array}$$

Subtract.

$$\begin{array}{r} 8 \\ -2 \\ \hline \end{array} \quad \begin{array}{r} 8 \\ -6 \\ \hline \end{array} \qquad \begin{array}{r} 7 \\ -4 \\ \hline \end{array} \quad \begin{array}{r} 7 \\ -3 \\ \hline \end{array} \qquad \begin{array}{r} 9 \\ -6 \\ \hline \end{array} \quad \begin{array}{r} 9 \\ -3 \\ \hline \end{array}$$

$$\begin{array}{r} 6 \\ -4 \\ \hline \end{array} \quad \begin{array}{r} 6 \\ -2 \\ \hline \end{array} \qquad \begin{array}{r} 9 \\ -5 \\ \hline \end{array} \quad \begin{array}{r} 9 \\ -4 \\ \hline \end{array} \qquad \begin{array}{r} 10 \\ -\ 2 \\ \hline \end{array} \quad \begin{array}{r} 10 \\ -\ 8 \\ \hline \end{array}$$

$$\begin{array}{r} 8 \\ -5 \\ \hline \end{array} \quad \begin{array}{r} 8 \\ -3 \\ \hline \end{array} \qquad \begin{array}{r} 10 \\ -\ 6 \\ \hline \end{array} \quad \begin{array}{r} 10 \\ -\ 4 \\ \hline \end{array} \qquad \begin{array}{r} 9 \\ -7 \\ \hline \end{array} \quad \begin{array}{r} 9 \\ -2 \\ \hline \end{array}$$

$$\begin{array}{r} 6 \\ -6 \\ \hline \end{array} \qquad \begin{array}{r} 9 \\ -0 \\ \hline \end{array} \qquad \begin{array}{r} 10 \\ -\ 1 \\ \hline \end{array} \qquad \begin{array}{r} 8 \\ -8 \\ \hline \end{array} \qquad \begin{array}{r} 10 \\ -\ 9 \\ \hline \end{array}$$

Name ______________________

Add. 

7 + 2 = ___	8 + 1 = ___	8 + 2 = ___
1 + 9 = ___	3 + 3 = ___	0 + 9 = ___
2 + 7 = ___	9 + 1 = ___	9 + 0 = ___
7 + 0 = ___	1 + 8 = ___	1 + 7 = ___
0 + 7 = ___	2 + 8 = ___	7 + 3 = ___

FIELD TRIP

Complete the wheels.

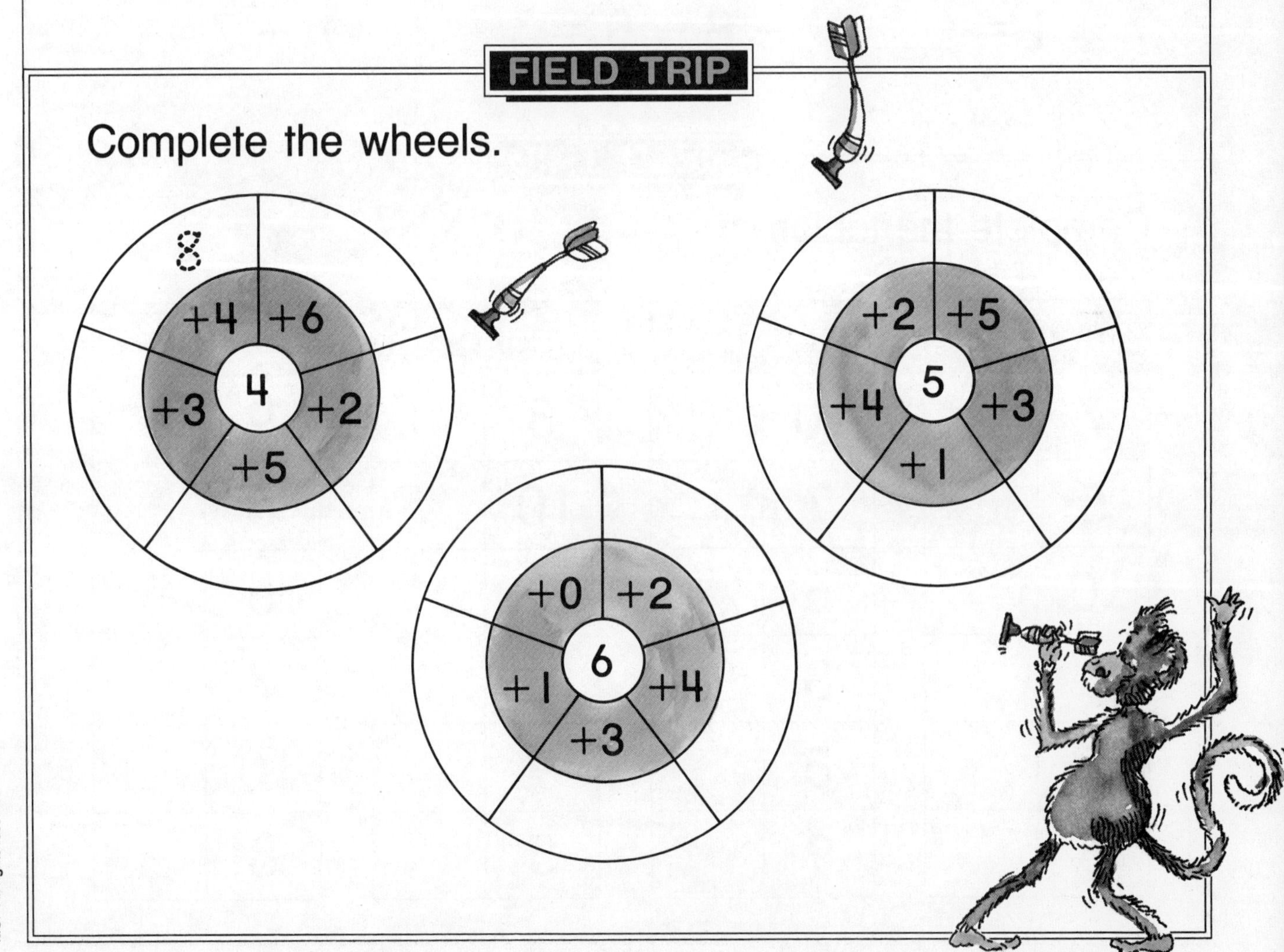

Subtract.

10 − 7 = ___	6 − 1 = ___	8 − 7 = ___
8 − 1 = ___	9 − 9 = ___	7 − 5 = ___
6 − 3 = ___	10 − 3 = ___	9 − 1 = ___
10 − 5 = ___	8 − 4 = ___	7 − 2 = ___
9 − 8 = ___	7 − 6 = ___	6 − 5 = ___
7 − 1 = ___	8 − 0 = ___	7 − 7 = ___

FIELD TRIP

Complete the tables.

Subtract 5	
7	2
5	
10	
8	
9	
6	

Subtract 2	
10	
7	
6	
8	
5	
9	

Subtract 4	
8	
10	
7	
6	
9	
5	

Subtract 3	
9	
6	
5	
7	
10	
8	

Name ______________________

Add or subtract.

$7 + 2 =$ ___ $6 + 2 =$ ___ $5 + 0 =$ ___

$4 - 1 =$ ___ $6 - 2 =$ ___ $7 - 2 =$ ___

$7 + 1 =$ ___ $4 + 2 =$ ___ $9 - 3 =$ ___

$3 + 2 =$ ___ $9 - 6 =$ ___ $6 + 3 =$ ___

$4 - 4 =$ ___ $10 - 2 =$ ___ $5 - 4 =$ ___

$5 + 2 =$ ___ $8 - 2 =$ ___ $1 + 2 =$ ___

$\begin{array}{r} 3 \\ -2 \\ \hline \end{array}$ $\begin{array}{r} 9 \\ -7 \\ \hline \end{array}$ $\begin{array}{r} 10 \\ -\ 5 \\ \hline \end{array}$ $\begin{array}{r} 9 \\ -1 \\ \hline \end{array}$ $\begin{array}{r} 3 \\ +7 \\ \hline \end{array}$ $\begin{array}{r} 10 \\ -\ 7 \\ \hline \end{array}$

$\begin{array}{r} 2 \\ +2 \\ \hline \end{array}$ $\begin{array}{r} 10 \\ -\ 3 \\ \hline \end{array}$ $\begin{array}{r} 9 \\ +1 \\ \hline \end{array}$ $\begin{array}{r} 2 \\ +7 \\ \hline \end{array}$ $\begin{array}{r} 8 \\ +2 \\ \hline \end{array}$ $\begin{array}{r} 6 \\ -3 \\ \hline \end{array}$

$\begin{array}{r} 0 \\ +7 \\ \hline \end{array}$ $\begin{array}{r} 6 \\ -4 \\ \hline \end{array}$ $\begin{array}{r} 2 \\ +1 \\ \hline \end{array}$ $\begin{array}{r} 6 \\ -5 \\ \hline \end{array}$ $\begin{array}{r} 4 \\ +5 \\ \hline \end{array}$ $\begin{array}{r} 2 \\ +3 \\ \hline \end{array}$

Add or subtract.

$0 + 3 =$ ___ $9 - 0 =$ ___ $4 + 4 =$ ___

$2 + 5 =$ ___ $4 - 3 =$ ___ $7 - 3 =$ ___

$10 - 6 =$ ___ $4 + 6 =$ ___ $5 + 3 =$ ___

$7 - 4 =$ ___ $3 - 1 =$ ___ $1 + 4 =$ ___

$1 + 7 =$ ___ $4 + 3 =$ ___ $7 - 6 =$ ___

$8 - 1 =$ ___ $9 - 4 =$ ___ $0 + 5 =$ ___

$\begin{array}{r} 2 \\ +4 \\ \hline \end{array}$ $\begin{array}{r} 6 \\ -6 \\ \hline \end{array}$ $\begin{array}{r} 8 \\ -3 \\ \hline \end{array}$ $\begin{array}{r} 3 \\ +3 \\ \hline \end{array}$ $\begin{array}{r} 5 \\ -3 \\ \hline \end{array}$ $\begin{array}{r} 9 \\ -8 \\ \hline \end{array}$

$\begin{array}{r} 3 \\ +4 \\ \hline \end{array}$ $\begin{array}{r} 1 \\ +5 \\ \hline \end{array}$ $\begin{array}{r} 8 \\ -7 \\ \hline \end{array}$ $\begin{array}{r} 7 \\ -5 \\ \hline \end{array}$ $\begin{array}{r} 2 \\ +6 \\ \hline \end{array}$ $\begin{array}{r} 8 \\ -5 \\ \hline \end{array}$

$\begin{array}{r} 2 \\ +8 \\ \hline \end{array}$ $\begin{array}{r} 5 \\ -2 \\ \hline \end{array}$ $\begin{array}{r} 8 \\ -6 \\ \hline \end{array}$ $\begin{array}{r} 3 \\ +5 \\ \hline \end{array}$ $\begin{array}{r} 5 \\ -0 \\ \hline \end{array}$ $\begin{array}{r} 7 \\ +3 \\ \hline \end{array}$

Name ______________________

Find the cost and add.

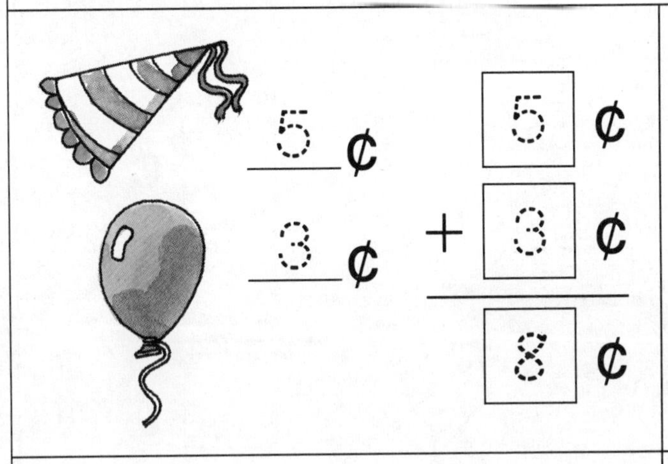

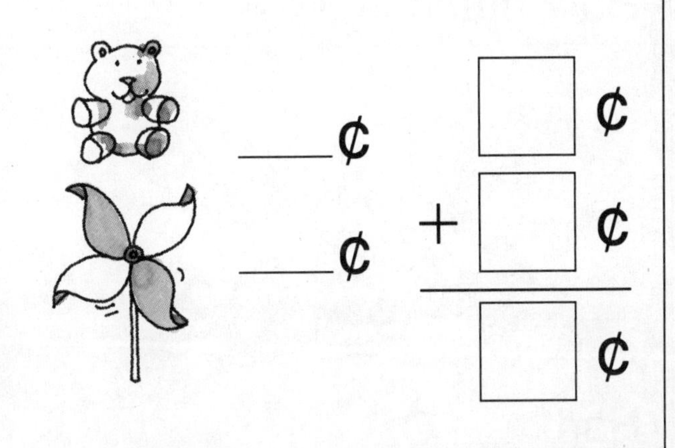

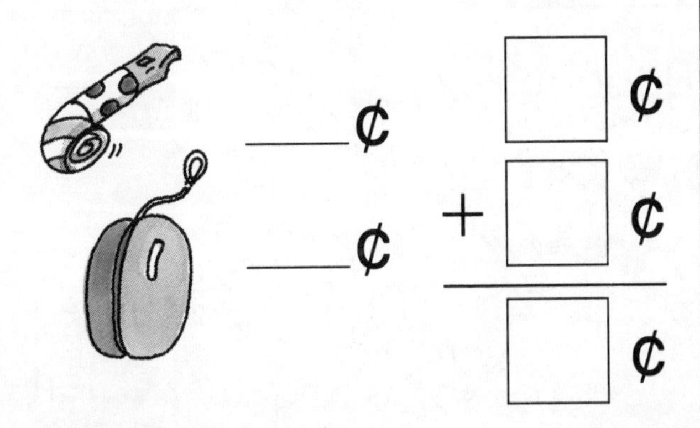

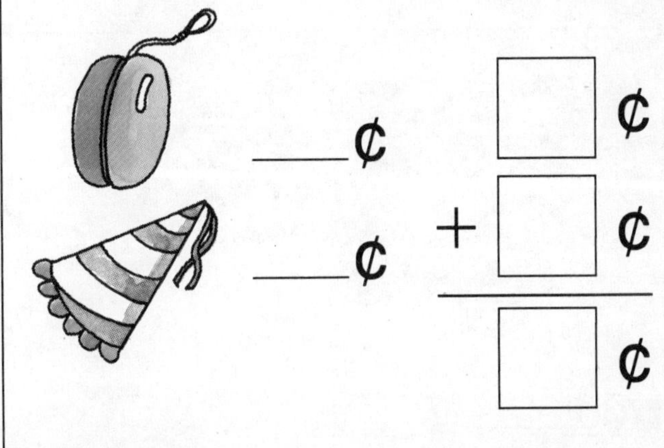

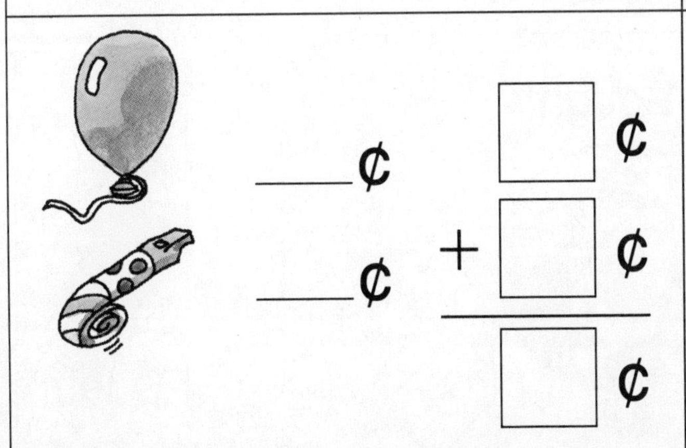

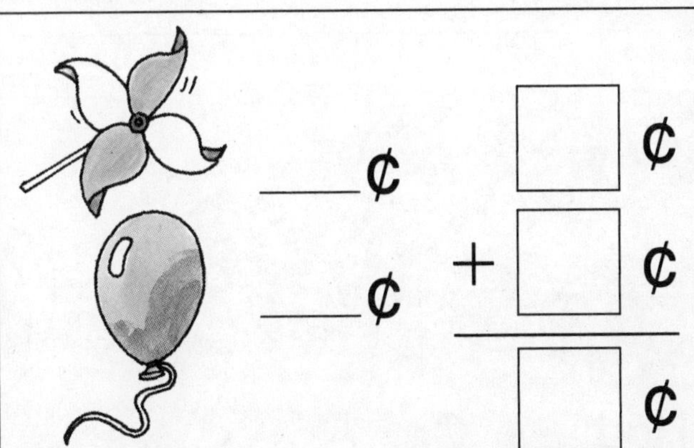

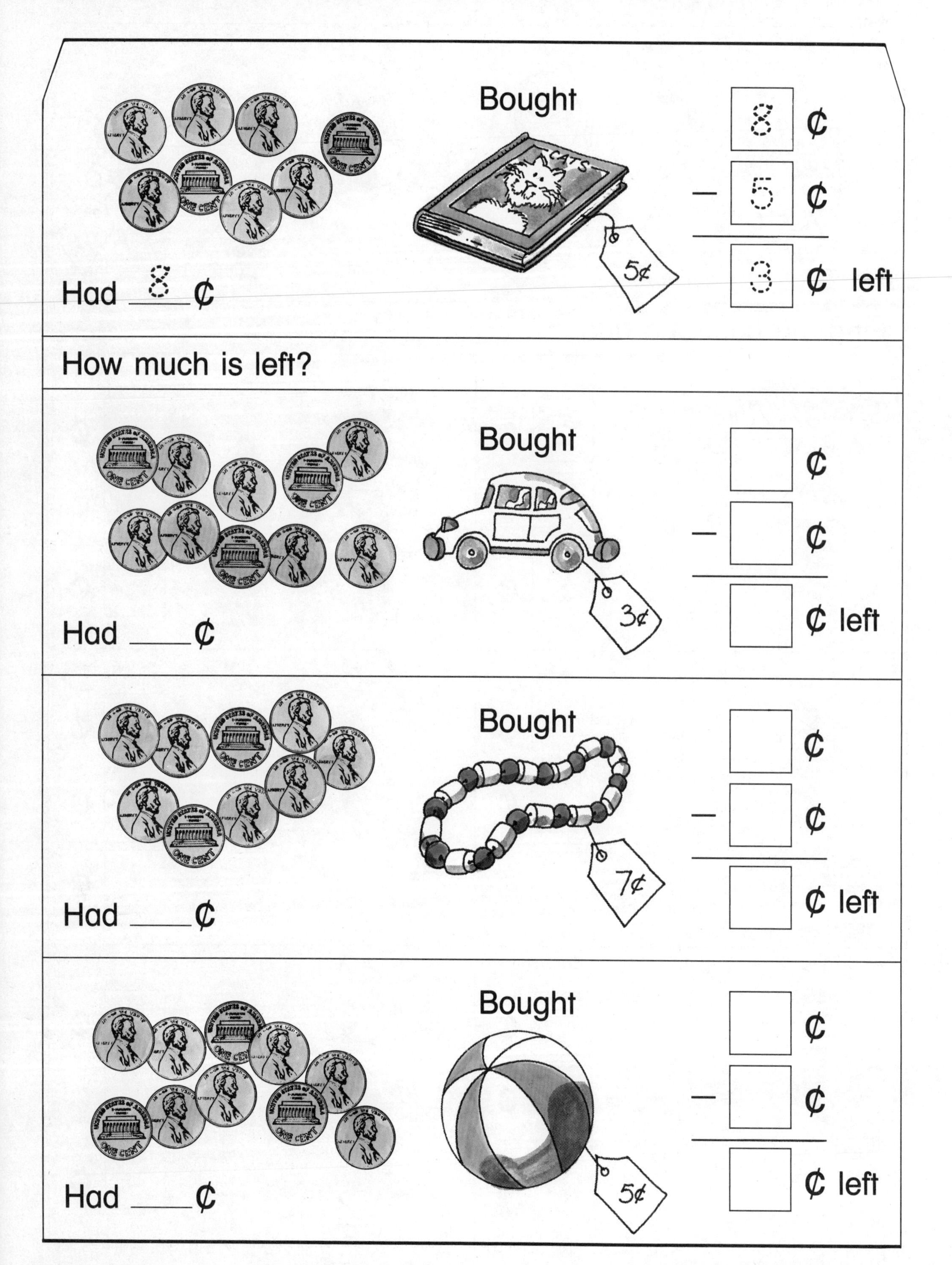

Bought
8 ¢
− 5 ¢
3 ¢ left
CATS
5¢
Had 8 ¢
How much is left?
Bought
¢
− ¢
¢ left
3¢
Had ¢
Bought
¢
− ¢
¢ left
7¢
Had ¢
Bought
¢
− ¢
¢ left
5¢
Had ¢

Name ______________________________

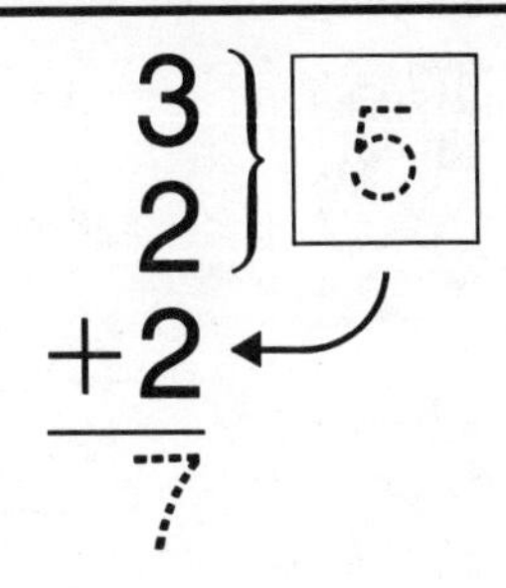

Add.

2 1 +5	3 2 +4	7 1 +2	1 3 +4

3 3 +3	3 1 +2	2 2 +3	9 0 +1	2 5 +2	6 1 +1
2 1 +7	5 3 +1	8 1 +1	4 1 +3	6 1 +3	5 1 +3
1 5 +2	6 2 +2	7 2 +1	2 4 +3	5 2 +3	3 4 +2

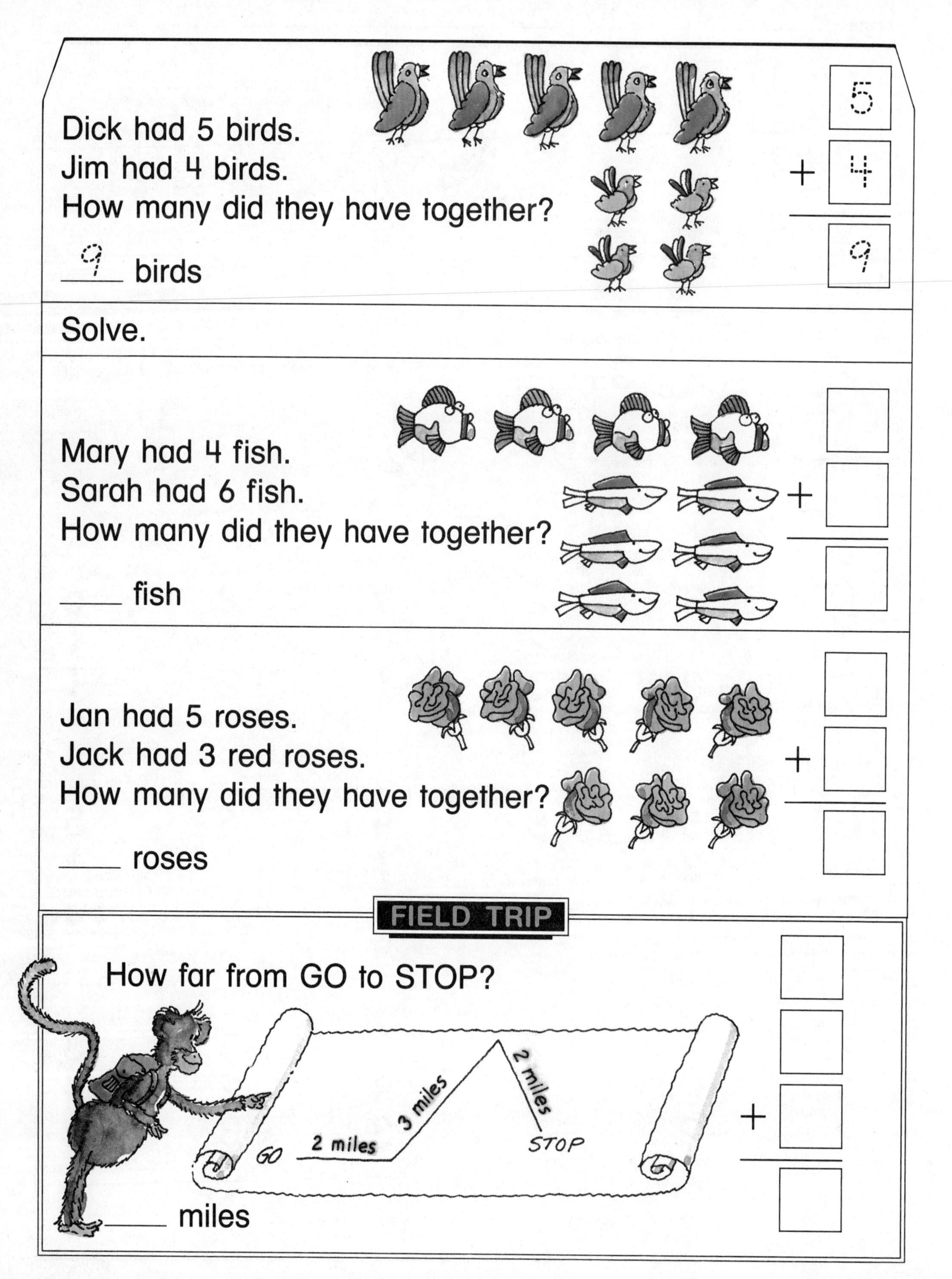

Dick had 5 birds.
Jim had 4 birds.
How many did they have together?

9 birds

$$\begin{array}{r} 5 \\ +\ 4 \\ \hline 9 \end{array}$$

Solve.

Mary had 4 fish.
Sarah had 6 fish.
How many did they have together?

____ fish

Jan had 5 roses.
Jack had 3 red roses.
How many did they have together?

____ roses

FIELD TRIP

How far from GO to STOP?

____ miles

Name ____________________

CHAPTER CHECKUP

Add or subtract.

7	3	1	5	9	2
+2	−2	+7	+3	−2	+4

5	6	10	8	8	7
−2	+4	− 1	−5	+2	−3

4	10	2	9	10	3
+4	− 4	+5	−6	− 7	+6

Solve.

How much did both cost?

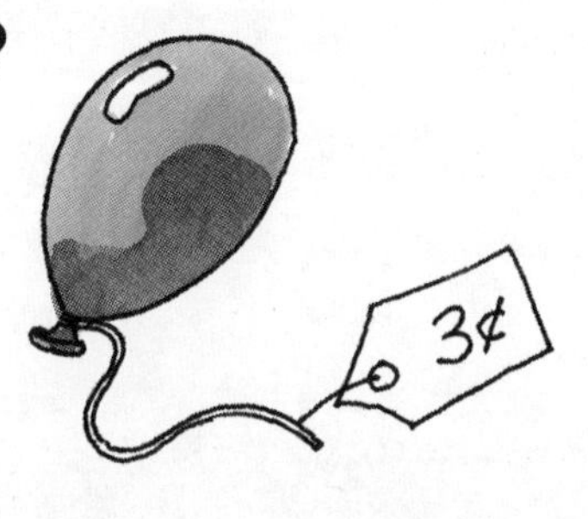

____¢

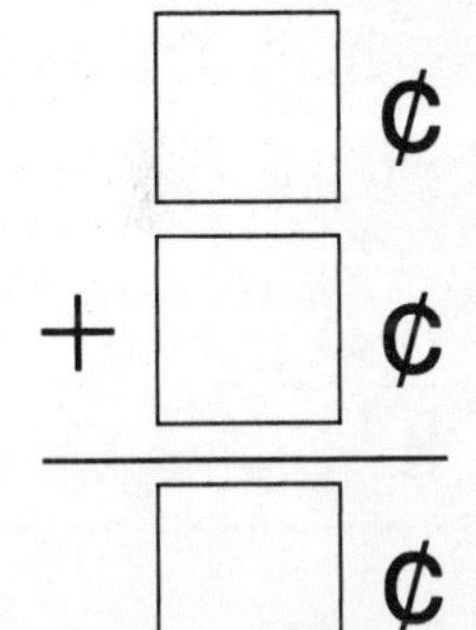

How much money was left?

____¢

Bought

☐ ¢
− ☐ ¢
☐ ¢

ROUNDUP REVIEW

Write the missing numbers.

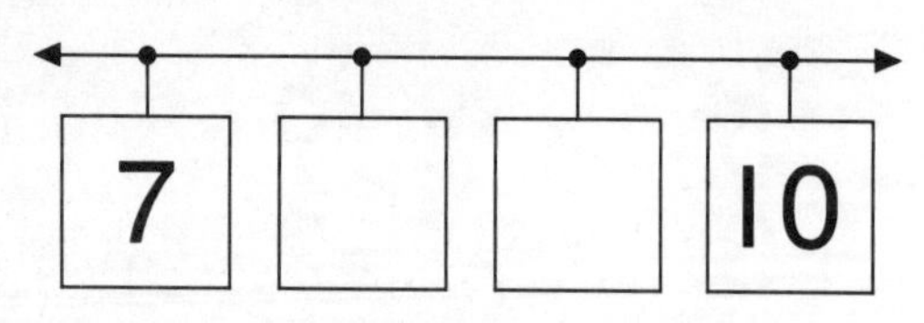

Count.

How much money? ____¢

How much money in all?

$$\begin{array}{r} 3¢ \\ +4¢ \\ \hline ¢ \end{array}$$

Add or subtract.

$$\begin{array}{r} 3 \\ +6 \\ \hline \end{array} \quad \begin{array}{r} 7 \\ -2 \\ \hline \end{array} \quad \begin{array}{r} 5 \\ +5 \\ \hline \end{array} \quad \begin{array}{r} 2 \\ +6 \\ \hline \end{array} \quad \begin{array}{r} 8 \\ -1 \\ \hline \end{array} \quad \begin{array}{r} 10 \\ -\ 7 \\ \hline \end{array}$$

$$\begin{array}{r} 3 \\ +4 \\ \hline \end{array} \quad \begin{array}{r} 8 \\ -3 \\ \hline \end{array} \quad \begin{array}{r} 10 \\ -\ 4 \\ \hline \end{array} \quad \begin{array}{r} 7 \\ +1 \\ \hline \end{array} \quad \begin{array}{r} 6 \\ +4 \\ \hline \end{array} \quad \begin{array}{r} 10 \\ -\ 2 \\ \hline \end{array}$$

Add.

$$\begin{array}{r} 1 \\ 2 \\ +3 \\ \hline \end{array} \quad \begin{array}{r} 4 \\ 3 \\ +2 \\ \hline \end{array} \quad \begin{array}{r} 6 \\ 1 \\ +1 \\ \hline \end{array}$$

How much money is left?

Had	7¢
Spent	−5¢
	¢

Name ____________________

5 PLACE VALUE THROUGH 99

How many are there in all?

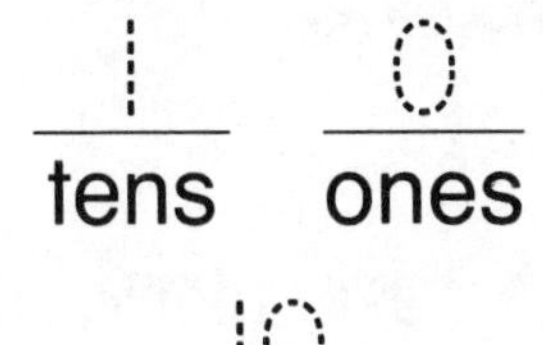

1 tens 0 ones

10

___ tens ___ ones
___

___ tens ___ ones
___

___ tens ___ ones
___

___ tens ___ ones
___

___ tens ___ ones
___

___ tens ___ ones
___

___ tens ___ ones
___

___ tens ___ ones
___

___ tens ___ ones
___

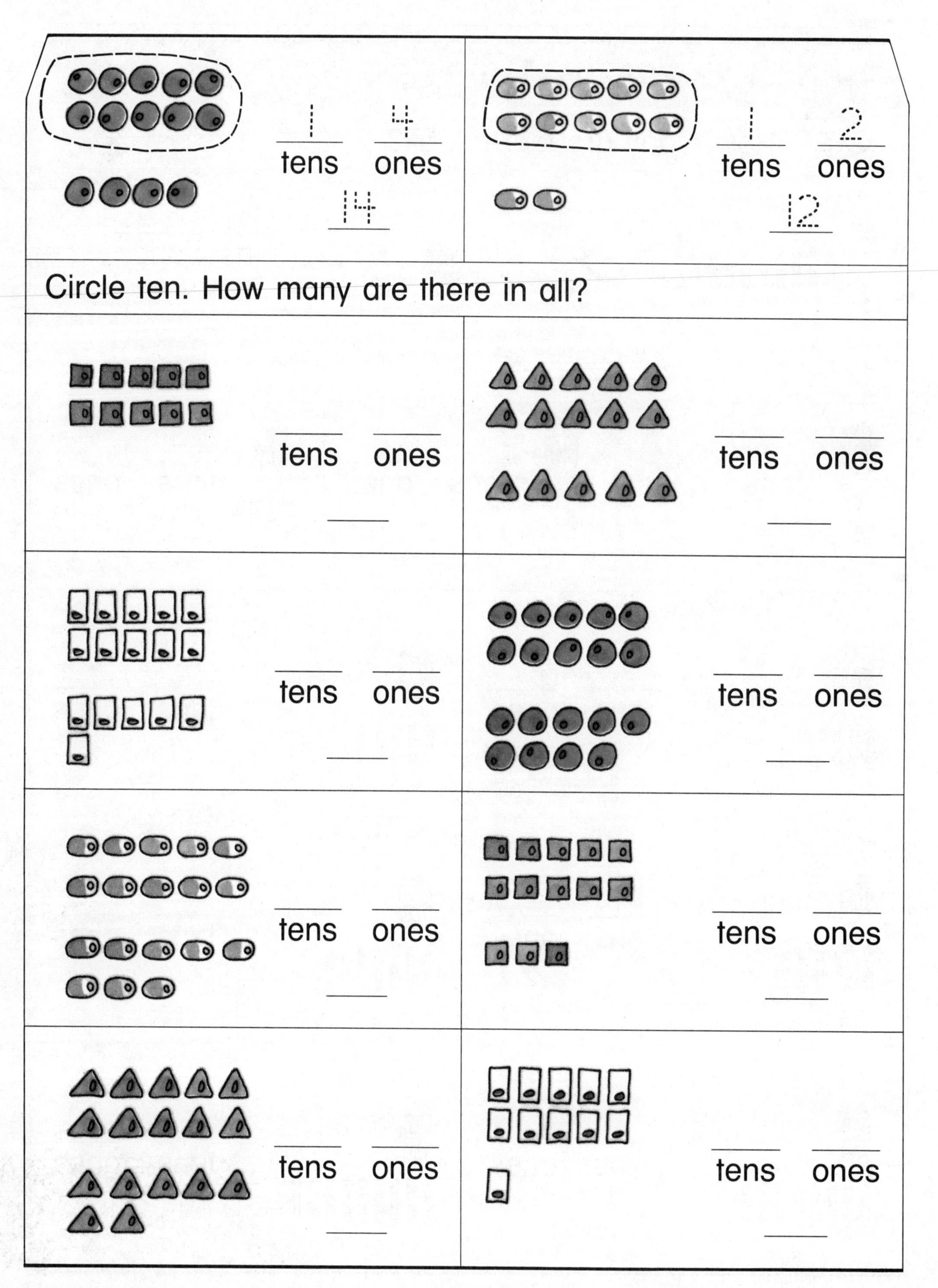
1
4
tens
ones
14
1
2
tens
ones
12
Circle ten. How many are there in all?
tens
ones
tens
ones
tens
ones
tens
ones
tens
ones
tens
ones
tens
ones
tens
ones

Name ______________________________

ten 10

Read and write the number.

eleven ____

twelve ____

thirteen ____

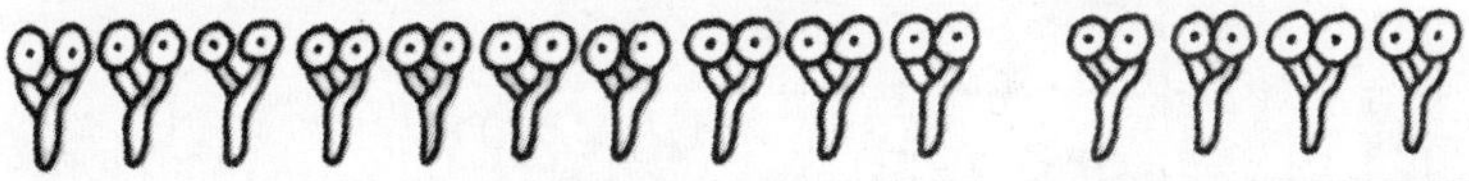

fourteen ____

fifteen ____

sixteen ____

seventeen ____

eighteen ____

nineteen ____

How many are there in all?

12

____

____

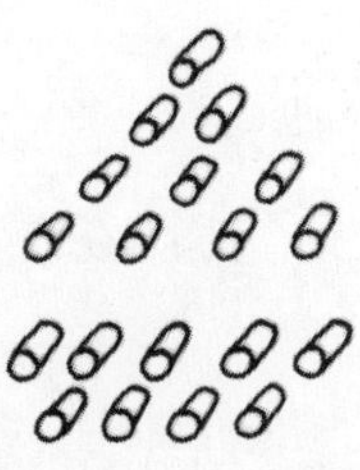

____

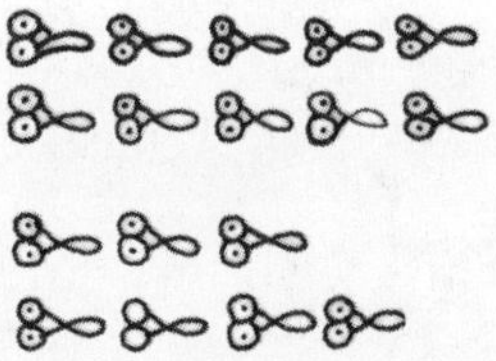

____

____

How many are there in all?

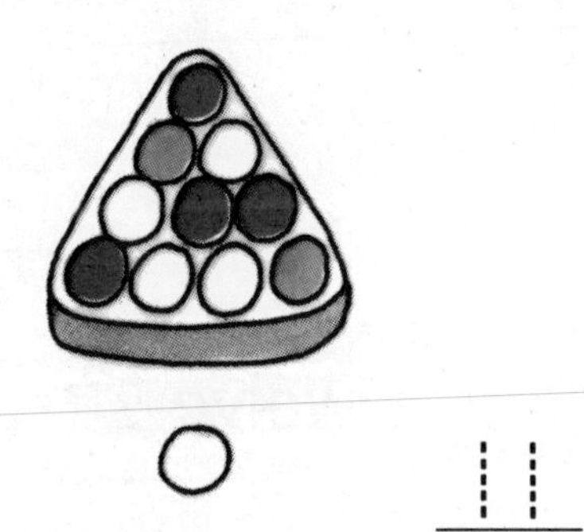

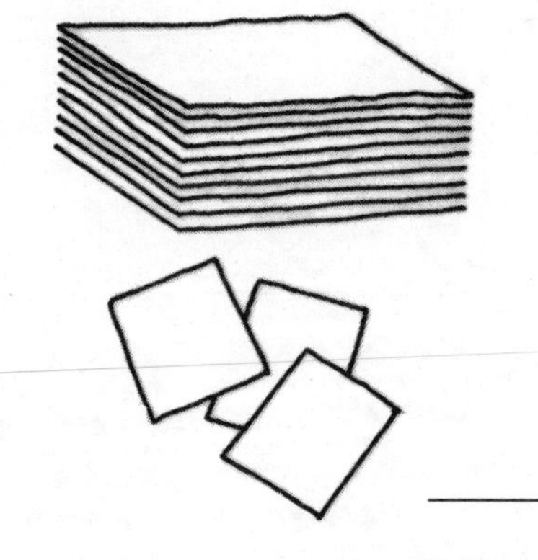

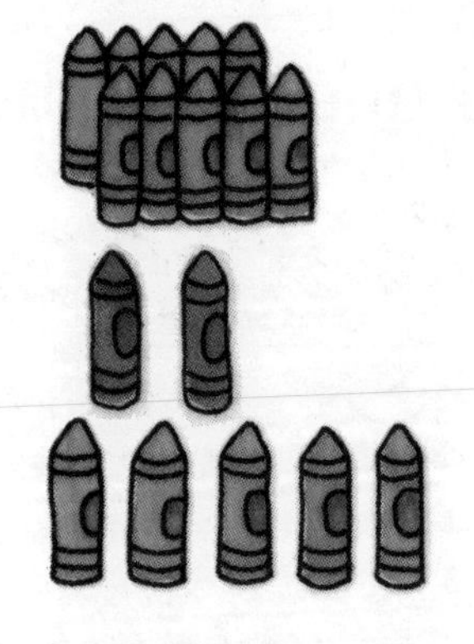

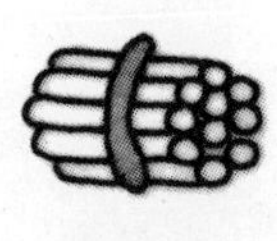

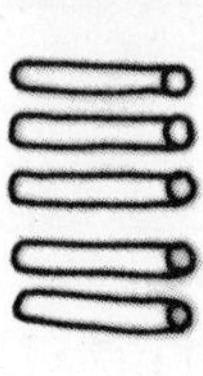

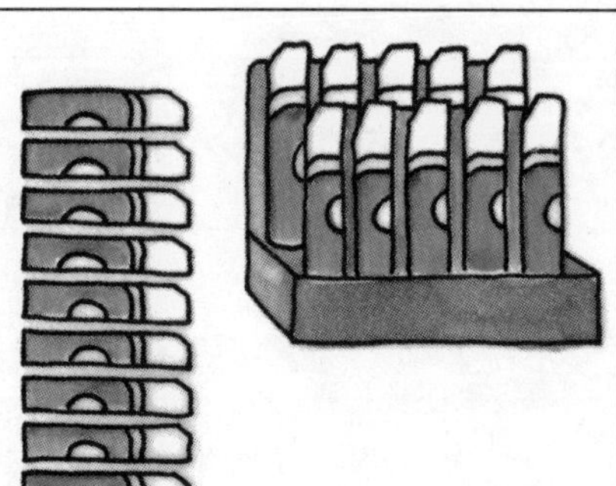

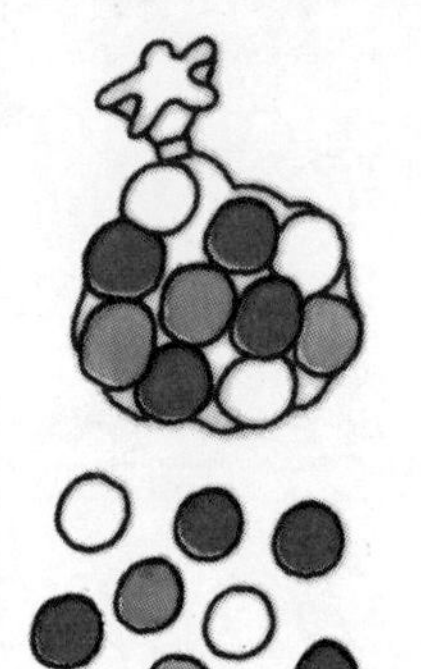

Match the number with its name.

13	ten	12	fourteen
17	thirteen	14	eighteen
10	fifteen	11	sixteen
19	seventeen	16	twelve
15	nineteen	18	eleven

Name ____________________

1 ten 10 ten

2 tens 20 twenty

3 tens 30 thirty

4 tens 40 forty

How many are there in all?

3 tens 0 ones

30

___ tens ___ ones

___

___ tens ___ ones

___

___ tens ___ ones

___

___ tens ___ ones

___

___ tens ___ ones

___

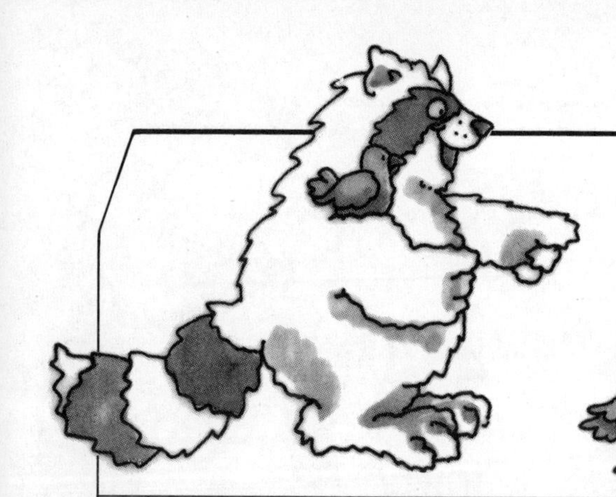

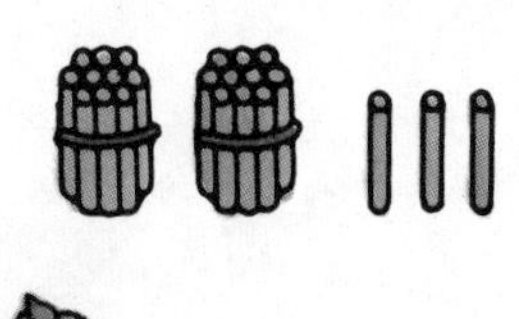

2 tens 3 ones

23

How many are there in all?

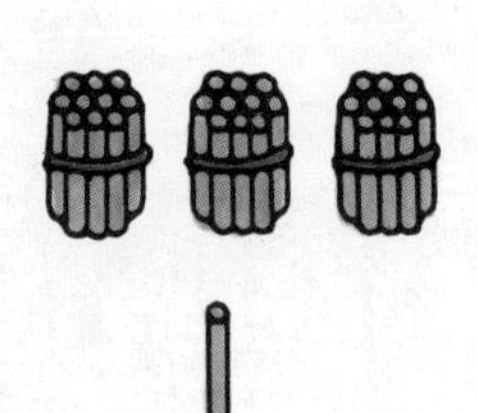

___ tens ___ ones

___

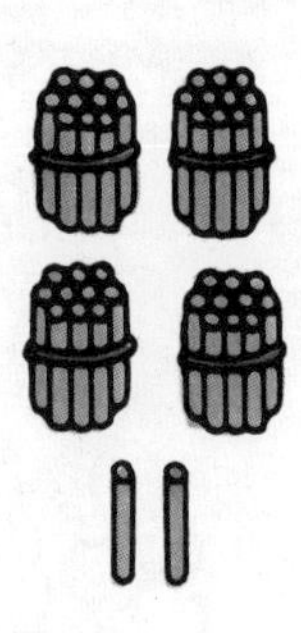

___ tens ___ ones

___

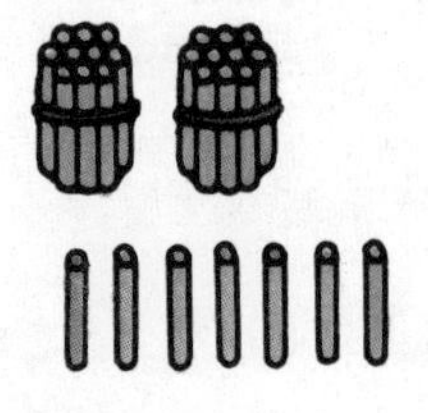

___ tens ___ ones

___

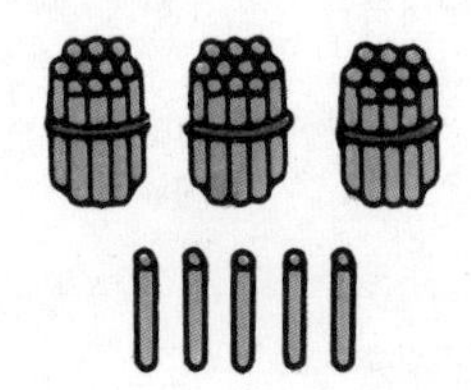

___ tens ___ ones

___

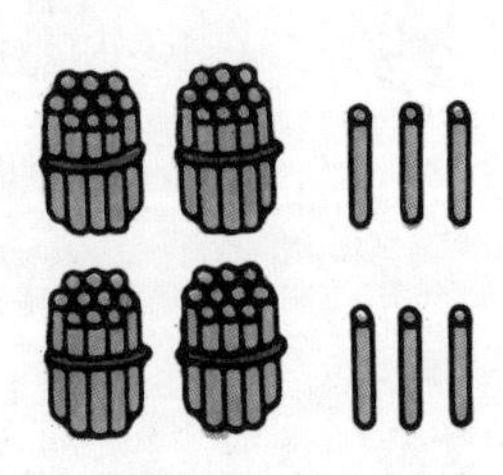

___ tens ___ ones

___

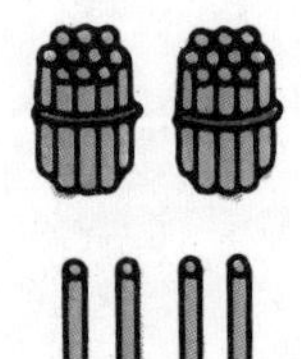

___ tens ___ ones

___

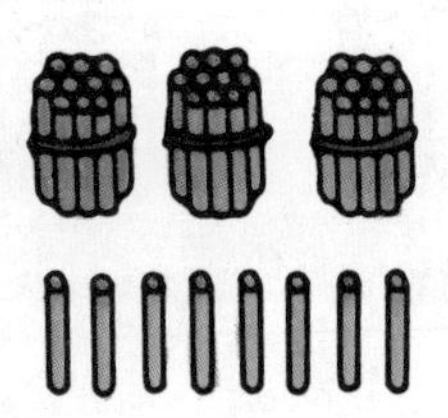

___ tens ___ ones

___

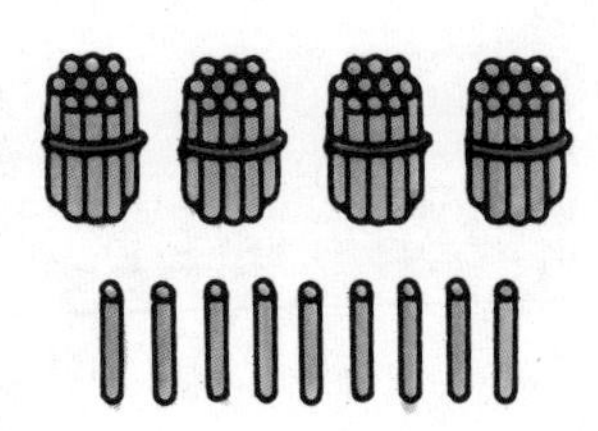

___ tens ___ ones

___

Name ________________

Write the numbers.

2 tens 0 ones

20 twenty

___ tens ___ ones

___ twenty-one

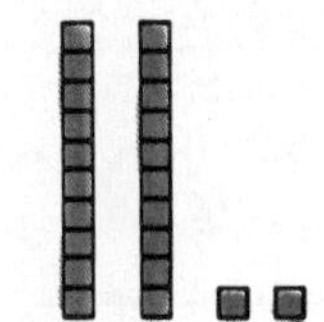

___ tens ___ ones

___ twenty-two

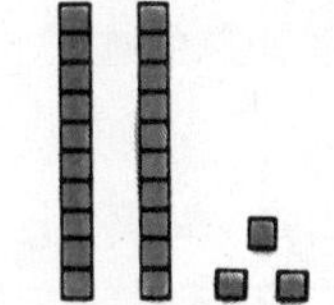

___ tens ___ ones

___ twenty-three

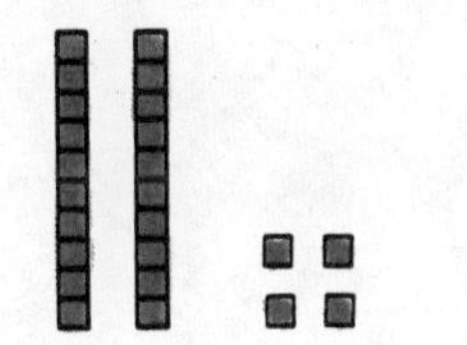

___ tens ___ ones

___ twenty-four

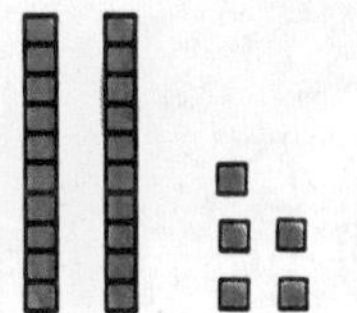

___ tens ___ ones

___ twenty-five

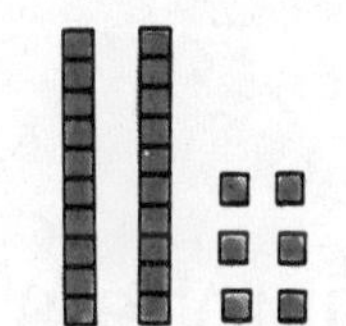

___ tens ___ ones

___ twenty-six

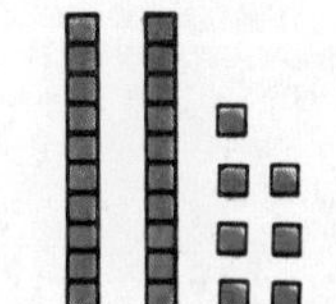

___ tens ___ ones

___ twenty-seven

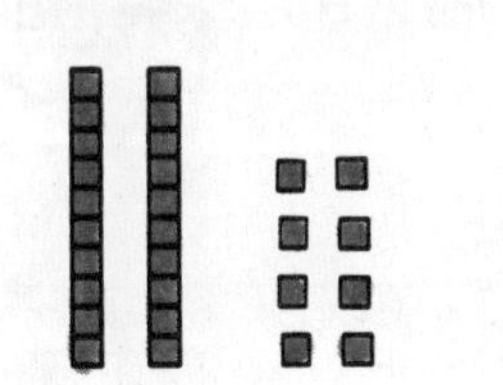

___ tens ___ ones

___ twenty-eight

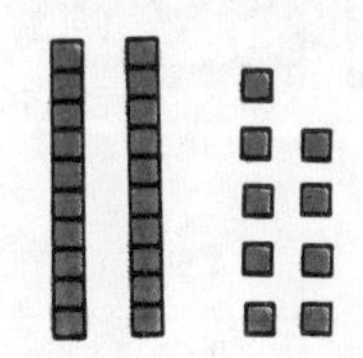

___ tens ___ ones

___ twenty-nine

Write the missing numbers.

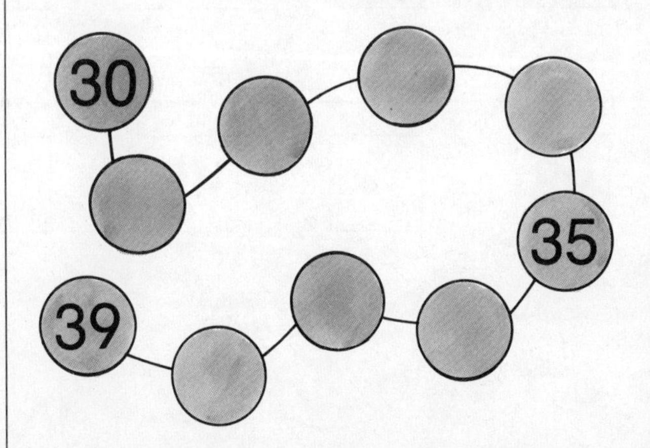

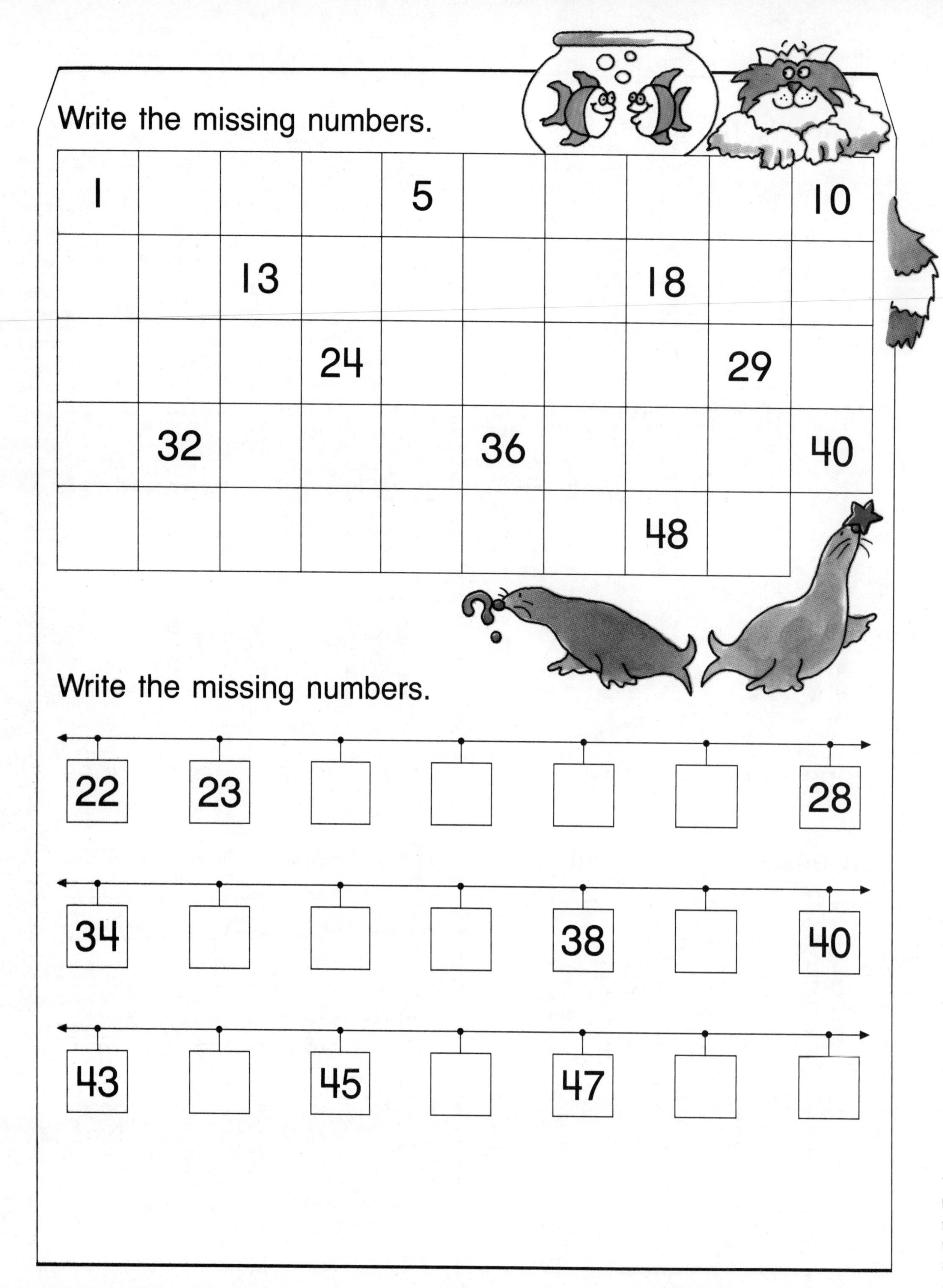

Write the missing numbers.

1				5					10
		13					18		
			24					29	
	32				36				40
							48	

Write the missing numbers.

22	23					28
34				38		40
43		45		47		

Name ______________________________

Can be traded for

1 dime

10 pennies 10 ¢

10 ¢

How much money?

____ dimes

____ ¢

____ dimes

____ ¢

____ dimes

____ ¢

____ dimes

____ ¢

____ dimes

____ ¢

____ dimes

____ ¢

____ dimes

____ ¢

____ dimes

____ ¢

Write the number.

ten	10	forty	___	seventy	___
twenty	___	fifty	___	eighty	___
thirty	___	sixty	___	ninety	___

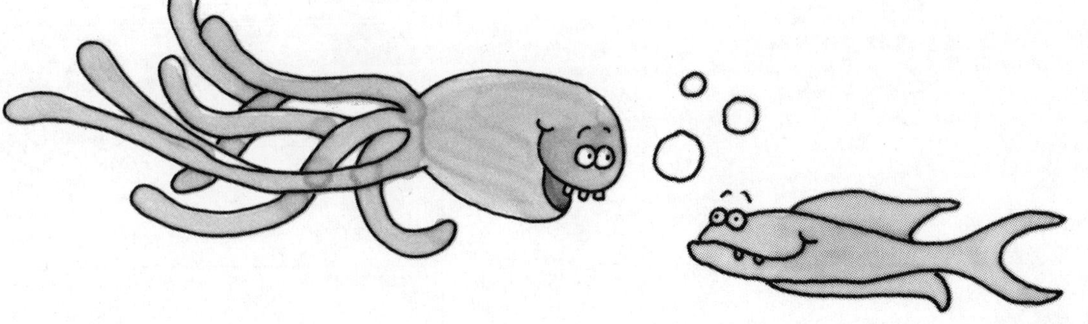

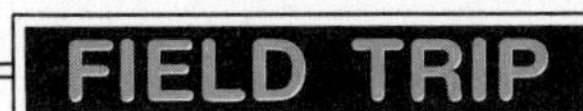

FIELD TRIP

Count by tens.

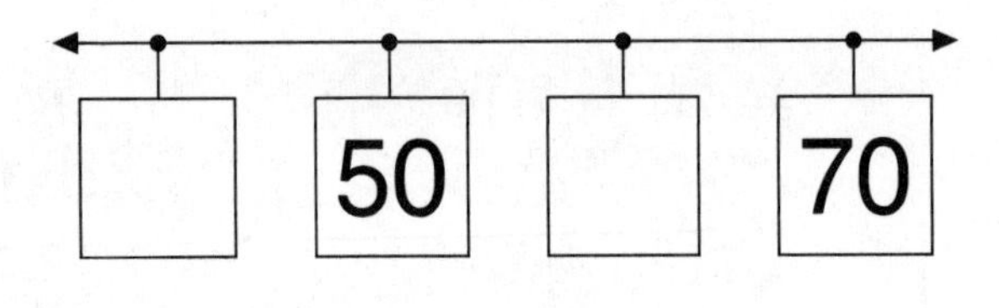

70 ___ 90

Name ______________________

2 dimes 4 pennies

24¢

How much money?

____ dimes ____ pennies

____¢

____ dimes ____ pennies

____¢

____ dimes ____ pennies

____¢

____ dimes ____ pennies

____¢

____ dimes ____ pennies

____¢

____ dimes ____ pennies

____¢

10¢ 20¢ 30¢ 40¢ 50¢ 51¢ 52¢ 53¢

I have 53 ¢.

How much money?

I have ____¢.

I have ____¢.

I have ____¢.

I have ____¢.

I have ____¢.

I have ____¢.

I have ____¢.

I have ____¢.

Name ______________________________

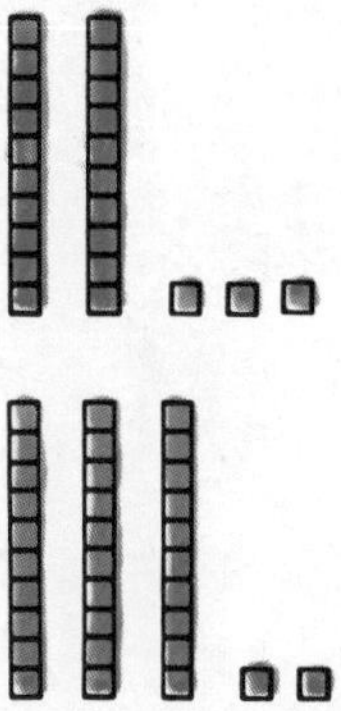

32 is greater than 23.

23

(32)

Circle the number that is greater.

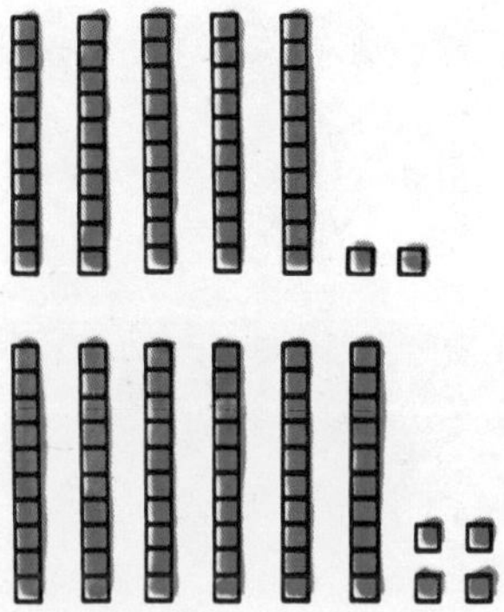

52

64

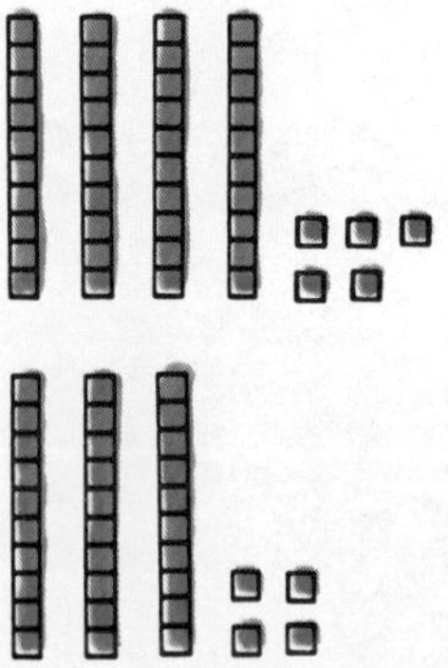

45

34

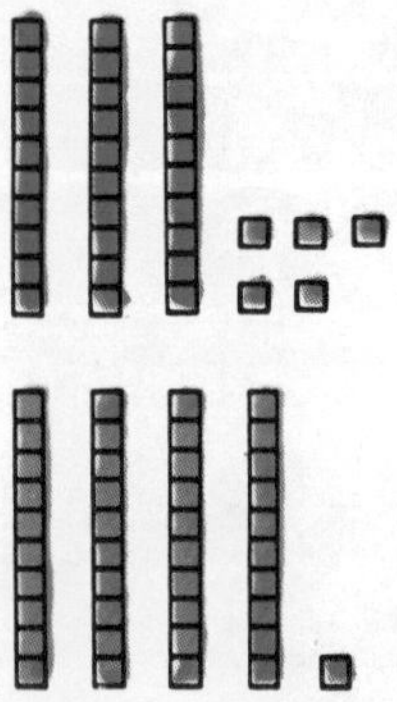

35

41

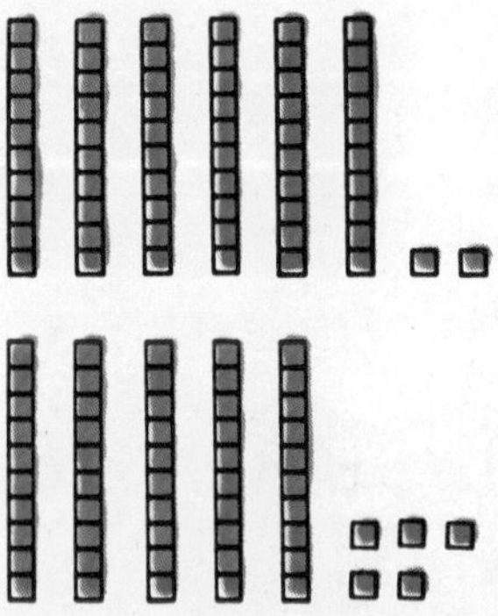

62

55

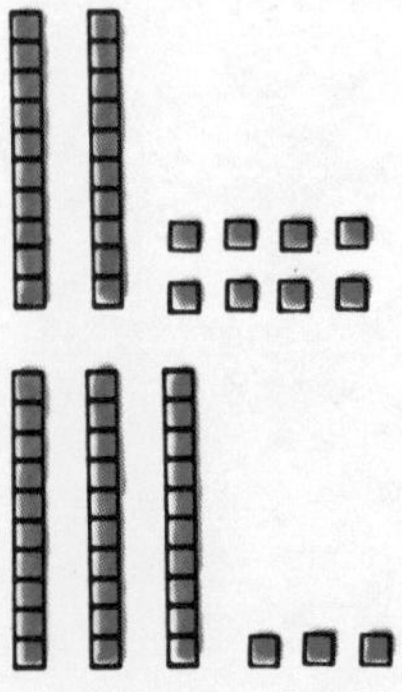

28

33

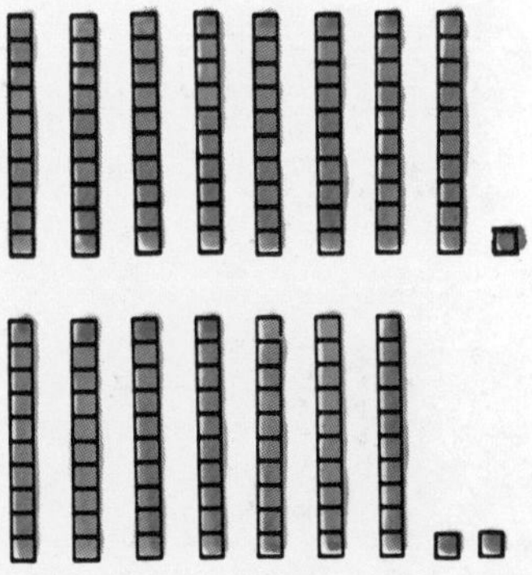

81

72

Circle the amount that is less.

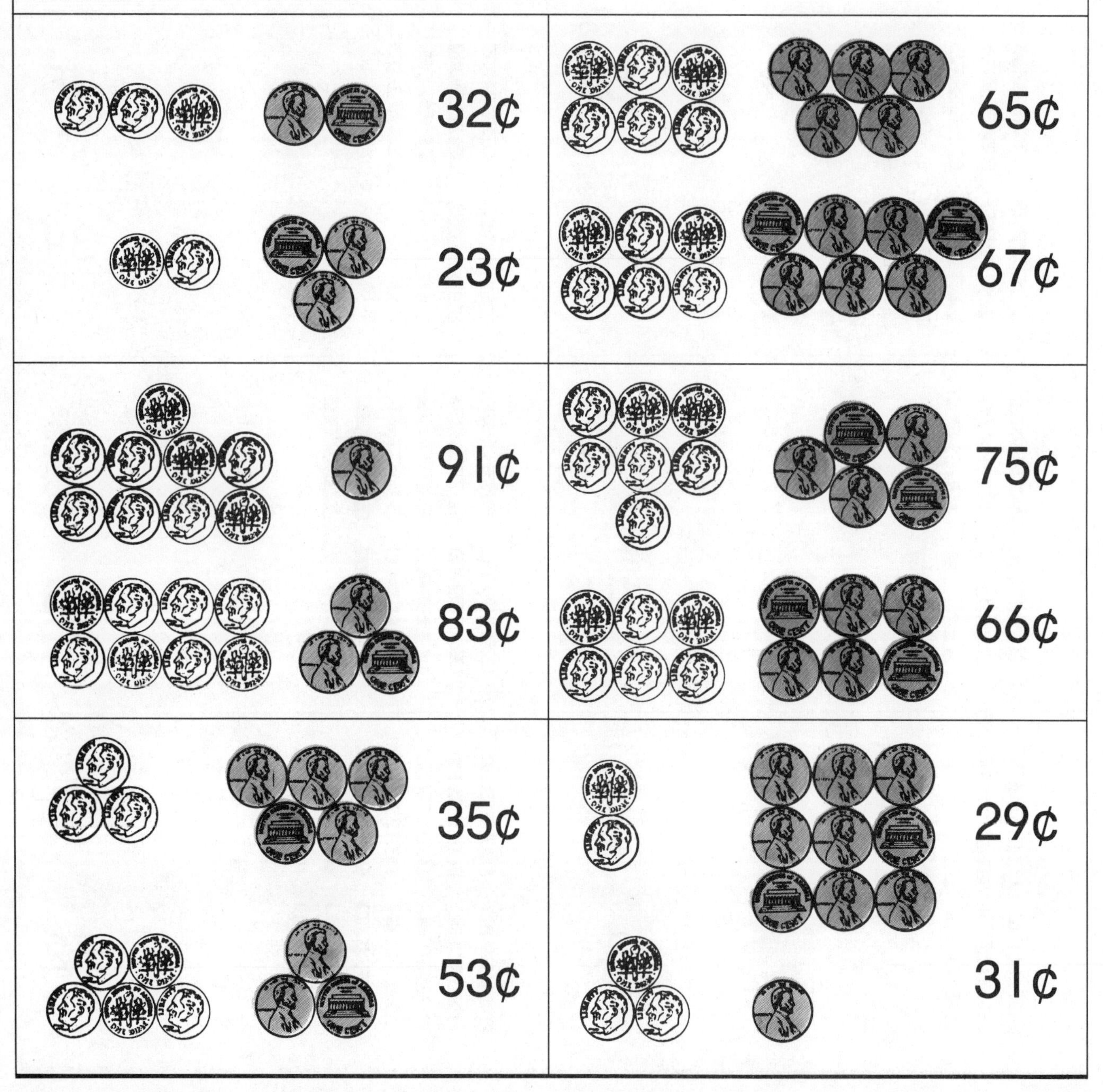

Name ______________________________

◯ fifth

╳ ninth

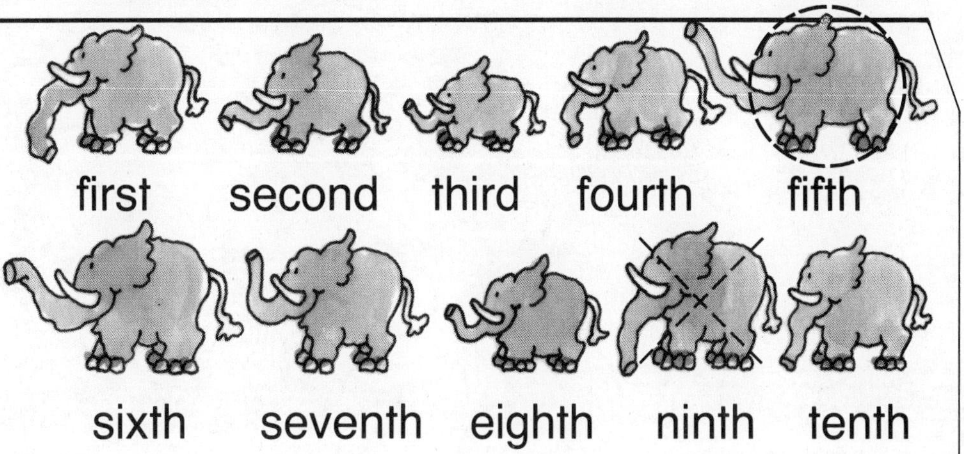

first second third fourth fifth

sixth seventh eighth ninth tenth

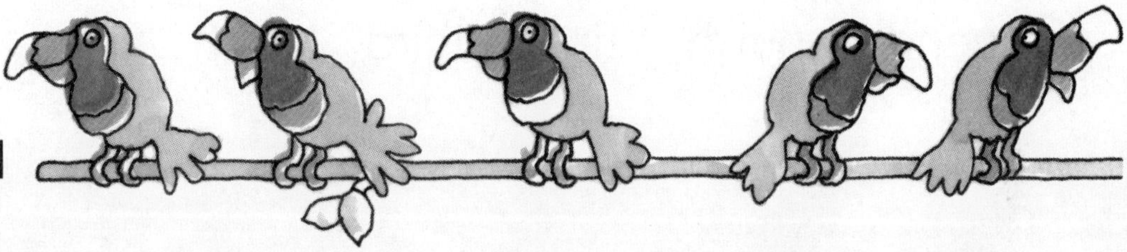

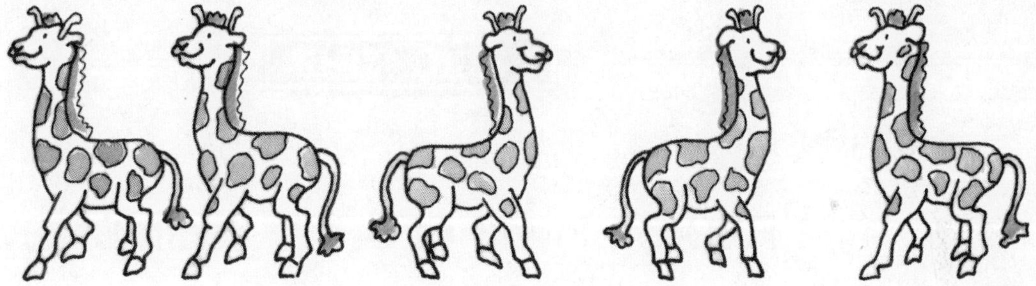

Mark the number.

◯ fourth

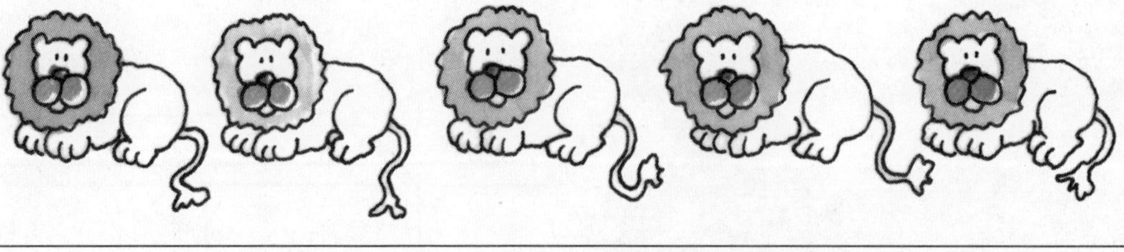

╳ second

◯ fifth

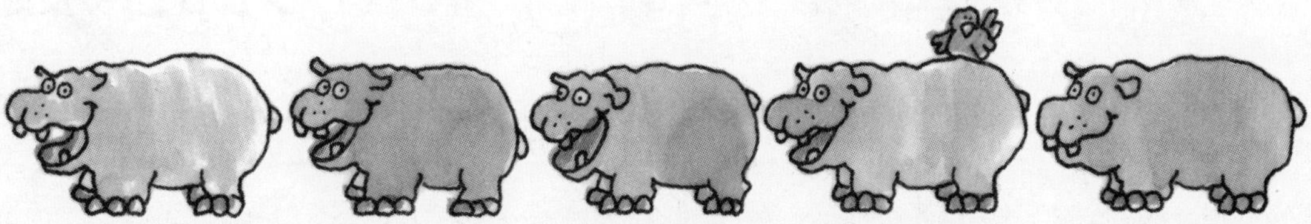

╳ first

◯ third

╳ fourth

◯ third

╳ fifth

Match.

second fourth first third sixth seventh fifth

FIELD TRIP

Color the cars.

first RED fourth BLUE tenth BROWN

seventh GREEN third PURPLE fifth YELLOW

Name ______________________________

CHAPTER CHECKUP

How many?

____ tens ____ ones

____

Match.

11	twelve
12	eighteen
15	eleven
18	fifteen

How many?

____ tens

____

____ tens ____ ones

____

Write the missing numbers.

36	37					42	

How much money?

____ dimes

____¢

____ dimes ____ pennies

____¢

Circle the greater.

32

23

Circle the second dog.

ROUNDUP REVIEW

Write the missing numbers.

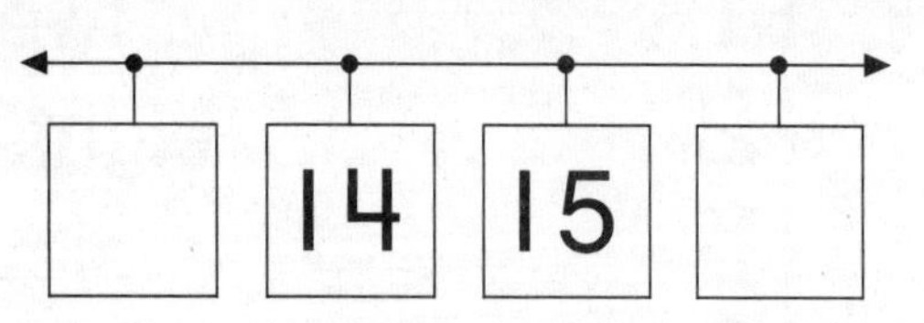

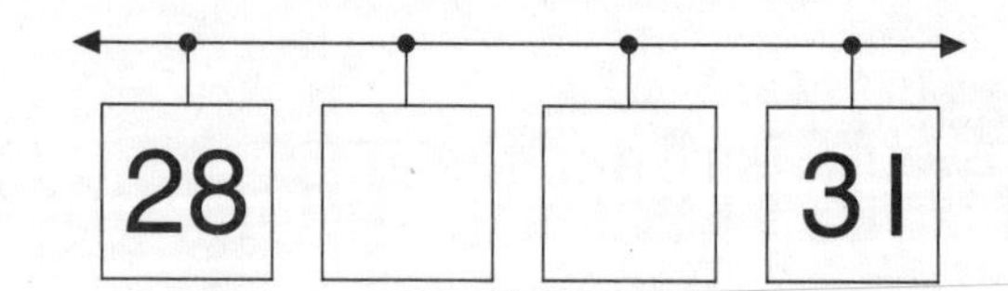

Add or subtract.

$\begin{array}{r} 3 \\ +4 \\ \hline \end{array}$ $\begin{array}{r} 6 \\ +3 \\ \hline \end{array}$ $\begin{array}{r} 1 \\ +7 \\ \hline \end{array}$ $\begin{array}{r} 2 \\ +4 \\ \hline \end{array}$ $\begin{array}{r} 5 \\ +2 \\ \hline \end{array}$ $\begin{array}{r} 9 \\ +1 \\ \hline \end{array}$

$\begin{array}{r} 5 \\ +3 \\ \hline \end{array}$ $\begin{array}{r} 4 \\ +6 \\ \hline \end{array}$ $\begin{array}{r} 3 \\ +2 \\ \hline \end{array}$ $\begin{array}{r} 4 \\ +4 \\ \hline \end{array}$ $\begin{array}{r} 2 \\ +2 \\ \hline \end{array}$ $\begin{array}{r} 3 \\ +3 \\ \hline \end{array}$

$\begin{array}{r} 8 \\ -3 \\ \hline \end{array}$ $\begin{array}{r} 9 \\ -5 \\ \hline \end{array}$ $\begin{array}{r} 7 \\ -4 \\ \hline \end{array}$ $\begin{array}{r} 5 \\ -3 \\ \hline \end{array}$ $\begin{array}{r} 8 \\ -4 \\ \hline \end{array}$ $\begin{array}{r} 10 \\ -\ 5 \\ \hline \end{array}$

$\begin{array}{r} 6 \\ -2 \\ \hline \end{array}$ $\begin{array}{r} 10 \\ -\ 3 \\ \hline \end{array}$ $\begin{array}{r} 9 \\ -2 \\ \hline \end{array}$ $\begin{array}{r} 8 \\ -6 \\ \hline \end{array}$ $\begin{array}{r} 7 \\ -2 \\ \hline \end{array}$ $\begin{array}{r} 10 \\ -\ 4 \\ \hline \end{array}$

$3 + 3 =$ ____ $10 - 6 =$ ____ $4 + 5 =$ ____

$7 + 2 =$ ____ $9 - 4 =$ ____ $8 - 2 =$ ____

Name ______________________________

ADDITION, SUMS THROUGH 18

Add.

$3 + 5 =$ 8

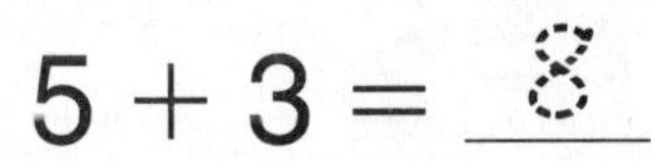

$5 + 3 =$ 8

$7 + 3 =$ ____

$3 + 7 =$ ____

$4 + 5 =$ ____

$5 + 4 =$ ____

$5 + 5 =$ ____

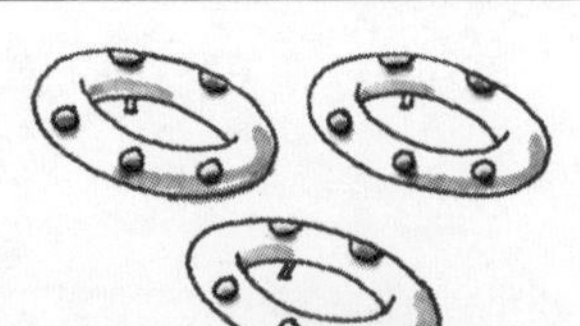

$3 + 3 =$ ____

$4 + 4 =$ ____

$6 + 2 =$ ____

Add.

9 + 0 = ___	4 + 3 = ___	6 + 0 = ___
2 + 8 = ___	1 + 4 = ___	7 + 2 = ___
1 + 2 = ___	4 + 2 = ___	4 + 6 = ___
2 + 4 = ___	1 + 9 = ___	3 + 2 = ___
3 + 4 = ___	8 + 2 = ___	5 + 0 = ___
8 + 1 = ___	5 + 1 = ___	7 + 1 = ___
6 + 4 = ___	1 + 7 = ___	2 + 3 = ___
3 + 6 = ___	6 + 3 = ___	9 + 1 = ___
2 + 7 = ___	2 + 5 = ___	0 + 4 = ___
1 + 6 = ___	1 + 8 = ___	5 + 2 = ___

Reviewing addition facts, sums through 10

Name ______________________

Add.

  5 +3	 4 +5
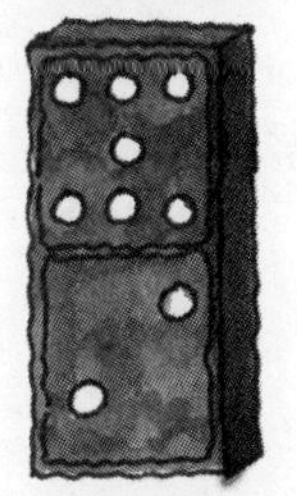 7 +2	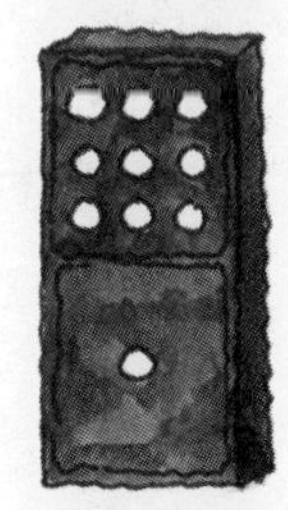 9 +1
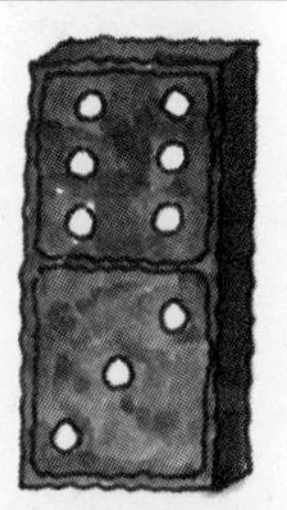 6 +3	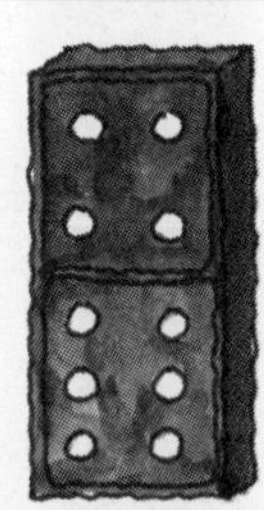 4 +6
 2 +6	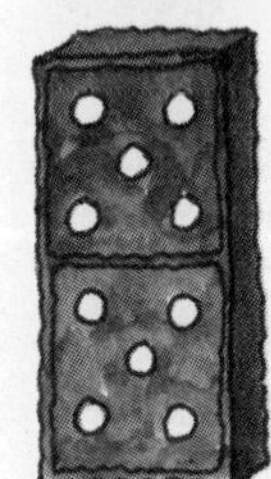 5 +5
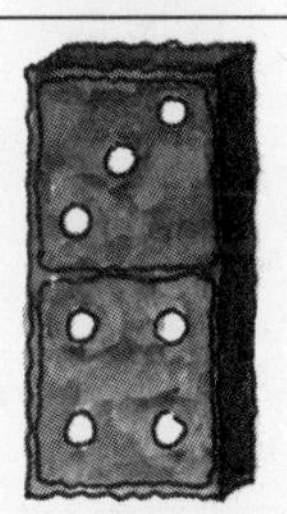 3 +4	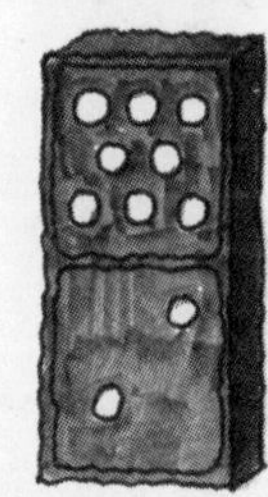 8 +2
 7 +3	 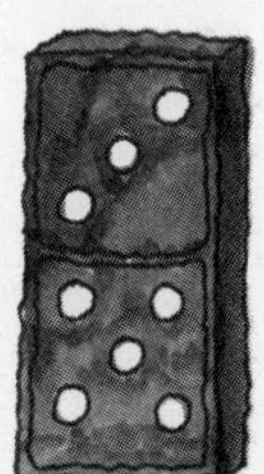 3 +5

Add.

8	5	6	4	3	5	9
+1	+4	+2	+3	+2	+2	+0

3	7	2	3	6	2	5
+3	+1	+5	+6	+4	+8	+1

2	4	8	4	3	2	2
+4	+2	+0	+4	+7	+7	+3

FIELD TRIP

Complete the tables.

Add 3	
2	5
6	
3	
5	
7	
4	

Add 4	
3	
0	
6	
4	
2	
5	

Add 5	
1	
5	
0	
2	
4	
3	

Name ______________________________

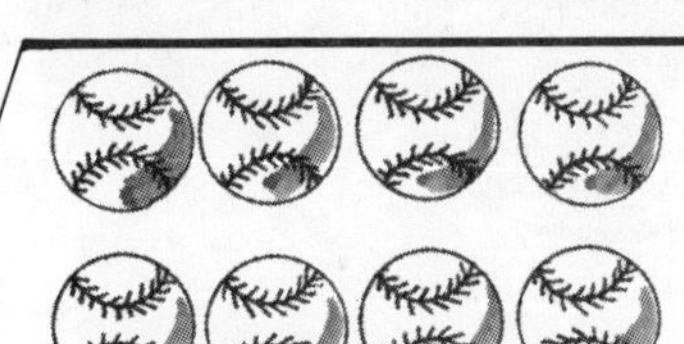

$8 + 3 = \underline{11}$

$$\begin{array}{r} 7 \\ +4 \\ \hline 11 \end{array}$$

Add.

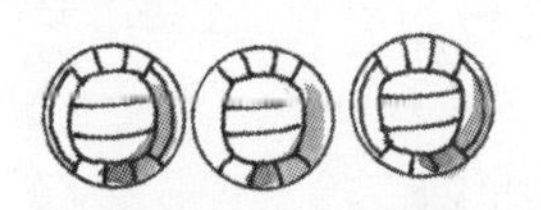
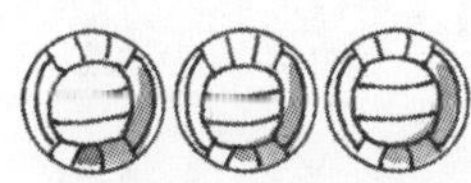

$6 + 6 = \underline{\quad}$

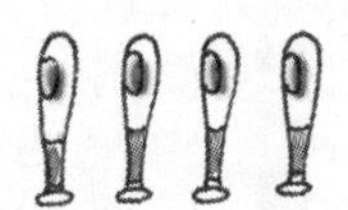

$$\begin{array}{r} 4 \\ +8 \\ \hline \end{array}$$

$7 + 5 = \underline{\quad}$

$$\begin{array}{r} 2 \\ +9 \\ \hline \end{array}$$

$3 + 9 = \underline{\quad}$

$$\begin{array}{r} 6 \\ +5 \\ \hline \end{array}$$

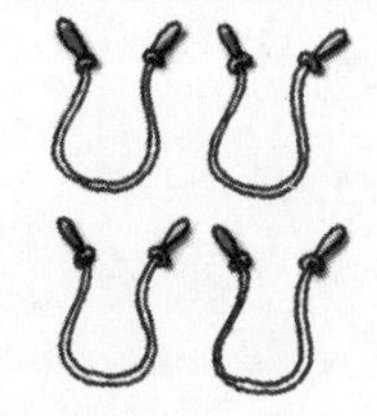
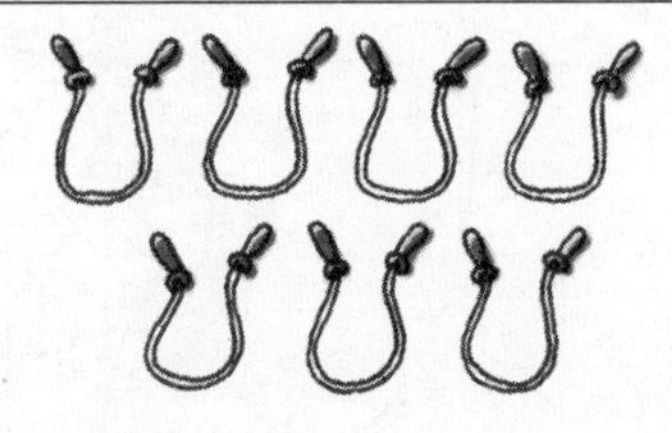

$4 + 7 = \underline{\quad}$

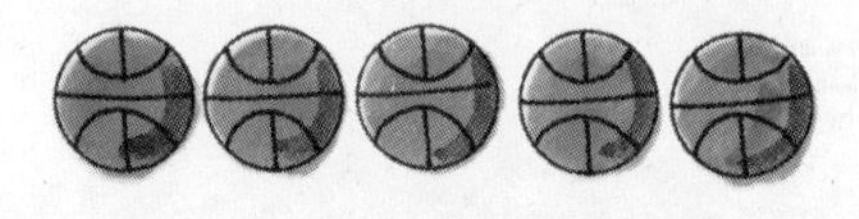

$$\begin{array}{r} 5 \\ +7 \\ \hline \end{array}$$

9 + 2	7 + 3	6 + 6	8 + 2	7 + 5	8 + 3	5 + 5
8 + 4	4 + 5	3 + 9	5 + 6	4 + 8	6 + 4	3 + 8
5 + 7	3 + 6	4 + 7	9 + 3	6 + 5	4 + 6	2 + 9

FIELD TRIP

Complete the wheels.

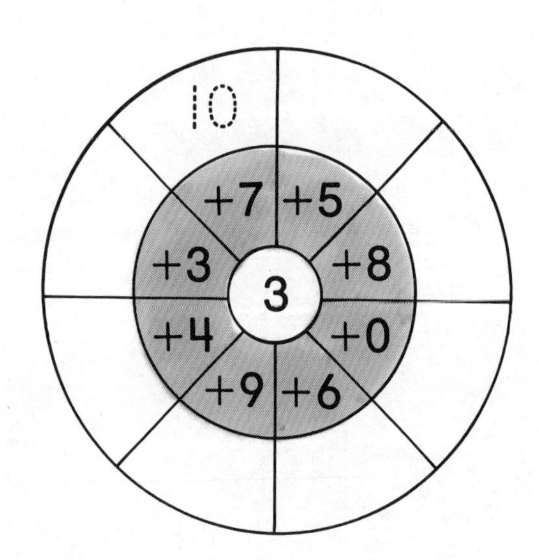

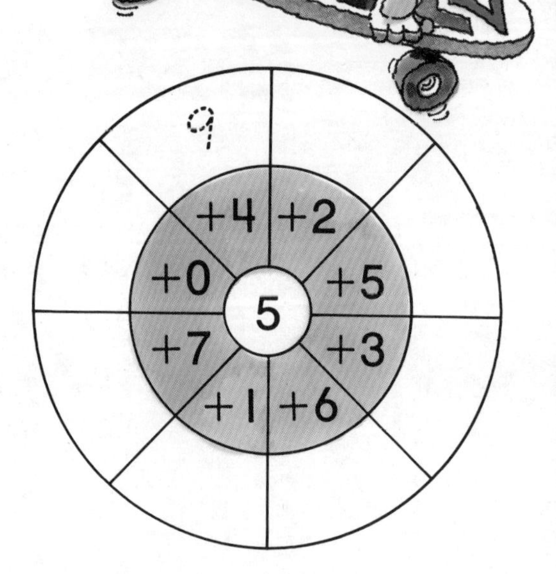

Name ______________________________

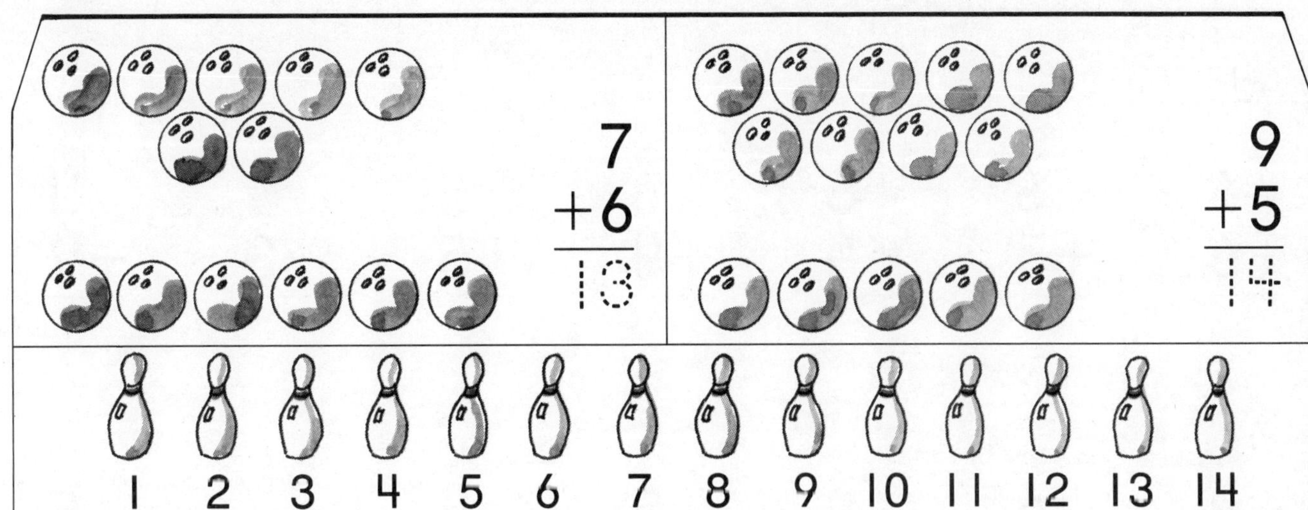

Add.

$\begin{array}{r} 9 \\ +4 \\ \hline \end{array}$	$\begin{array}{r} 7 \\ +4 \\ \hline \end{array}$	$\begin{array}{r} 5 \\ +8 \\ \hline \end{array}$	$\begin{array}{r} 7 \\ +6 \\ \hline \end{array}$	$\begin{array}{r} 4 \\ +7 \\ \hline \end{array}$	$\begin{array}{r} 8 \\ +3 \\ \hline \end{array}$
$\begin{array}{r} 6 \\ +8 \\ \hline \end{array}$	$\begin{array}{r} 8 \\ +3 \\ \hline \end{array}$	$\begin{array}{r} 9 \\ +2 \\ \hline \end{array}$	$\begin{array}{r} 3 \\ +8 \\ \hline \end{array}$	$\begin{array}{r} 5 \\ +9 \\ \hline \end{array}$	$\begin{array}{r} 6 \\ +6 \\ \hline \end{array}$
$\begin{array}{r} 8 \\ +5 \\ \hline \end{array}$	$\begin{array}{r} 5 \\ +6 \\ \hline \end{array}$	$\begin{array}{r} 2 \\ +9 \\ \hline \end{array}$	$\begin{array}{r} 9 \\ +5 \\ \hline \end{array}$	$\begin{array}{r} 4 \\ +8 \\ \hline \end{array}$	$\begin{array}{r} 7 \\ +7 \\ \hline \end{array}$
$\begin{array}{r} 4 \\ +9 \\ \hline \end{array}$	$\begin{array}{r} 6 \\ +7 \\ \hline \end{array}$	$\begin{array}{r} 8 \\ +6 \\ \hline \end{array}$	$\begin{array}{r} 6 \\ +5 \\ \hline \end{array}$	$\begin{array}{r} 4 \\ +7 \\ \hline \end{array}$	$\begin{array}{r} 3 \\ +9 \\ \hline \end{array}$

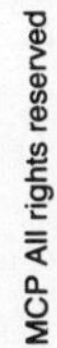

Add.

$$\begin{array}{r}6\\+6\\\hline\end{array}\quad\begin{array}{r}6\\+5\\\hline\end{array}\quad\begin{array}{r}8\\+4\\\hline\end{array}\quad\begin{array}{r}6\\+4\\\hline\end{array}\quad\begin{array}{r}5\\+5\\\hline\end{array}\quad\begin{array}{r}9\\+3\\\hline\end{array}\quad\begin{array}{r}4\\+9\\\hline\end{array}$$

$$\begin{array}{r}9\\+4\\\hline\end{array}\quad\begin{array}{r}6\\+7\\\hline\end{array}\quad\begin{array}{r}8\\+5\\\hline\end{array}\quad\begin{array}{r}5\\+7\\\hline\end{array}\quad\begin{array}{r}4\\+8\\\hline\end{array}\quad\begin{array}{r}7\\+5\\\hline\end{array}\quad\begin{array}{r}5\\+9\\\hline\end{array}$$

$$\begin{array}{r}7\\+6\\\hline\end{array}\quad\begin{array}{r}7\\+7\\\hline\end{array}\quad\begin{array}{r}8\\+6\\\hline\end{array}\quad\begin{array}{r}5\\+8\\\hline\end{array}\quad\begin{array}{r}6\\+8\\\hline\end{array}\quad\begin{array}{r}9\\+5\\\hline\end{array}\quad\begin{array}{r}4\\+7\\\hline\end{array}$$

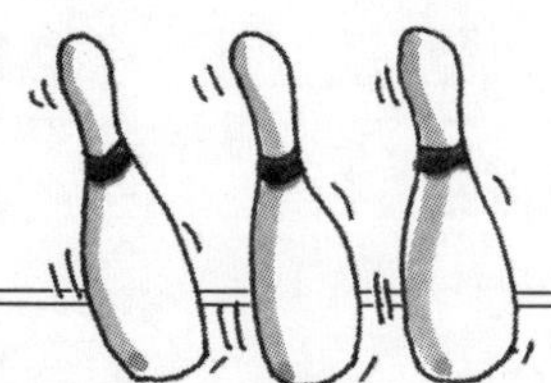

FIELD TRIP

Complete the tables.

Add 5	
6	11
8	
9	
7	

Add 6	
6	
7	
8	
5	

Add 7	
5	
7	
4	
6	

Add 8	
4	
6	
3	
5	

Name ____

1 2 3 4 5 6 7 8 9 10 11 12 13 14

Add.

8	9	7	6	8	5	4
+3	+2	+5	+3	+2	+4	+8
7	5	9	5	8	6	8
+3	+6	+3	+5	+4	+4	+5
4	4	7	4	9	3	5
+9	+6	+6	+7	+4	+8	+7
6	5	7	6	8	2	9
+5	+9	+4	+6	+6	+8	+5
3	6	3	5	7	6	2
+9	+8	+7	+8	+7	+7	+9

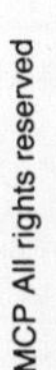

Complete the tables.

Add 4	
3	7
0	
6	
7	
5	
9	
8	

Add 5	
3	
4	
6	
5	
8	
9	
7	

Add 2	
5	
0	
8	
6	
7	
2	
9	

Add 6	
2	
4	
3	
6	
5	
8	
7	

Add 3	
2	
7	
4	
6	
9	
5	
8	

Add 7	
2	
5	
3	
0	
6	
4	
7	

Name ______

$$\begin{array}{r} 9 \\ +6 \\ \hline 15 \end{array}$$

$$\begin{array}{r} 6 \\ +9 \\ \hline 15 \end{array}$$

Add.

$$\begin{array}{r} 8 \\ +7 \\ \hline \end{array}$$

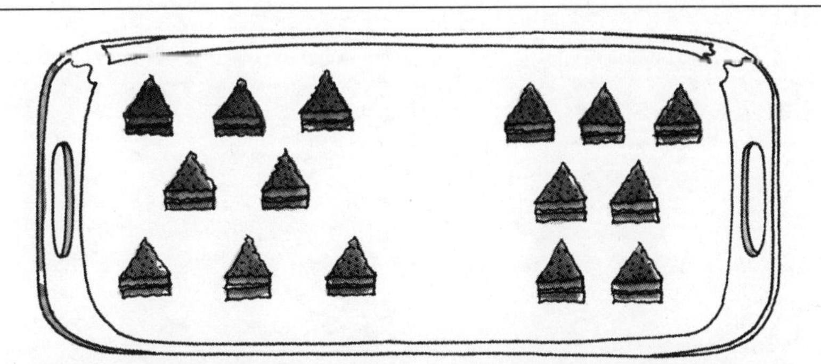

$$\begin{array}{r} 7 \\ +8 \\ \hline \end{array}$$

$$\begin{array}{r} 9 \\ +7 \\ \hline \end{array}$$

$$\begin{array}{r} 7 \\ +9 \\ \hline \end{array}$$

$$\begin{array}{r} 8 \\ +7 \\ \hline \end{array}$$

$$\begin{array}{r} 7 \\ +8 \\ \hline \end{array}$$

$$\begin{array}{r} 6 \\ +9 \\ \hline \end{array} \quad \begin{array}{r} 8 \\ +8 \\ \hline \end{array} \quad \begin{array}{r} 7 \\ +9 \\ \hline \end{array} \quad \begin{array}{r} 9 \\ +6 \\ \hline \end{array} \quad \begin{array}{r} 9 \\ +7 \\ \hline \end{array} \quad \begin{array}{r} 8 \\ +7 \\ \hline \end{array}$$

Add.

4	8	8	9	7	8	7
+8	+7	+5	+3	+4	+3	+9

6	4	7	3	8	6	9
+8	+9	+7	+8	+7	+5	+4

5	8	6	5	8	5	9
+7	+8	+9	+8	+4	+6	+5

7	7	9	5	4	8	9
+8	+9	+6	+9	+7	+6	+7

Solve.

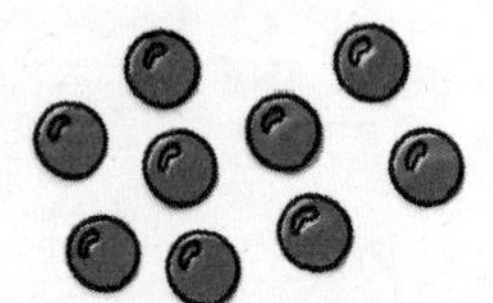

Juan had 9 marbles.
He bought 6 more.
How many in all?

9
+ 6
____

____ marbles

Maria had 8¢.
Mother gave her
8¢ more.
How much in all?

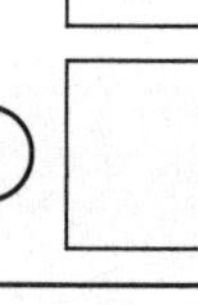
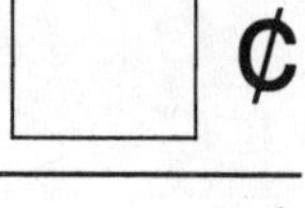

___ ¢
○ ___ ¢
____
___ ¢

____¢

Name ________________________________

$$\begin{array}{r} 9 \\ +8 \\ \hline 17 \end{array}$$

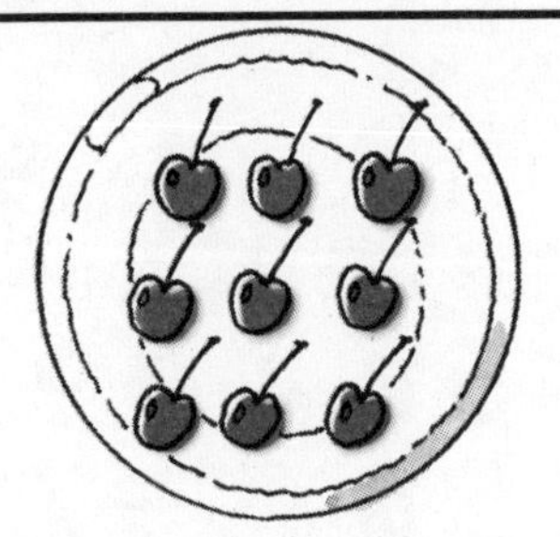

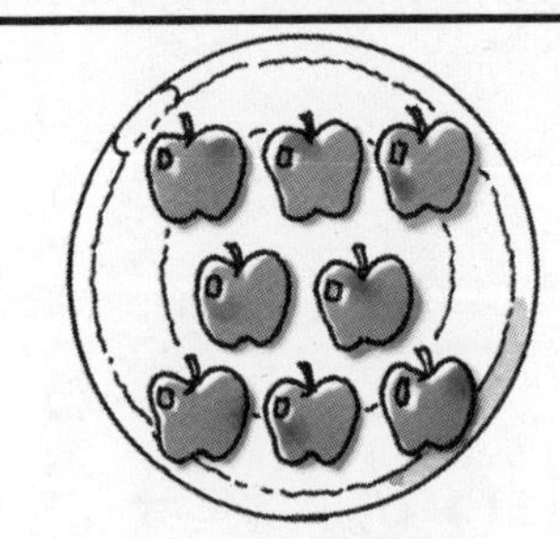

$$\begin{array}{r} 8 \\ +9 \\ \hline 17 \end{array}$$

$$\begin{array}{r} 9 \\ +9 \\ \hline 18 \end{array}$$

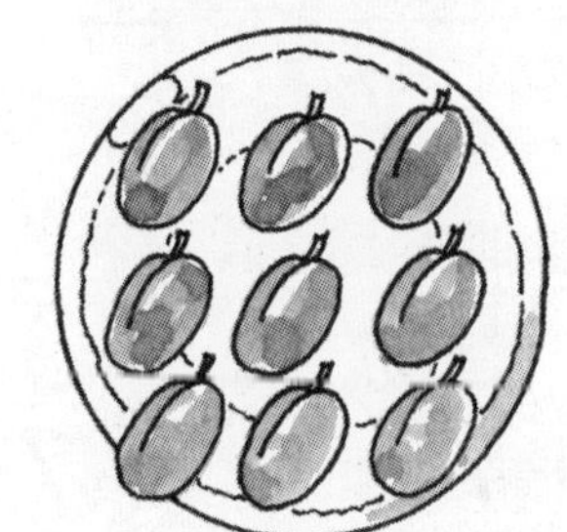

Add.

$\begin{array}{r} 9 \\ +6 \\ \hline \end{array}$	$\begin{array}{r} 3 \\ +6 \\ \hline \end{array}$	$\begin{array}{r} 2 \\ +9 \\ \hline \end{array}$	$\begin{array}{r} 1 \\ +8 \\ \hline \end{array}$	$\begin{array}{r} 9 \\ +8 \\ \hline \end{array}$	$\begin{array}{r} 7 \\ +5 \\ \hline \end{array}$
$\begin{array}{r} 9 \\ +7 \\ \hline \end{array}$	$\begin{array}{r} 6 \\ +8 \\ \hline \end{array}$	$\begin{array}{r} 4 \\ +7 \\ \hline \end{array}$	$\begin{array}{r} 5 \\ +9 \\ \hline \end{array}$	$\begin{array}{r} 9 \\ +3 \\ \hline \end{array}$	$\begin{array}{r} 9 \\ +9 \\ \hline \end{array}$
$\begin{array}{r} 5 \\ +6 \\ \hline \end{array}$	$\begin{array}{r} 3 \\ +7 \\ \hline \end{array}$	$\begin{array}{r} 6 \\ +4 \\ \hline \end{array}$	$\begin{array}{r} 7 \\ +8 \\ \hline \end{array}$	$\begin{array}{r} 5 \\ +7 \\ \hline \end{array}$	$\begin{array}{r} 8 \\ +9 \\ \hline \end{array}$
$\begin{array}{r} 6 \\ +6 \\ \hline \end{array}$	$\begin{array}{r} 9 \\ +5 \\ \hline \end{array}$	$\begin{array}{r} 8 \\ +5 \\ \hline \end{array}$	$\begin{array}{r} 5 \\ +5 \\ \hline \end{array}$	$\begin{array}{r} 6 \\ +9 \\ \hline \end{array}$	$\begin{array}{r} 8 \\ +8 \\ \hline \end{array}$

Add.

4¢	7¢	8¢	5¢	9¢	6¢
+5¢	+6¢	+8¢	+5¢	+7¢	+6¢
9¢	¢	¢	¢	¢	¢

9¢	5¢	8¢	9¢	8¢	7¢
+8¢	+7¢	+7¢	+9¢	+5¢	+8¢
¢	¢	¢	¢	¢	¢

FIELD TRIP

Complete the tables.

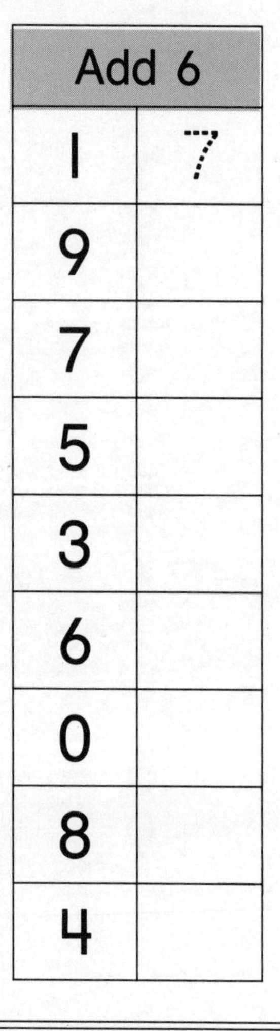

Add 6	
1	7
9	
7	
5	
3	
6	
0	
8	
4	

Add 7	
2	
4	
0	
3	
5	
9	
7	
8	
6	

Add 8	
0	
3	
5	
2	
4	
6	
8	
7	
9	

Name ______________________

Add.

2 +2	4 +4	0 +5	4 +2	1 +1	3 +0
3 +4	5 +1	2 +3	6 +1	3 +2	1 +8
1 +2	5 +0	5 +4	0 +9	4 +3	2 +5
5 +2	3 +3	2 +7	6 +2	4 +5	1 +4
2 +4	3 +1	6 +3	1 +5	8 +1	3 +5
1 +7	5 +3	3 +6	7 +2	2 +6	7 +1

Add.

$7 + 3$	$9 + 2$	$4 + 8$	$6 + 5$	$3 + 8$	$7 + 5$
$8 + 4$	$5 + 5$	$5 + 8$	$9 + 8$	$5 + 6$	$4 + 9$
$6 + 7$	$6 + 4$	$8 + 8$	$4 + 7$	$9 + 4$	$6 + 6$
$9 + 6$	$7 + 7$	$8 + 5$	$8 + 7$	$4 + 6$	$6 + 9$
$7 + 8$	$9 + 3$	$7 + 6$	$5 + 9$	$7 + 9$	$6 + 8$
$8 + 9$	$9 + 5$	$9 + 7$	$5 + 7$	$8 + 6$	$9 + 9$

Name ____________________

Write the missing numbers.

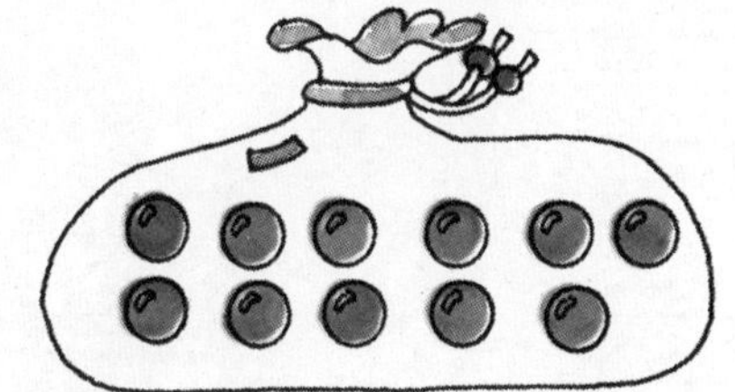

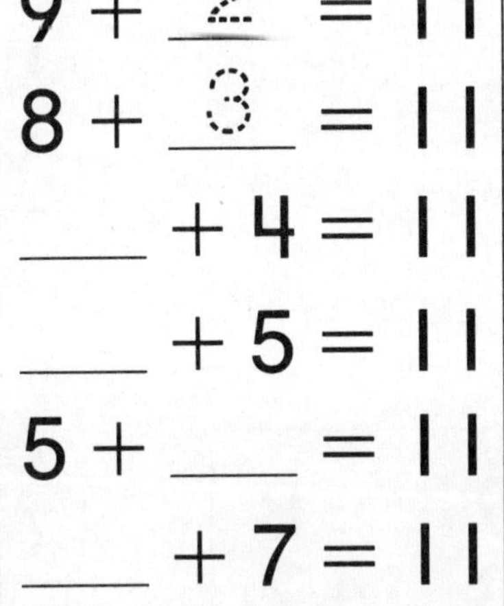

9 + 2 = 11

8 + 3 = 11

___ + 4 = 11

___ + 5 = 11

5 + ___ = 11

___ + 7 = 11

___ + 8 = 11

2 + ___ = 11

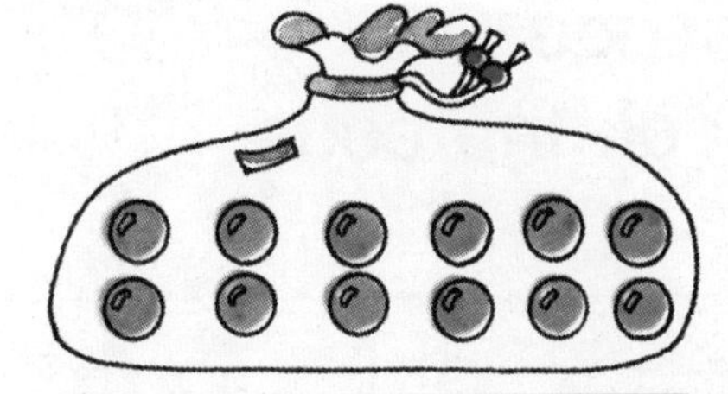

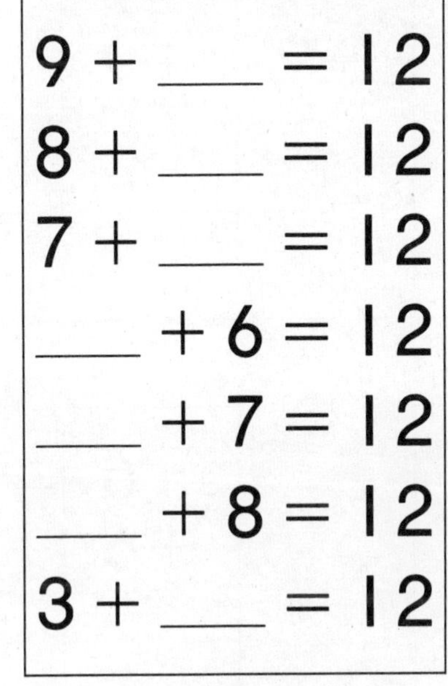

9 + ___ = 12

8 + ___ = 12

7 + ___ = 12

___ + 6 = 12

___ + 7 = 12

___ + 8 = 12

3 + ___ = 12

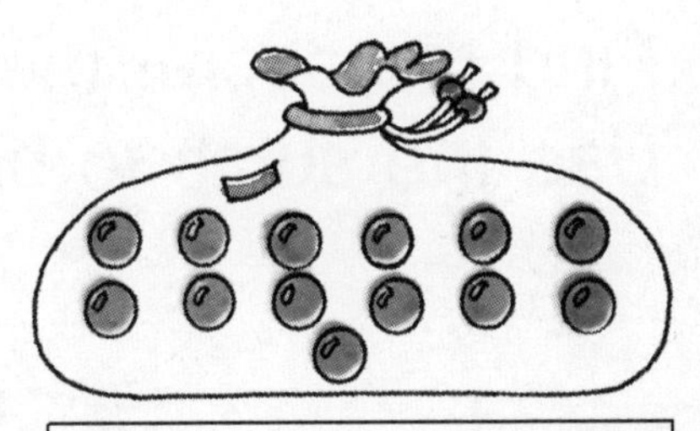

9 + ___ = 13

___ + 5 = 13

7 + ___ = 13

6 + ___ = 13

___ + 8 = 13

___ + 9 = 13

9 + ___ = 14

8 + ___ = 14

___ + 7 = 14

___ + 8 = 14

5 + ___ = 14

9 + ___ = 15

___ + 7 = 15

7 + ___ = 15

6 + ___ = 15

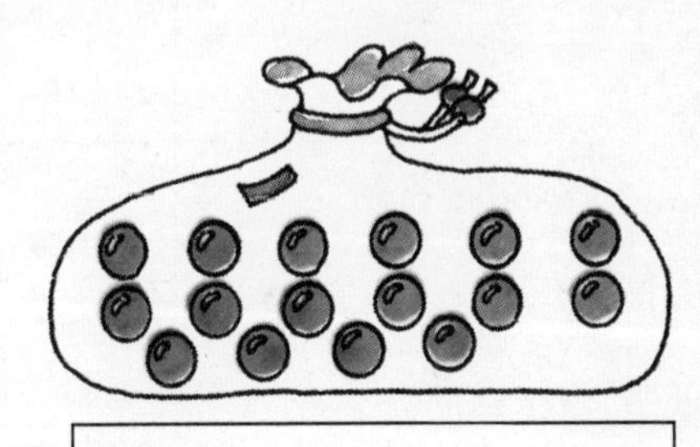

9 + ___ = 16

8 + ___ = 16

___ + 9 = 16

FIELD TRIP

Find the secret message.
Use the sums to break the code.

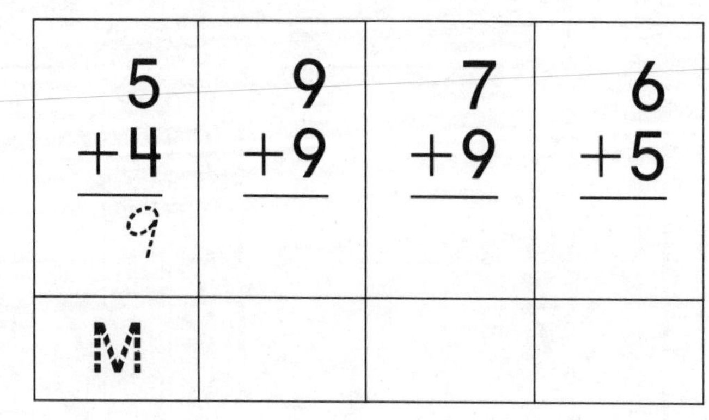

$5 + 4 = 9$	$9 + 9$	$7 + 9$	$6 + 5$
M			

$6 + 4$	$8 + 5$

$6 + 6$	$9 + 8$	$8 + 7$

$8 + 8$	$5 + 9$

$3 + 5$	$7 + 7$

Code

8	9	10	11	12	13	14	15	16	17	18
D	M	I	H	F	S	O	N	T	U	A

Name ______________________________

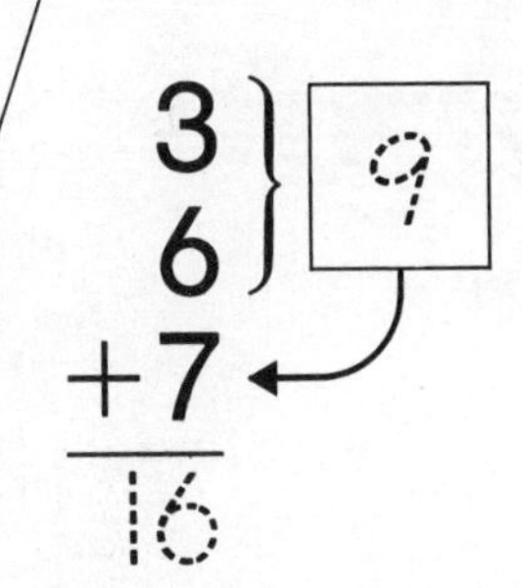

Add the two top numbers.
$3 + 6 = 9$

Add the bottom number.
$9 + 7 = 16$

Add.

4 3 +8	5 4 +6	7 1 +4

1 2 +5	6 2 +5	4 1 +9	3 3 +3	5 3 +7	9 1 +7
7 2 +7	2 6 +3	3 4 +5	6 3 +7	8 1 +3	4 4 +4
1 1 +9	4 5 +6	6 3 +9	9 0 +7	5 3 +9	3 5 +7

Solve.

Super Girl jumped over 3 wagons. Then she jumped over 8 more. How many wagons did she jump?

3
+ 8

____ wagons

Jump Man leaped over 8 wagons. He then jumped over 7 more. How many wagons did he leap over?

____ wagons

Fast Guy passed 5 wagons, and then 3 more. Then he passed 5 more wagons. How many wagons did Fast Guy pass in all?

____ wagons

Speedy Fran passed 4 wagons and then 3 more. Then she passed 7 more. How many wagons did Speedy Fran pass in all?

____ wagons

FIELD TRIP

How far?

A — 4 steps — B — 5 steps — C — 5 steps — D

+

steps

Name ______________________________

How much do they cost?

9 ¢
+ 6 ¢
15 ¢

¢
+ ¢
¢

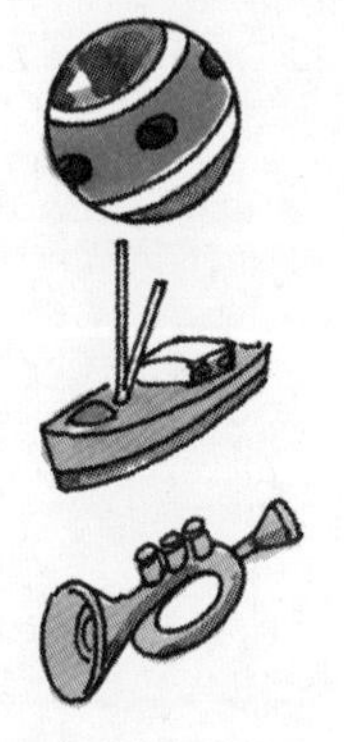

¢
¢
+ ¢
¢

¢
+ ¢
¢

¢
¢
+ ¢
¢

¢
¢
+ ¢
¢

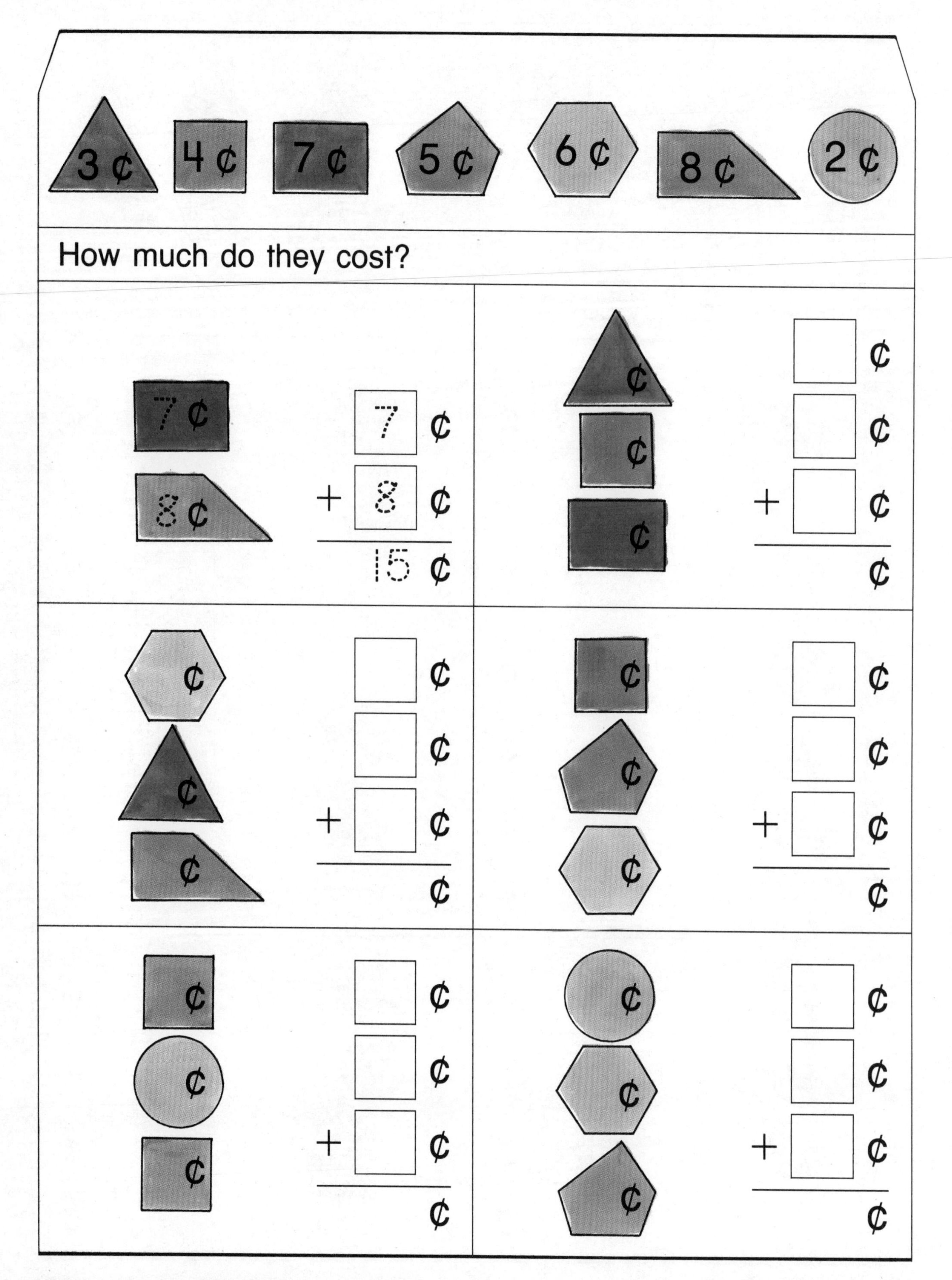
3 ¢
4 ¢
7 ¢
5 ¢
6 ¢
8 ¢
2 ¢
How much do they cost?
7 ¢
8 ¢
7 ¢
+ 8 ¢
15 ¢

Name ______________________________

CHAPTER CHECKUP

Add.

2 +9	9 +8	7 +5	6 +8	5 +9	4 +7	9 +3
5 +7	6 +9	5 +6	4 +9	8 +3	9 +7	4 +8

$9 + 5 =$ ____ $8 + 8 =$ ____ $6 + 6 =$ ____

$7 + 4 =$ ____ $9 + 6 =$ ____ $8 + 6 =$ ____

$7 + 8 =$ ____ $7 + 7 =$ ____ $6 + 7 =$ ____

$3 + 9 =$ ____ $8 + 9 =$ ____ $8 + 5 =$ ____

$8 + 4 =$ ____ $7 + 6 =$ ____ $9 + 9 =$ ____

$6 + 5 =$ ____ $9 + 4 =$ ____ $8 + 7 =$ ____

How much?

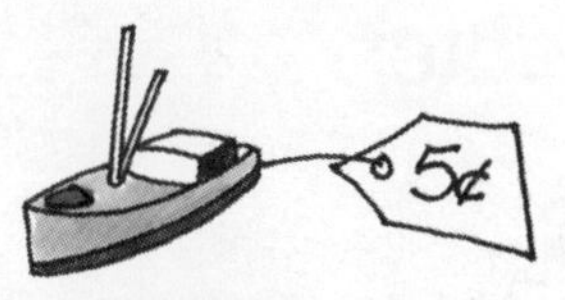

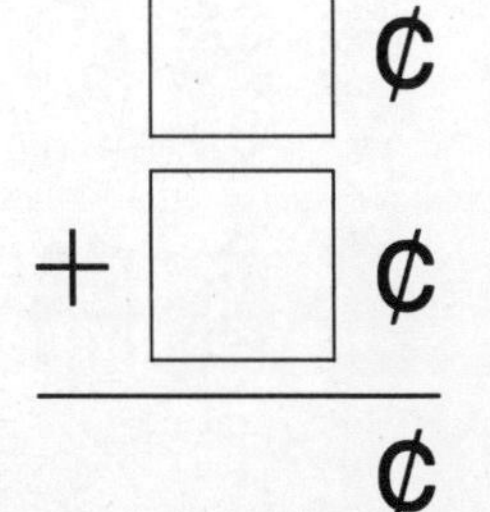

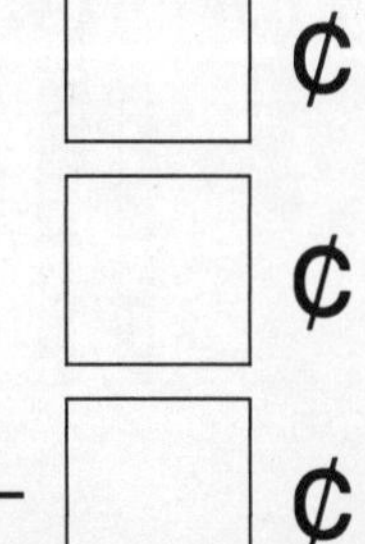

ROUNDUP REVIEW

Add or subtract.

$\begin{array}{r} 3 \\ +4 \\ \hline \end{array}$	$\begin{array}{r} 9 \\ +6 \\ \hline \end{array}$	$\begin{array}{r} 7 \\ -4 \\ \hline \end{array}$	$\begin{array}{r} 8 \\ -3 \\ \hline \end{array}$	$\begin{array}{r} 4 \\ +7 \\ \hline \end{array}$	$\begin{array}{r} 5 \\ +5 \\ \hline \end{array}$
$\begin{array}{r} 10 \\ -\ 3 \\ \hline \end{array}$	$\begin{array}{r} 8 \\ -5 \\ \hline \end{array}$	$\begin{array}{r} 9 \\ -4 \\ \hline \end{array}$	$\begin{array}{r} 4 \\ +4 \\ \hline \end{array}$	$\begin{array}{r} 0 \\ +8 \\ \hline \end{array}$	$\begin{array}{r} 5 \\ -3 \\ \hline \end{array}$
$\begin{array}{r} 9 \\ -5 \\ \hline \end{array}$	$\begin{array}{r} 9 \\ +9 \\ \hline \end{array}$	$\begin{array}{r} 10 \\ -\ 5 \\ \hline \end{array}$	$\begin{array}{r} 10 \\ -\ 2 \\ \hline \end{array}$	$\begin{array}{r} 6 \\ +7 \\ \hline \end{array}$	$\begin{array}{r} 4 \\ +8 \\ \hline \end{array}$

Count by tens.

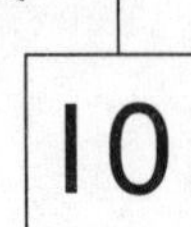
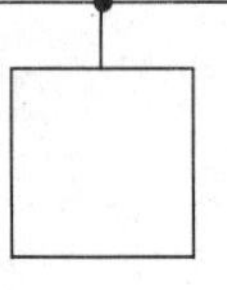
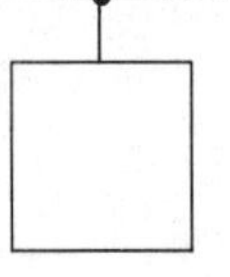
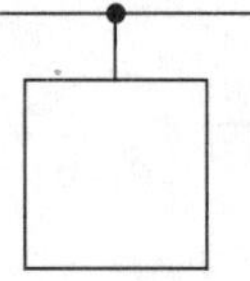
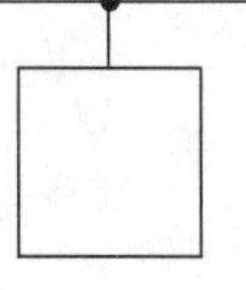
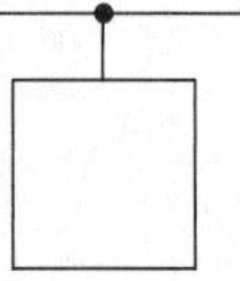
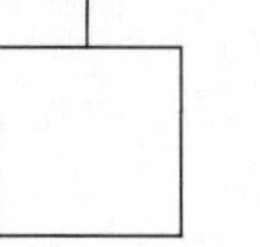

10	20							

How many?

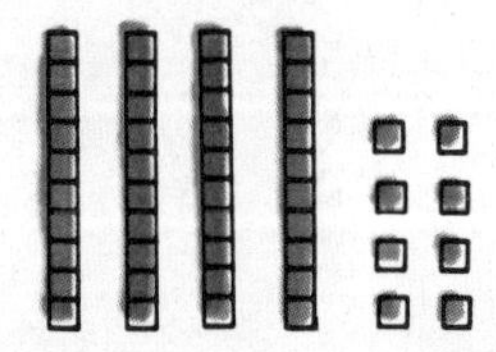

_____ tens _____ ones

_____

How many?
Circle the greater.

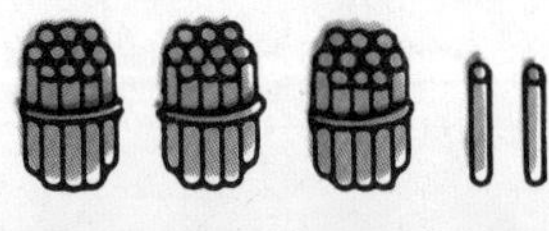

_____

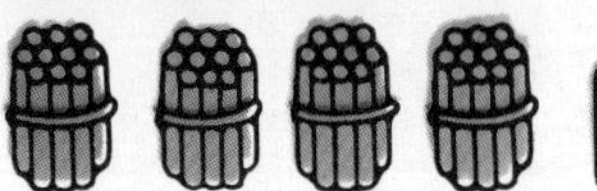

_____

Name ____

7 SUBTRACTION, MINUENDS THROUGH 18

How many taken away? How many left?

How many horses?  7

How many taken away? − 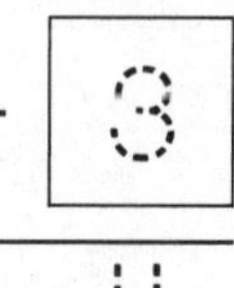 3

How many are left? 4

$\begin{array}{r} 8 \\ -2 \\ \hline \end{array}$

$\begin{array}{r} 9 \\ -5 \\ \hline \end{array}$

$\begin{array}{r} 7 \\ -6 \\ \hline \end{array}$

$\begin{array}{r} 7 \\ -4 \\ \hline \end{array}$

$\begin{array}{r} 9 \\ -4 \\ \hline \end{array}$

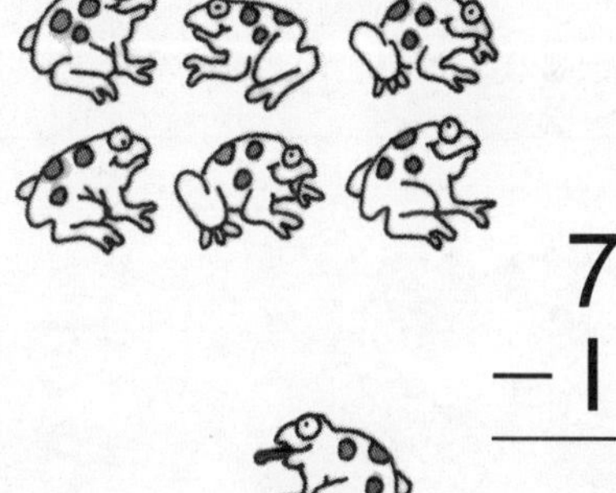

$\begin{array}{r} 7 \\ -1 \\ \hline \end{array}$

$\begin{array}{r} 5 \\ -4 \\ \hline \end{array}$

$\begin{array}{r} 6 \\ -5 \\ \hline \end{array}$

$\begin{array}{r} 8 \\ -4 \\ \hline \end{array}$

How many taken away? How many left?

 2 −1 1	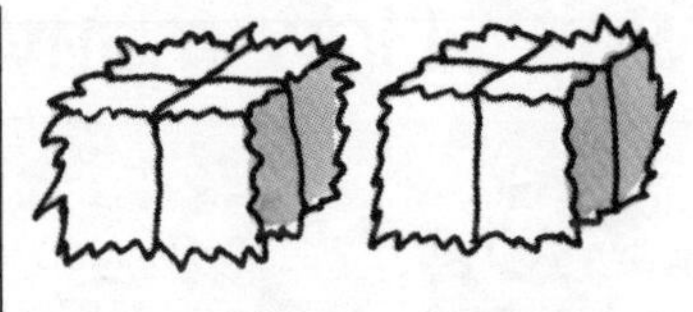 4 −2	 5 −2
 5 −3	  7 −2	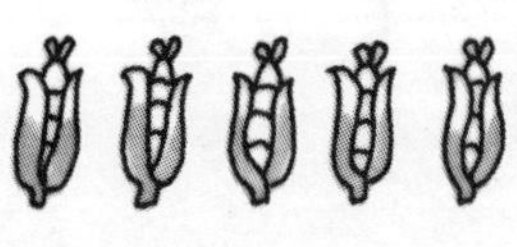 8 −3
 9 −2	  6 −2	 4 −1
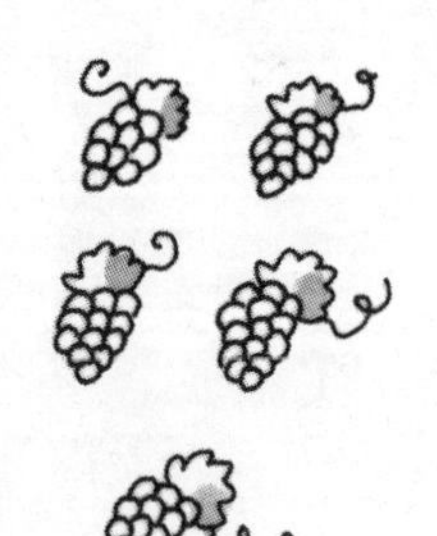 5 −5	 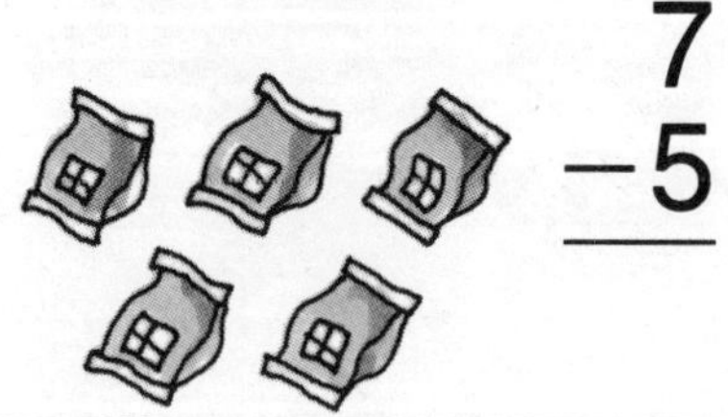 7 −5	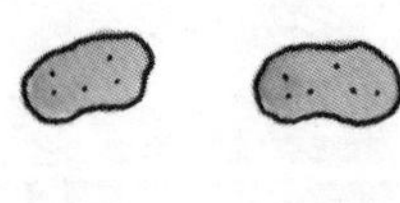 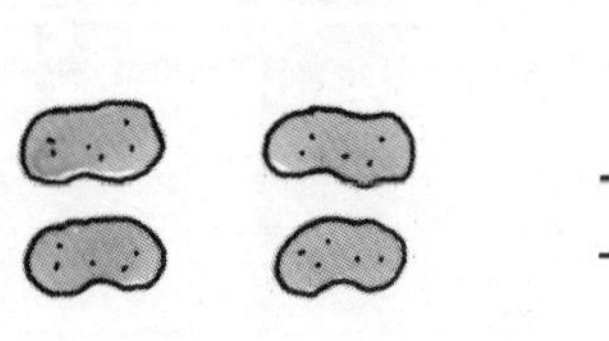 6 −4
  8 −6	  9 −3	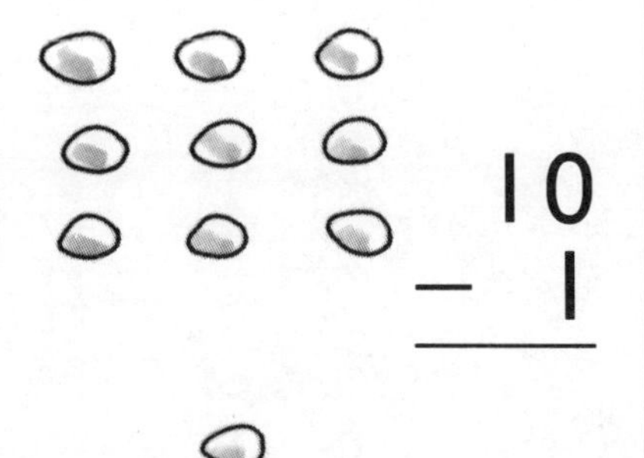 10 − 1

Name ______________________________

Subtract.

$9 - 1 =$ ____	$9 - 7 =$ ____	$10 - 8 =$ ____
$4 - 4 =$ ____	$6 - 1 =$ ____	$8 - 0 =$ ____
$3 - 2 =$ ____	$7 - 7 =$ ____	$6 - 4 =$ ____
$8 - 5 =$ ____	$10 - 6 =$ ____	$4 - 1 =$ ____
$9 - 6 =$ ____	$8 - 1 =$ ____	$3 - 3 =$ ____
$3 - 1 =$ ____	$7 - 5 =$ ____	$10 - 1 =$ ____

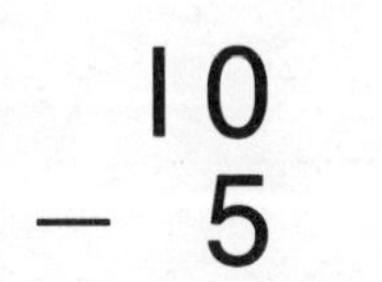

10	9	8	10	9	10
− 5	−8	−7	− 9	−4	− 7
7	9	10	6	10	8
−6	−5	− 2	−3	− 4	−4
7	8	6	9	10	8
−1	−2	−6	−0	− 3	−8

Complete the tables.

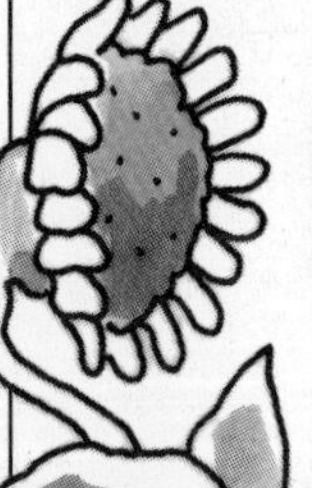

Subtract 3	
5	2
6	
10	
8	
9	

Subtract 4	
7	
10	
8	
6	
9	

Subtract 5	
6	
5	
10	
9	
8	

FIELD TRIP

Subtract. Use the numbers to write another fact.

$9 - 3 =$ 6

9 − 6 = 3

$4 - 4 =$ ___

☐ − ☐ = ___

$8 - 5 =$ ___

☐ − ☐ = ___

$10 - 7 =$ ___

☐ − ☐ = ___

$10 - 9 =$ ___

☐ − ☐ = ___

$7 - 0 =$ ___

☐ − ☐ = ___

Name ____________________

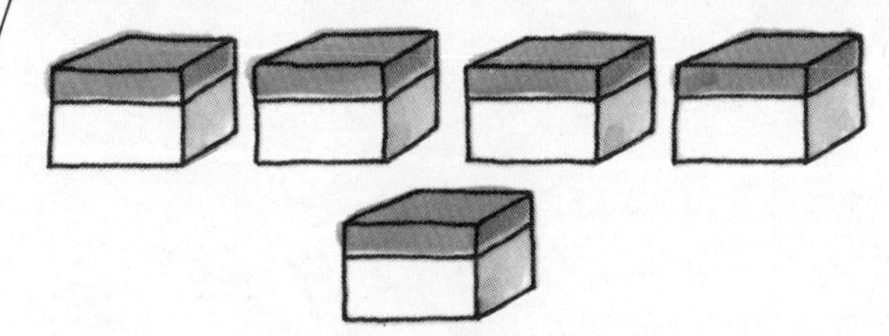

How many presents? 11

How many without ribbons? 5

How many with ribbons? 6

$\begin{array}{r} 11 \\ -\ 5 \\ \hline 6 \end{array}$ $\begin{array}{r} 11 \\ -\ 6 \\ \hline 5 \end{array}$

Subtract.

$\begin{array}{r} 11 \\ -\ 2 \\ \hline \end{array}$ $\begin{array}{r} 11 \\ -\ 9 \\ \hline \end{array}$

$\begin{array}{r} 11 \\ -\ 5 \\ \hline \end{array}$ $\begin{array}{r} 11 \\ -\ 6 \\ \hline \end{array}$

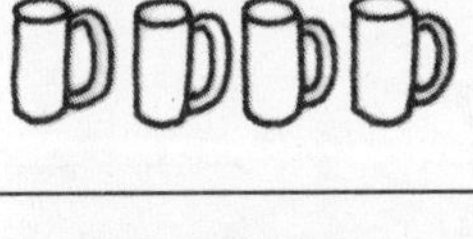

$\begin{array}{r} 11 \\ -\ 4 \\ \hline \end{array}$ $\begin{array}{r} 11 \\ -\ 7 \\ \hline \end{array}$

$\begin{array}{r} 12 \\ -\ 3 \\ \hline \end{array}$ $\begin{array}{r} 12 \\ -\ 9 \\ \hline \end{array}$

$\begin{array}{r} 12 \\ -\ 4 \\ \hline \end{array}$ $\begin{array}{r} 12 \\ -\ 8 \\ \hline \end{array}$

$\begin{array}{r} 12 \\ -\ 5 \\ \hline \end{array}$ $\begin{array}{r} 12 \\ -\ 7 \\ \hline \end{array}$

Subtract.

$8 - 3 =$ ___ $11 - 2 =$ ___ $9 - 7 =$ ___

$9 - 1 =$ ___ $12 - 4 =$ ___ $10 - 1 =$ ___

$10 - 2 =$ ___ $10 - 3 =$ ___ $8 - 5 =$ ___

$11 - 5 =$ ___ $12 - 5 =$ ___ $10 - 9 =$ ___

$9 - 9 =$ ___ $11 - 9 =$ ___ $11 - 6 =$ ___

$12 - 3 =$ ___ $9 - 3 =$ ___ $10 - 5 =$ ___

$\begin{array}{r} 9 \\ -2 \\ \hline \end{array}$ $\begin{array}{r} 10 \\ -\ 4 \\ \hline \end{array}$ $\begin{array}{r} 12 \\ -\ 7 \\ \hline \end{array}$ $\begin{array}{r} 9 \\ -6 \\ \hline \end{array}$ $\begin{array}{r} 11 \\ -\ 3 \\ \hline \end{array}$ $\begin{array}{r} 12 \\ -\ 9 \\ \hline \end{array}$

$\begin{array}{r} 8 \\ -2 \\ \hline \end{array}$ $\begin{array}{r} 10 \\ -\ 8 \\ \hline \end{array}$ $\begin{array}{r} 9 \\ -4 \\ \hline \end{array}$ $\begin{array}{r} 11 \\ -\ 8 \\ \hline \end{array}$ $\begin{array}{r} 12 \\ -\ 8 \\ \hline \end{array}$ $\begin{array}{r} 10 \\ -\ 7 \\ \hline \end{array}$

$\begin{array}{r} 11 \\ -\ 4 \\ \hline \end{array}$ $\begin{array}{r} 9 \\ -5 \\ \hline \end{array}$ $\begin{array}{r} 12 \\ -\ 6 \\ \hline \end{array}$ $\begin{array}{r} 11 \\ -\ 7 \\ \hline \end{array}$ $\begin{array}{r} 9 \\ -8 \\ \hline \end{array}$ $\begin{array}{r} 10 \\ -\ 6 \\ \hline \end{array}$

Name ______________________________

13 in all
− 5 flew away
8 stayed

13 in all
− 8 stayed
5 flew away

Subtract.

$\begin{array}{r} 14 \\ -\ 6 \\ \hline \end{array}$	$\begin{array}{r} 14 \\ -\ 8 \\ \hline \end{array}$

$\begin{array}{r} 13 \\ -\ 4 \\ \hline \end{array}$	$\begin{array}{r} 13 \\ -\ 5 \\ \hline \end{array}$	$\begin{array}{r} 13 \\ -\ 6 \\ \hline \end{array}$	$\begin{array}{r} 13 \\ -\ 7 \\ \hline \end{array}$	$\begin{array}{r} 13 \\ -\ 8 \\ \hline \end{array}$	$\begin{array}{r} 13 \\ -\ 9 \\ \hline \end{array}$
$\begin{array}{r} 14 \\ -\ 5 \\ \hline \end{array}$	$\begin{array}{r} 14 \\ -\ 6 \\ \hline \end{array}$	$\begin{array}{r} 14 \\ -\ 7 \\ \hline \end{array}$	$\begin{array}{r} 14 \\ -\ 8 \\ \hline \end{array}$	$\begin{array}{r} 14 \\ -\ 9 \\ \hline \end{array}$	$\begin{array}{r} 12 \\ -\ 5 \\ \hline \end{array}$
$\begin{array}{r} 14 \\ -\ 7 \\ \hline \end{array}$	$\begin{array}{r} 13 \\ -\ 9 \\ \hline \end{array}$	$\begin{array}{r} 13 \\ -\ 4 \\ \hline \end{array}$	$\begin{array}{r} 13 \\ -\ 6 \\ \hline \end{array}$	$\begin{array}{r} 14 \\ -\ 6 \\ \hline \end{array}$	$\begin{array}{r} 14 \\ -\ 8 \\ \hline \end{array}$

Subtract.

11	11	12	12	13	13	12
− 3	− 8	− 3	− 9	− 4	− 9	− 4

12	13	13	11	11	12	12
− 8	− 5	− 8	− 5	− 6	− 5	− 7

13	13	14	14	14	14	14
− 6	− 7	− 5	− 9	− 6	− 8	− 7

FIELD TRIP

Complete the wheels.

Name ______________________________

Subtract.

12 − 6 = ___	12 − 4 = ___	11 − 2 = ___
13 − 5 = ___	14 − 7 = ___	12 − 9 = ___
10 − 5 = ___	11 − 8 = ___	13 − 9 = ___
11 − 5 = ___	12 − 3 = ___	11 − 7 = ___
14 − 6 = ___	13 − 4 = ___	14 − 5 = ___
12 − 5 = ___	11 − 4 = ___	13 − 8 = ___
11 − 6 = ___	13 − 7 = ___	14 − 9 = ___
11 − 9 = ___	14 − 8 = ___	11 − 3 = ___
12 − 7 = ___	13 − 6 = ___	12 − 8 = ___

Solve.

Tom had 13¢.
He spent 8¢.
How much does he have left?

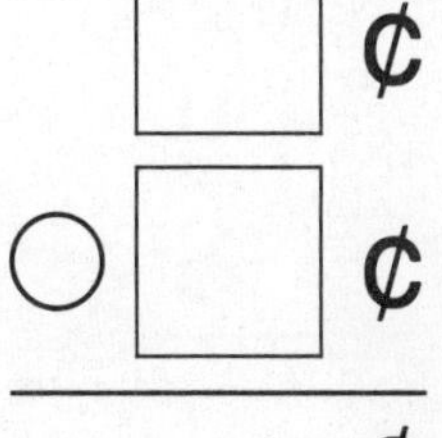

___¢

Ann had 15¢.
She bought a hat for 9¢.
How much does she have left?

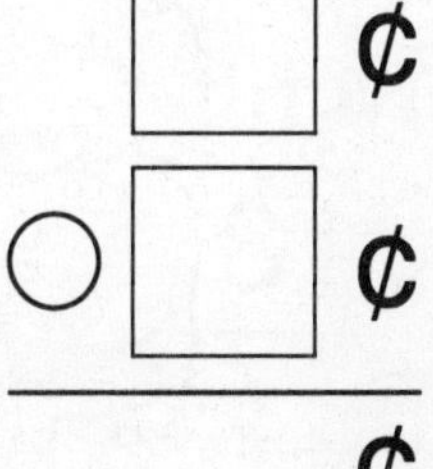

___¢

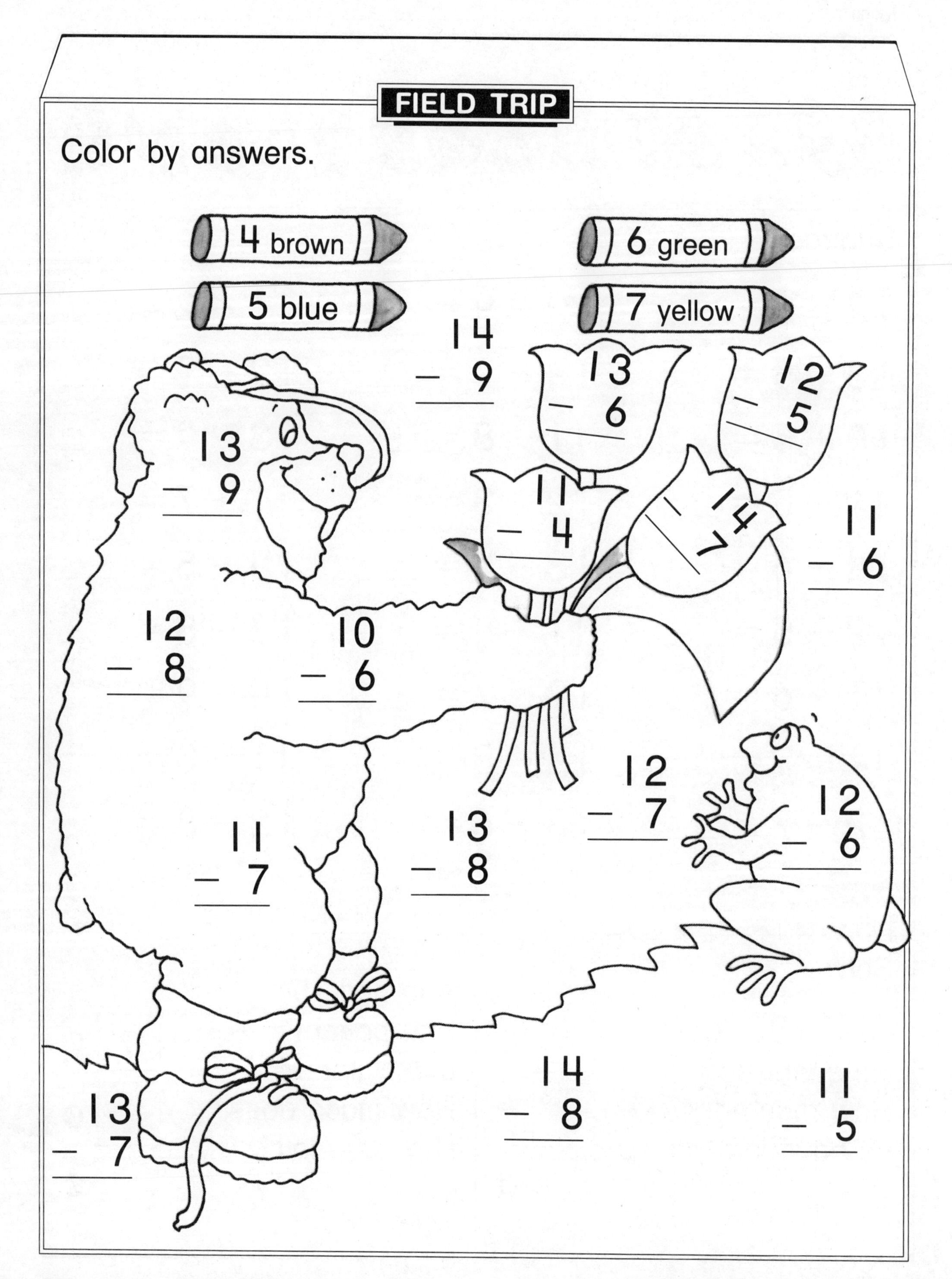
FIELD TRIP
Color by answers.
4 brown
6 green
5 blue
7 yellow
14 − 9
13 − 6
12 − 5
13 − 9
11 − 4
14 − 7
11 − 6
12 − 8
10 − 6
12 − 7
12 − 6
11 − 7
13 − 8
13 − 7
14 − 8
11 − 5

Name ______

How many in all? 15

15	15
− 6	− 9
9	6

Subtract.

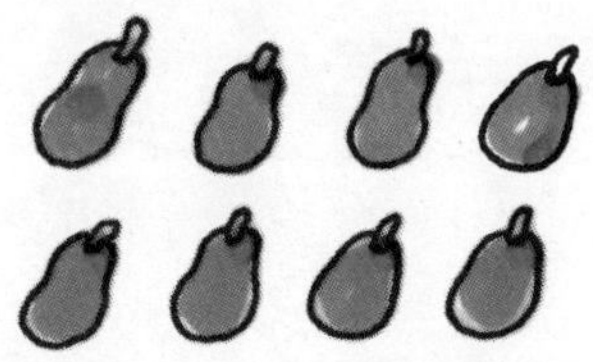

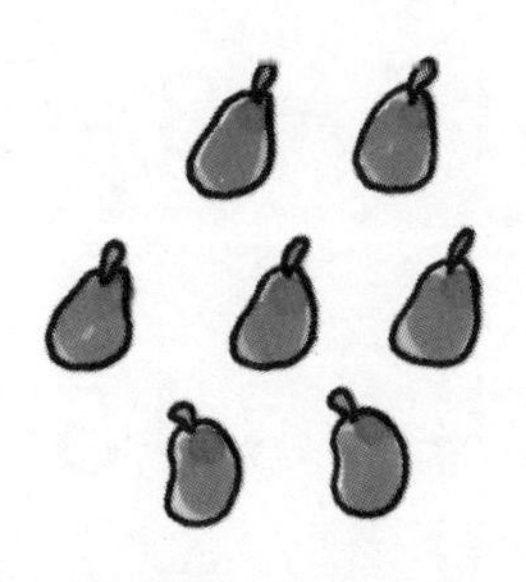

How many in all? ____

15	15
− 8	− 7

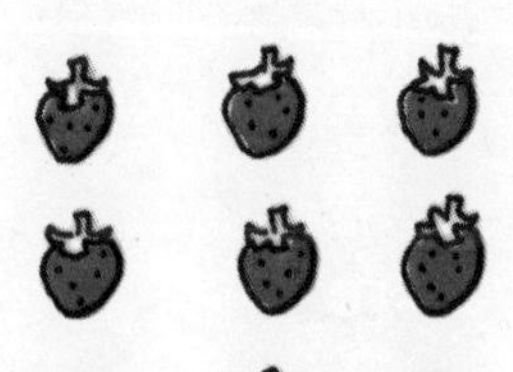

How many in all? ____

16	16
− 7	− 9

How many in all? ____

$$\begin{array}{r} 16 \\ -\ 8 \\ \hline \end{array}$$

Solve.

Jack saw 15 horses.
7 of them ran away. ◯ ☐ ☐
How many are left? ____

____ horses

Maria had 16 flowers.
She gave her
teacher 8. ◯ ☐ ☐
How many are left? ____

____ flowers

Subtract.

$15 - 6 =$ ___ $15 - 9 =$ ___ $16 - 7 =$ ___

$14 - 7 =$ ___ $16 - 9 =$ ___ $15 - 7 =$ ___

$16 - 8 =$ ___ $15 - 8 =$ ___ $14 - 5 =$ ___

14	16	14	13	15	13	16
− 7	− 8	− 9	− 7	− 8	− 6	− 7

14	13	16	13	15	14	15
− 8	− 9	− 9	− 8	− 9	− 6	− 7

Solve.

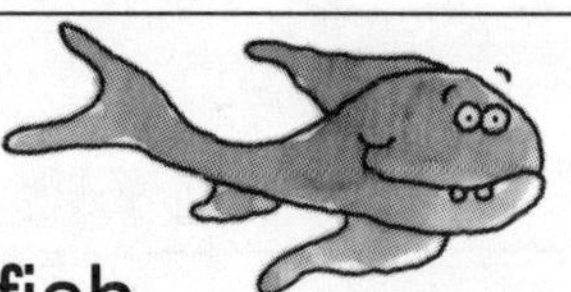

Sarah had 15 fish.
She gave 7 fish
to her brother.
How many does
she have left?

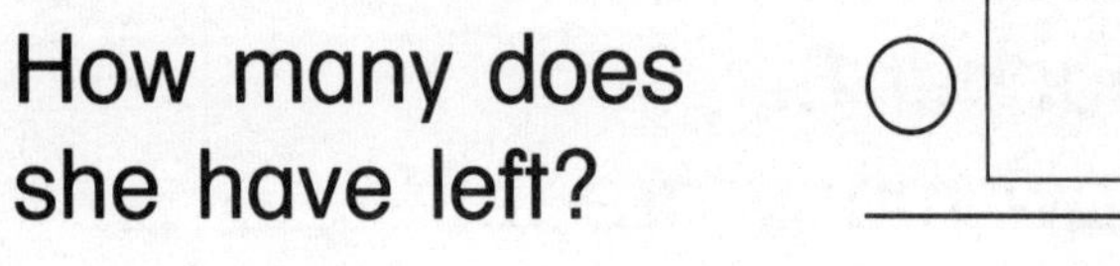

___ fish

Yang has 16 toy cars.
9 cars are red.
The rest are black.
How many black
cars are there?

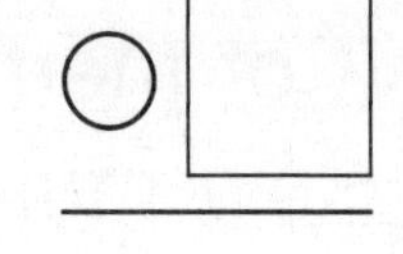

___ black cars

Name ____________________

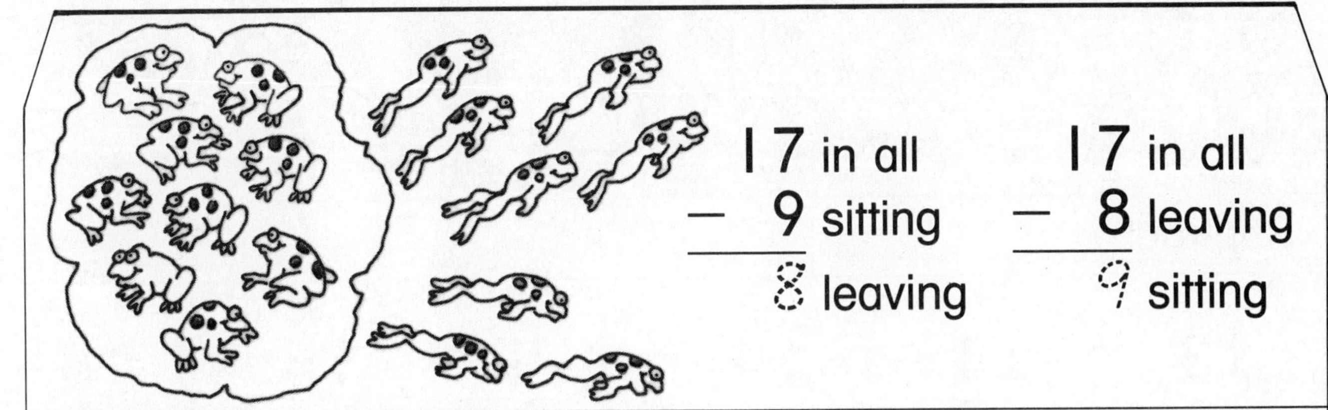

17	in all	17	in all
− 9	sitting	− 8	leaving
8	leaving	9	sitting

Subtract.

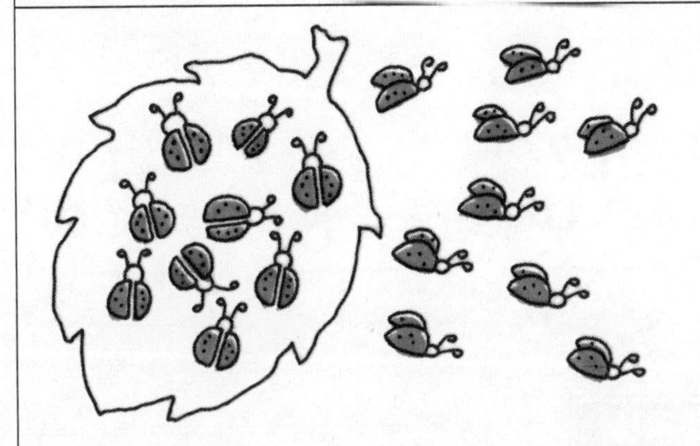

18	in all	18	in all
− 9	sitting	− 9	leaving
☐	leaving	☐	sitting

$$\begin{array}{r}15\\-\ 6\\\hline\end{array}\quad\begin{array}{r}13\\-\ 4\\\hline\end{array}\quad\begin{array}{r}16\\-\ 8\\\hline\end{array}\quad\begin{array}{r}15\\-\ 9\\\hline\end{array}\quad\begin{array}{r}14\\-\ 7\\\hline\end{array}\quad\begin{array}{r}17\\-\ 9\\\hline\end{array}$$

$$\begin{array}{r}14\\-\ 8\\\hline\end{array}\quad\begin{array}{r}16\\-\ 9\\\hline\end{array}\quad\begin{array}{r}14\\-\ 5\\\hline\end{array}\quad\begin{array}{r}18\\-\ 9\\\hline\end{array}\quad\begin{array}{r}13\\-\ 5\\\hline\end{array}\quad\begin{array}{r}15\\-\ 8\\\hline\end{array}$$

$$\begin{array}{r}13\\-\ 6\\\hline\end{array}\quad\begin{array}{r}15\\-\ 7\\\hline\end{array}\quad\begin{array}{r}14\\-\ 9\\\hline\end{array}\quad\begin{array}{r}16\\-\ 7\\\hline\end{array}\quad\begin{array}{r}14\\-\ 6\\\hline\end{array}\quad\begin{array}{r}17\\-\ 8\\\hline\end{array}$$

Subtract.

13	13	14	14	15	15
− 6	− 7	− 6	− 8	− 6	− 9

16	16	17	17	16	18
− 7	− 9	− 8	− 9	− 8	− 9

FIELD TRIP

Write the missing numbers.

7 + [6] = 13　　8 + [ ] = 17

6 + [ ] = 13　　17 − [ ] = 8

13 − [7] = 6　　9 + [ ] = 17

13 − [ ] = 7　　17 − [ ] = 9

Name ____________________

Subtract.

$11 - 4 =$ ___ $13 - 6 =$ ___ $11 - 9 =$ ___

$12 - 5 =$ ___ $16 - 8 =$ ___ $12 - 7 =$ ___

$11 - 2 =$ ___ $14 - 7 =$ ___ $13 - 4 =$ ___

$13 - 7 =$ ___ $12 - 3 =$ ___ $11 - 8 =$ ___

$15 - 8 =$ ___ $11 - 5 =$ ___ $14 - 6 =$ ___

$12 - 6 =$ ___ $15 - 6 =$ ___ $13 - 8 =$ ___

$$\begin{array}{r}13\\-\ 5\\\hline\end{array}\quad\begin{array}{r}15\\-\ 9\\\hline\end{array}\quad\begin{array}{r}11\\-\ 6\\\hline\end{array}\quad\begin{array}{r}17\\-\ 9\\\hline\end{array}\quad\begin{array}{r}15\\-\ 7\\\hline\end{array}\quad\begin{array}{r}14\\-\ 9\\\hline\end{array}$$

$$\begin{array}{r}14\\-\ 8\\\hline\end{array}\quad\begin{array}{r}12\\-\ 4\\\hline\end{array}\quad\begin{array}{r}13\\-\ 9\\\hline\end{array}\quad\begin{array}{r}11\\-\ 3\\\hline\end{array}\quad\begin{array}{r}16\\-\ 7\\\hline\end{array}\quad\begin{array}{r}12\\-\ 8\\\hline\end{array}$$

$$\begin{array}{r}11\\-\ 7\\\hline\end{array}\quad\begin{array}{r}18\\-\ 9\\\hline\end{array}\quad\begin{array}{r}12\\-\ 9\\\hline\end{array}\quad\begin{array}{r}14\\-\ 5\\\hline\end{array}\quad\begin{array}{r}16\\-\ 9\\\hline\end{array}\quad\begin{array}{r}17\\-\ 8\\\hline\end{array}$$

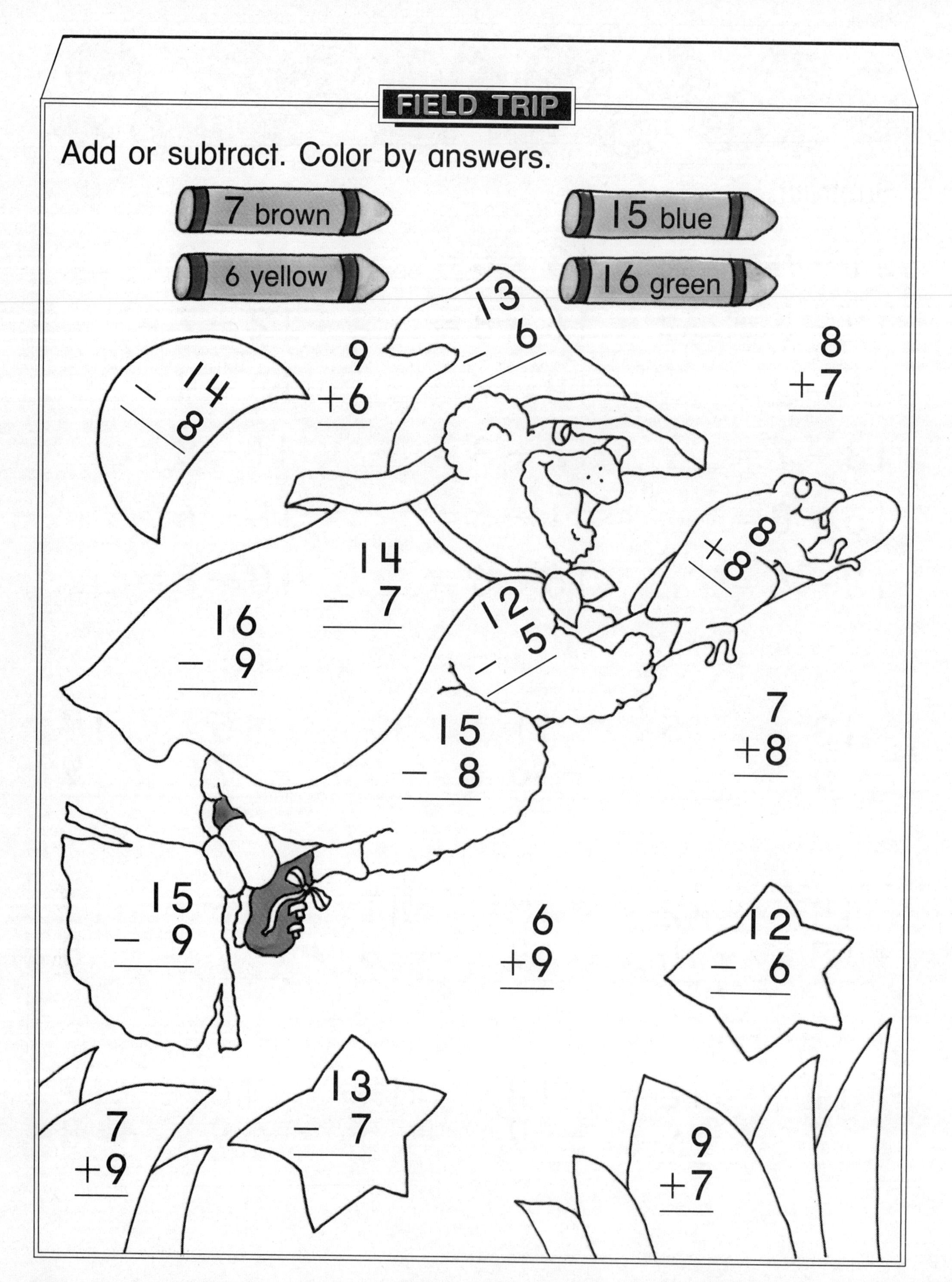
FIELD TRIP
Add or subtract. Color by answers.
7 brown
15 blue
6 yellow
16 green
14 − 8
9 + 6
13 − 6
8 + 7
14 − 7
16 − 9
12 − 5
8 + 8
15 − 8
7 + 8
15 − 9
6 + 9
12 − 6
13 − 7
7 + 9
9 + 7

Name ______________________________

How much is left?

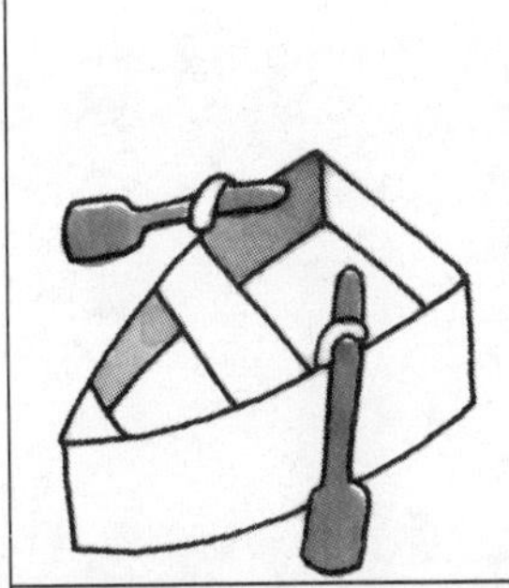

Had 14 ¢
Spent − 7 ¢
Left 7 ¢

Had 12 ¢
Spent − 6 ¢
Left 6 ¢

Had 16 ¢
Spent − ☐ ¢
Left ¢

Had 18 ¢
Spent − ☐ ¢
Left ¢

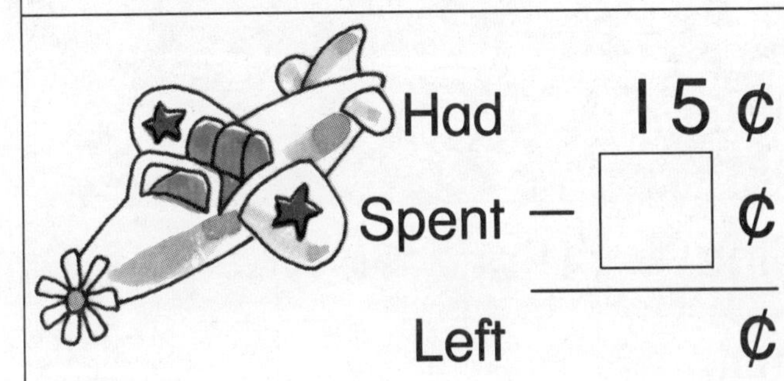

Had 15 ¢
Spent − ☐ ¢
Left ¢

Had 13 ¢
Spent − ☐ ¢
Left ¢

Had 16 ¢
Spent − ☐ ¢
Left ¢

Had 17 ¢
Spent − ☐ ¢
Left ¢

Subtract.

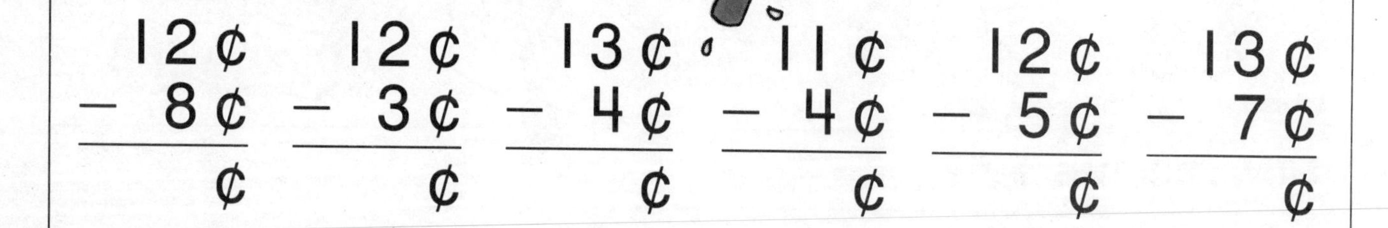

12¢	12¢	13¢	11¢	12¢	13¢
− 8¢	− 3¢	− 4¢	− 4¢	− 5¢	− 7¢
¢	¢	¢	¢	¢	¢

13¢	12¢	13¢	14¢	13¢	14¢
− 9¢	− 6¢	− 6¢	− 7¢	− 8¢	− 5¢
¢	¢	¢	¢	¢	¢

12¢	15¢	12¢	15¢	16¢	13¢
− 4¢	− 9¢	− 9¢	− 9¢	− 9¢	− 5¢
¢	¢	¢	¢	¢	¢

FIELD TRIP

Complete the charts.

Name	Had	Spent	Money Left	Name	Had	Spent	Money Left
Kay	12¢	9¢	3¢	Tina	14¢	9¢	¢
Dorothy	15¢	6¢	¢	Billy Jo	11¢	6¢	¢
Alan	18¢	9¢	¢	Kiku	17¢	9¢	¢
Sam	16¢	8¢	¢	Chris	15¢	8¢	¢
Rex	17¢	8¢	¢	Roy	14¢	6¢	¢

Name ______________________________

CHAPTER CHECKUP

Subtract.

$14 - 5 =$ ___	$16 - 9 =$ ___	$17 - 9 =$ ___
$14 - 8 =$ ___	$15 - 9 =$ ___	$12 - 5 =$ ___
$15 - 6 =$ ___	$13 - 6 =$ ___	$14 - 9 =$ ___
$13 - 5 =$ ___	$16 - 8 =$ ___	$16 - 7 =$ ___
$12 - 6 =$ ___	$14 - 9 =$ ___	$13 - 8 =$ ___

$\begin{array}{r} 12 \\ -\ 4 \\ \hline \end{array}$ $\begin{array}{r} 13 \\ -\ 9 \\ \hline \end{array}$ $\begin{array}{r} 15 \\ -\ 7 \\ \hline \end{array}$ $\begin{array}{r} 12 \\ -\ 9 \\ \hline \end{array}$ $\begin{array}{r} 14 \\ -\ 6 \\ \hline \end{array}$ $\begin{array}{r} 17 \\ -\ 8 \\ \hline \end{array}$

$\begin{array}{r} 15 \\ -\ 8 \\ \hline \end{array}$ $\begin{array}{r} 11 \\ -\ 2 \\ \hline \end{array}$ $\begin{array}{r} 18 \\ -\ 9 \\ \hline \end{array}$ $\begin{array}{r} 11 \\ -\ 4 \\ \hline \end{array}$ $\begin{array}{r} 13 \\ -\ 7 \\ \hline \end{array}$ $\begin{array}{r} 12 \\ -\ 7 \\ \hline \end{array}$

Solve.

Matt had 15¢.
He bought a toy car for 8¢.
How much does Matt have left?

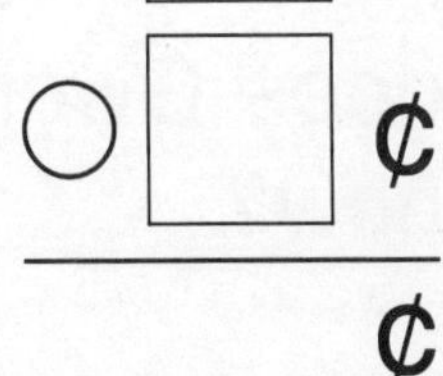
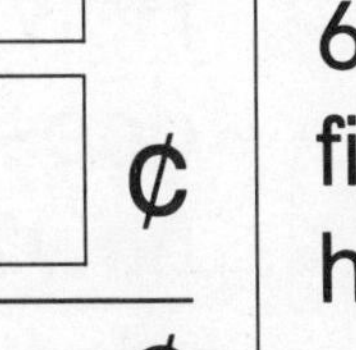

☐ ¢
○ ☐ ¢
______ ¢

_____¢

Terry had 13 fish.
She gave Juan 6 fish. How many fish does Terry have now?

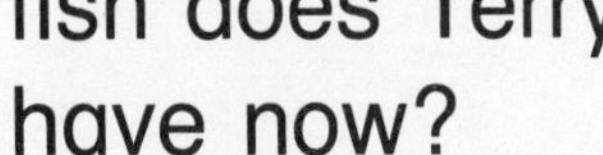

☐
○ ☐
______

_____ fish

ROUNDUP REVIEW

Add or subtract.

7	12	6	8	13	15	4
+8	− 4	+6	+9	− 6	− 7	+6

16	11	12	7	14	8	9
− 9	− 4	− 5	+7	− 5	+8	+5

Write the missing numbers.

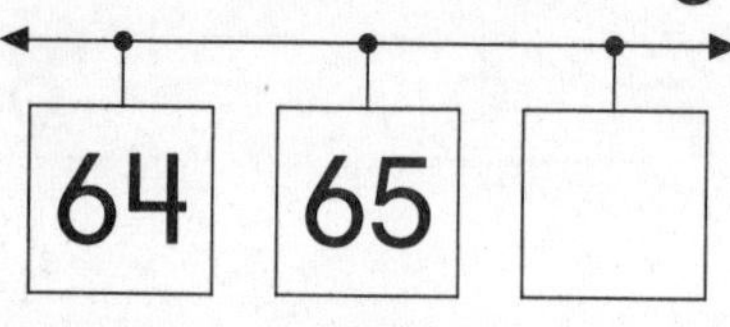

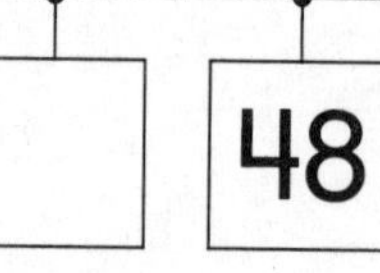

How many?

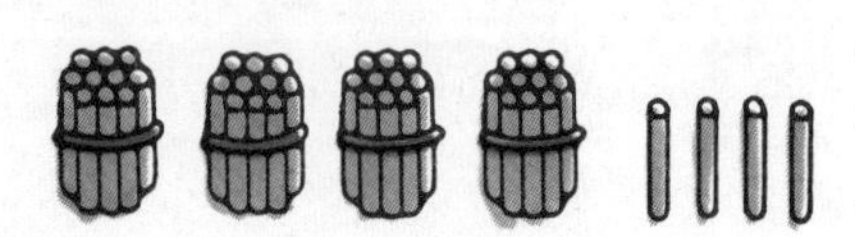

____ tens ____ ones

____

Solve.

Ken had 6 rabbits.
He bought 5 more.
How many rabbits
does Ken have
now?

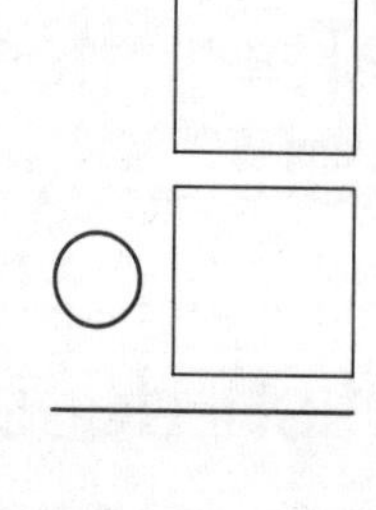

____ rabbits

Gwen had 15¢.
She spent 8¢.
How much money
does Gwen have
now?

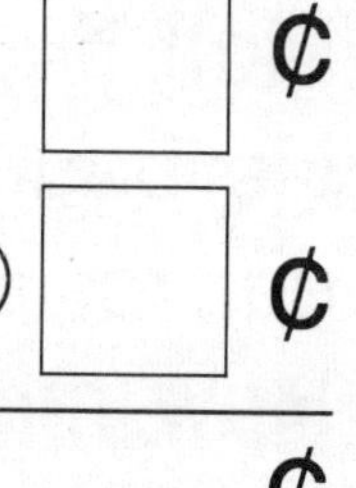

¢

¢

¢

____¢

Name ______________________

8 MONEY AND TIME

Count the money.

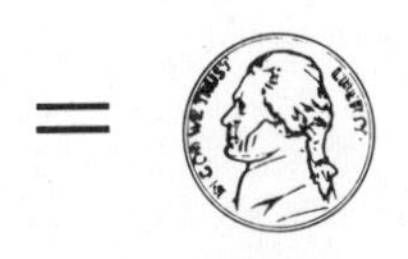

5 pennies = I nickel
5¢ 5¢

5 ¢

10 ¢

____ ¢

____ ¢

____ ¢

____ ¢

____ ¢

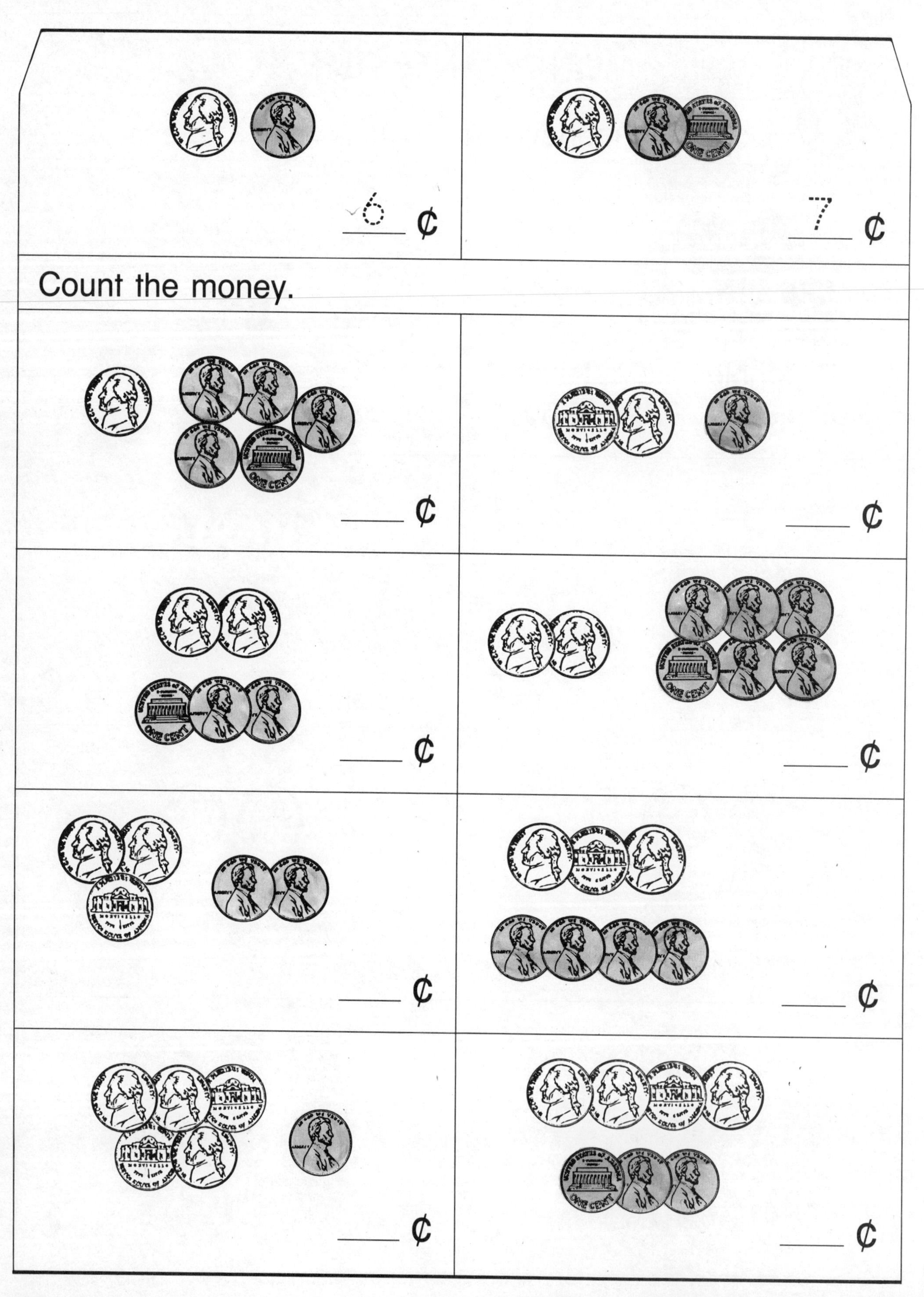
6 ¢
7 ¢
Count the money.
¢
¢
¢
¢
¢
¢
¢
¢

Name ______________________________

 = 

10 pennies = 1 dime
10¢ = 10¢

10 ¢

Count the money.

15 ¢

25 ¢

____ ¢

____ ¢

____ ¢

____ ¢

____ ¢

____ ¢

Match the bank with the money.

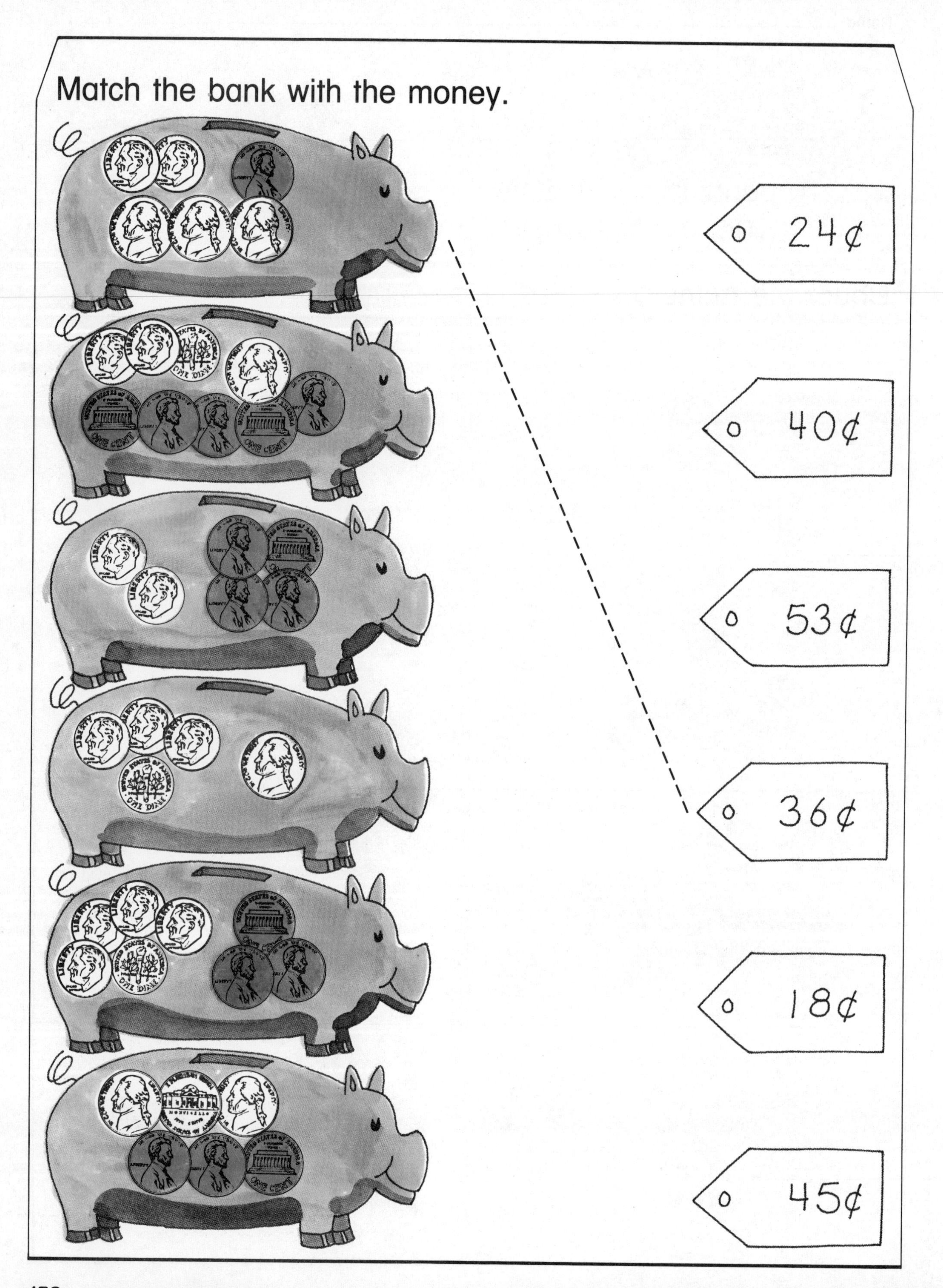

Name ______________________________

Check the coins you need to buy each toy.

Count the money. Write the cost.

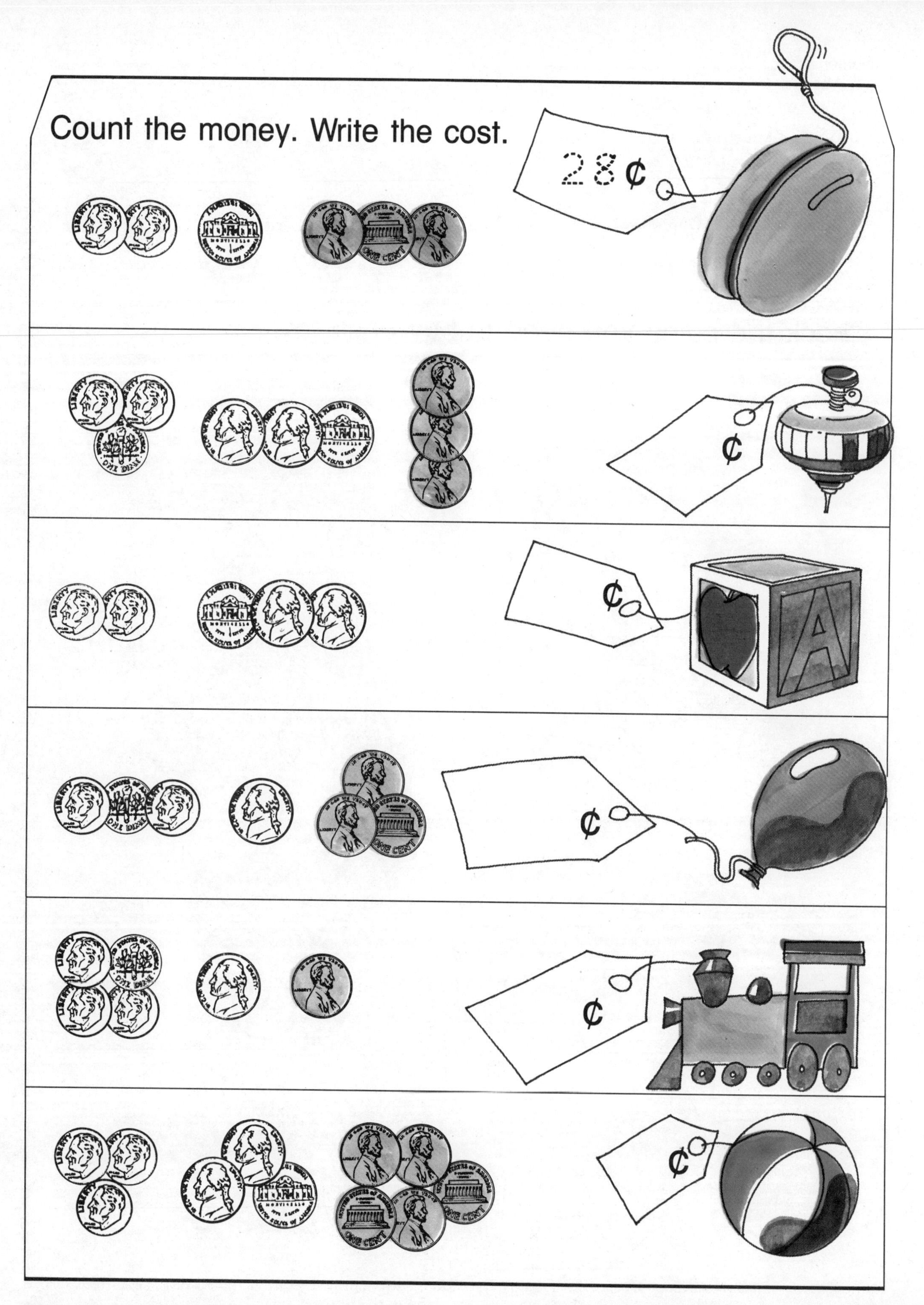

Name ______________________________

2 dimes 1 nickel

25¢ 25¢

25 ¢

Count the money.

30 ¢

____ ¢

____ ¢

____ ¢

____ ¢

____ ¢

____ ¢

____ ¢

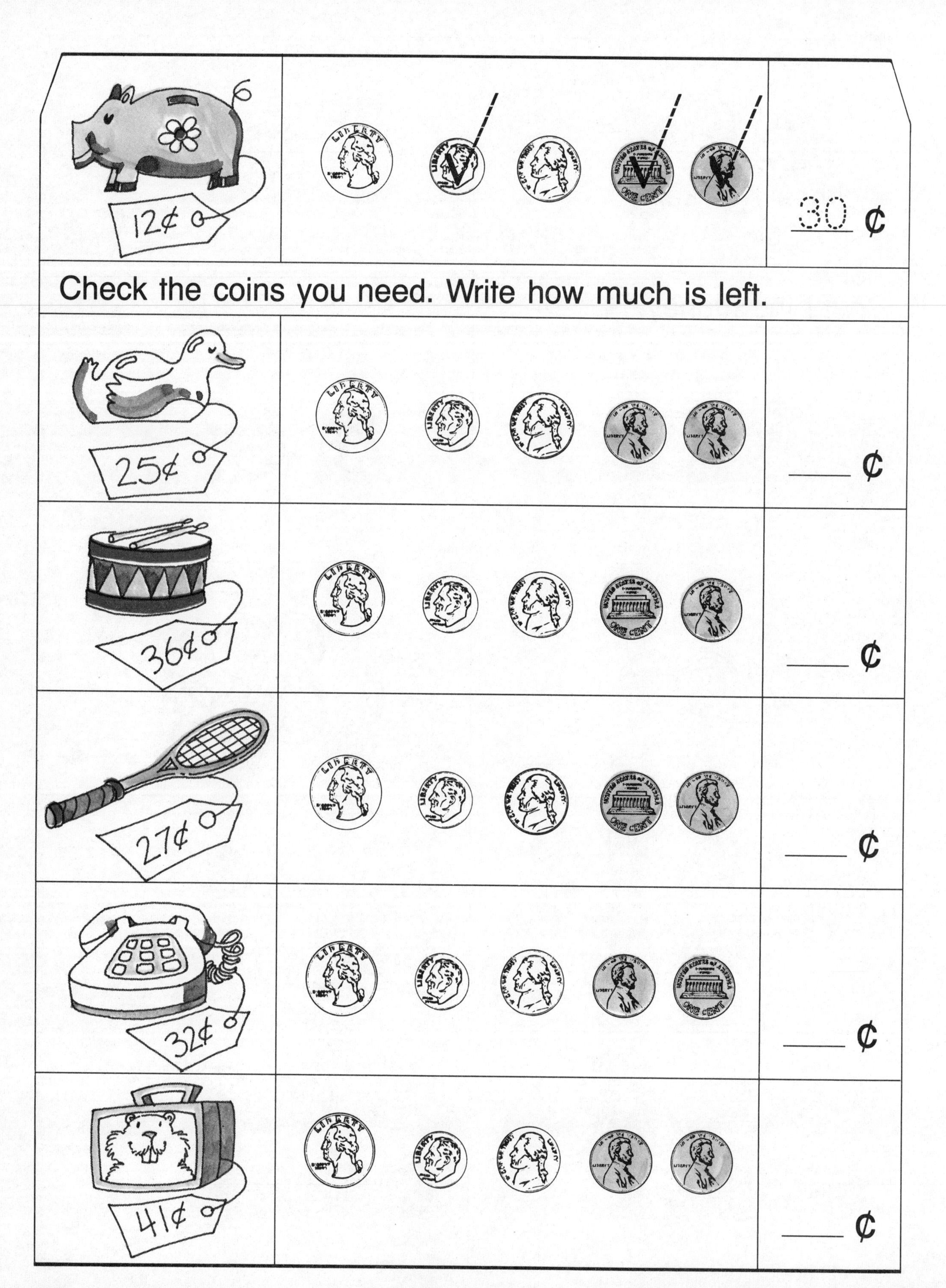
12¢
30 ¢
Check the coins you need. Write how much is left.
25¢
¢
36¢
¢
27¢
¢
32¢
¢
41¢
¢

Name ______________________________

YES

NO

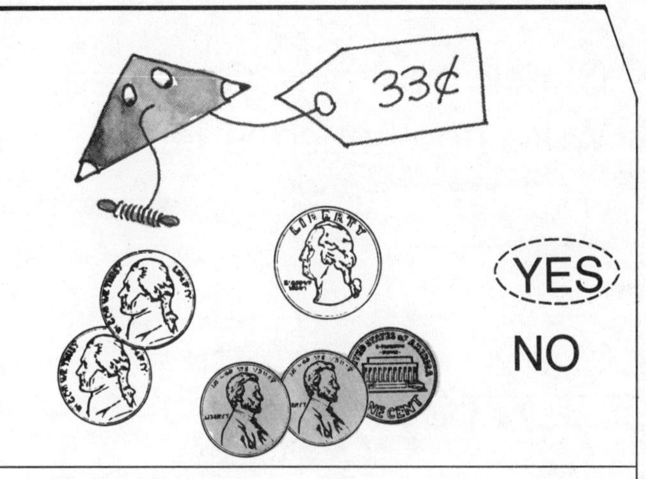

YES

NO

Is there enough money to buy the toy?

YES

NO

YES

NO

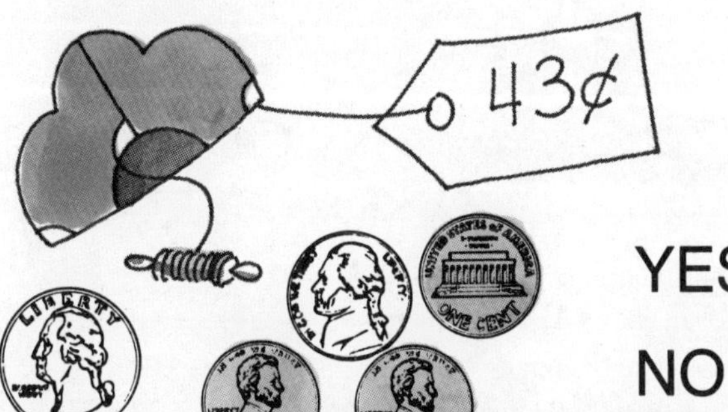

YES

NO

YES

NO

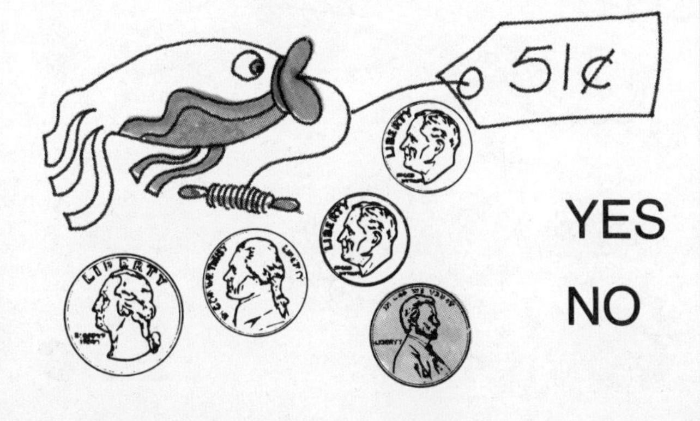

YES

NO

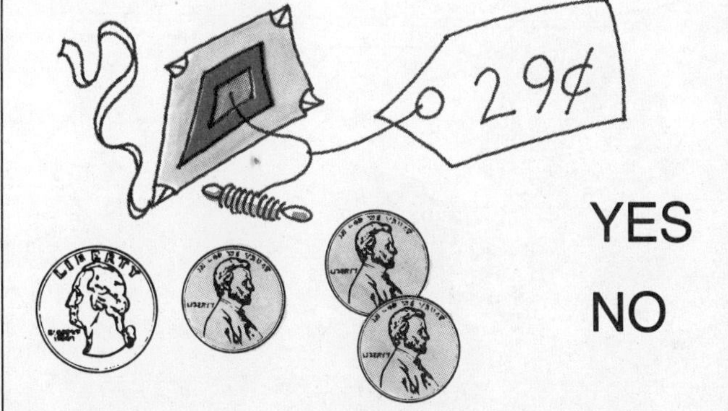

YES

NO

Check the coins you need.
Write how much is left.

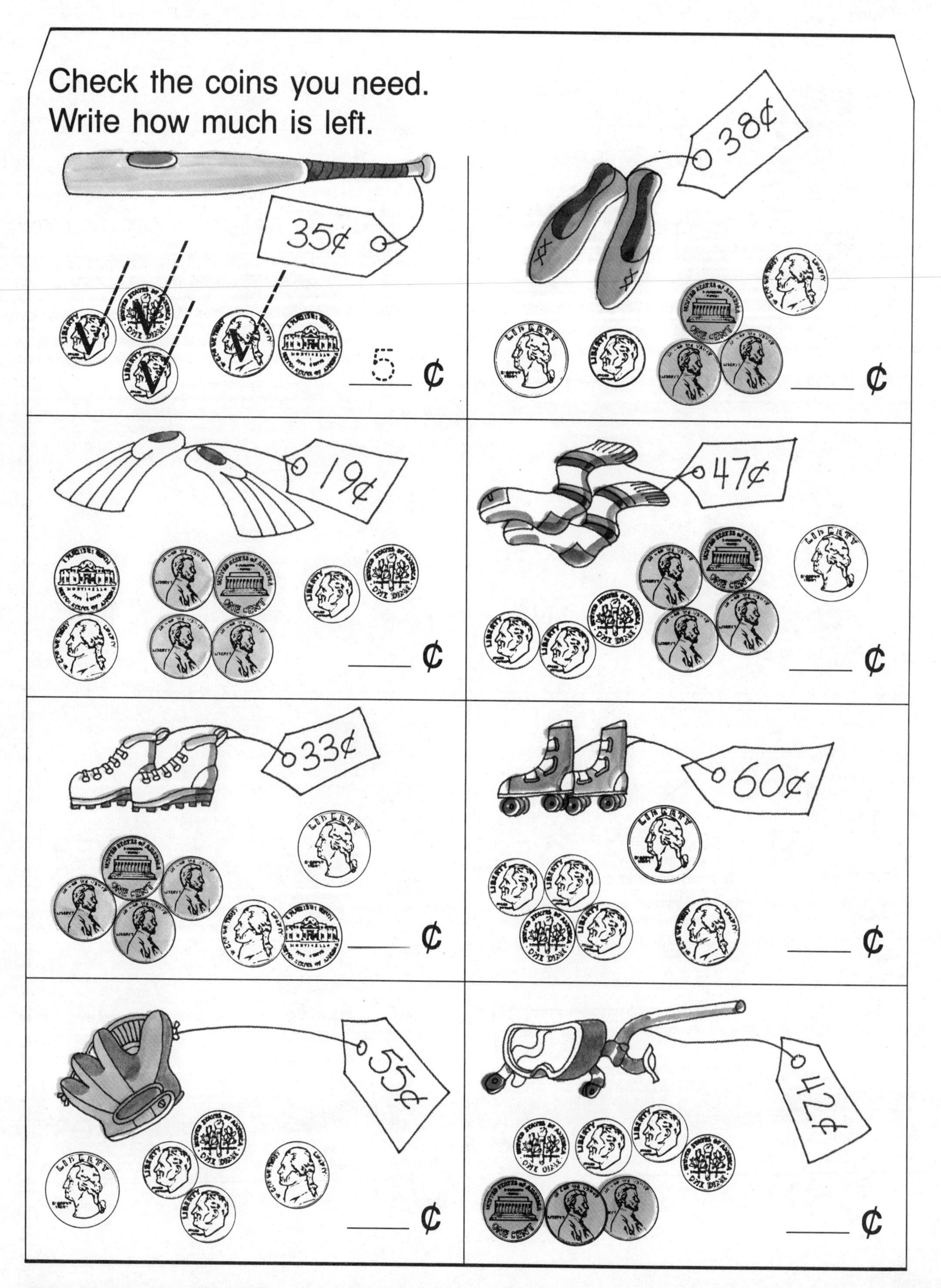

Name ____

Write the missing numbers on the clock.

Write the missing numbers.

The hour hand is on ____. Color it red.

The minute hand is on ____. Color it blue.

The time is ____ o'clock.

Circle the clock that shows the same time.

12:00

4:12

Write the times. Match the clocks.

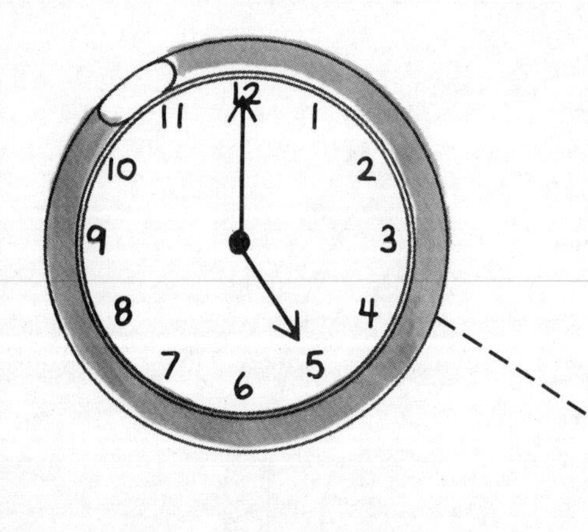

2:00

5:00

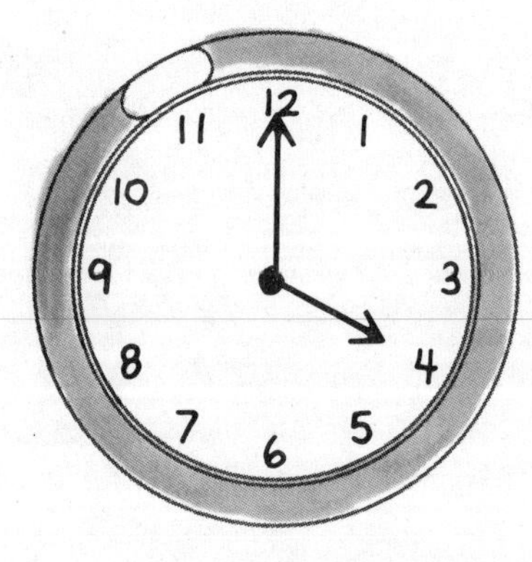

5 o'clock

___ o'clock

1:00

4:00

___ o'clock

___ o'clock

8:00

10:00

___ o'clock

___ o'clock

Name ____

The time is a half-hour after 9 o'clock

or

Write the times.

7:00

a half-hour later

7:30

a half-hour later

________ ________

a half-hour later

________ ________

a half-hour later

________ ________

Write the times.

Name ______________________________

Match the clocks.

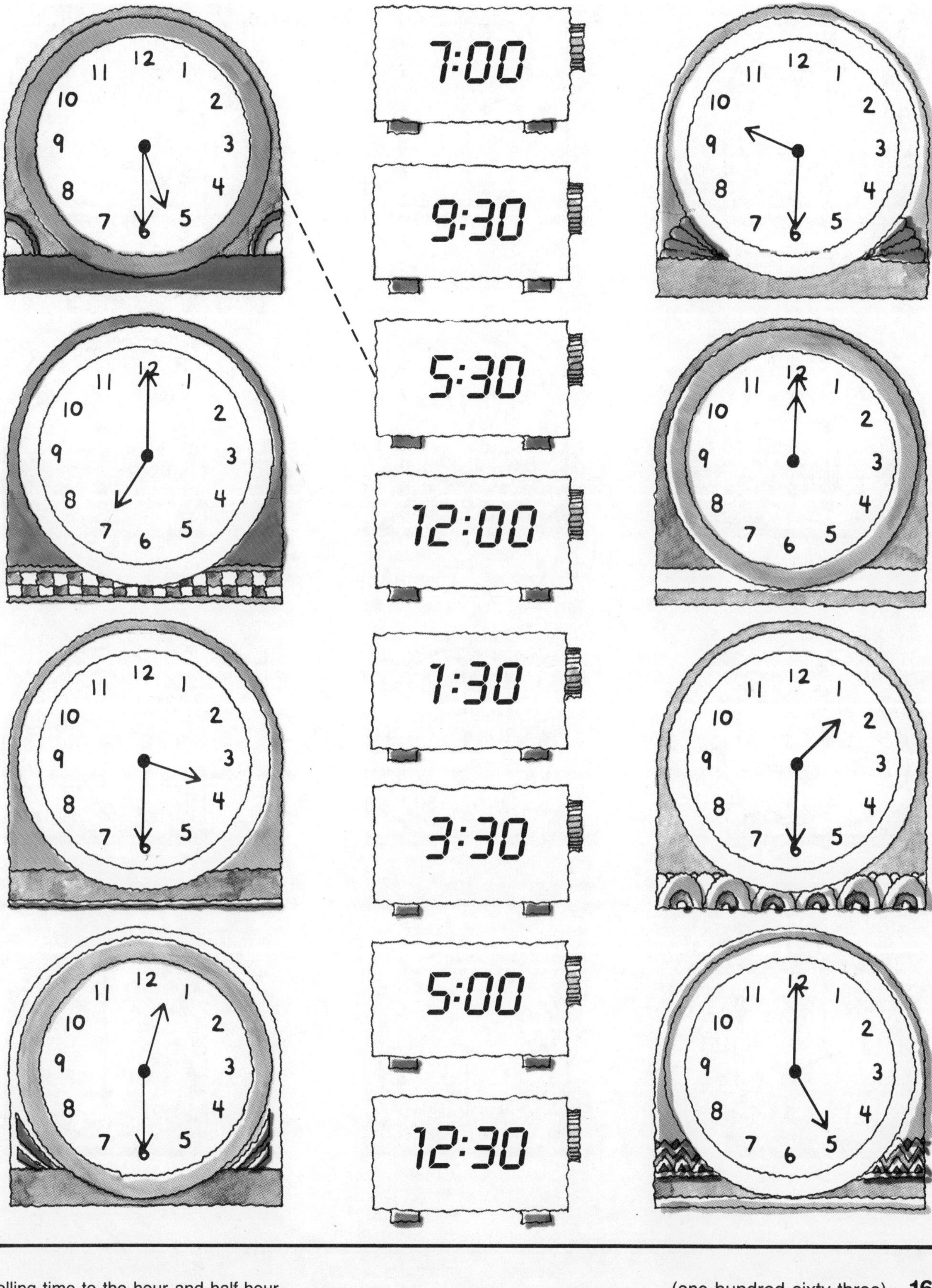

7:00

9:30

5:30

12:00

1:30

3:30

5:00

12:30

Write the times.

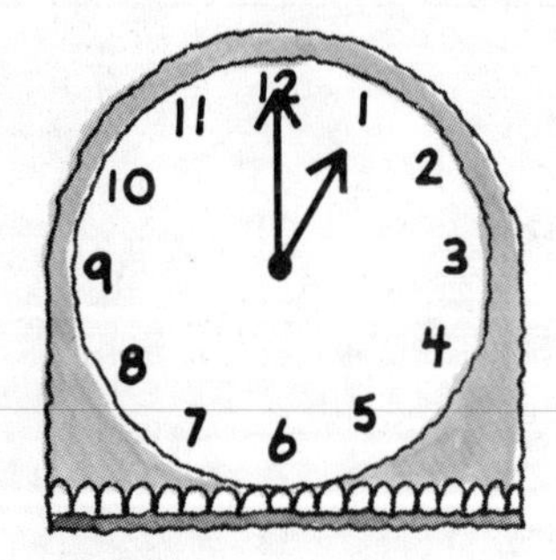

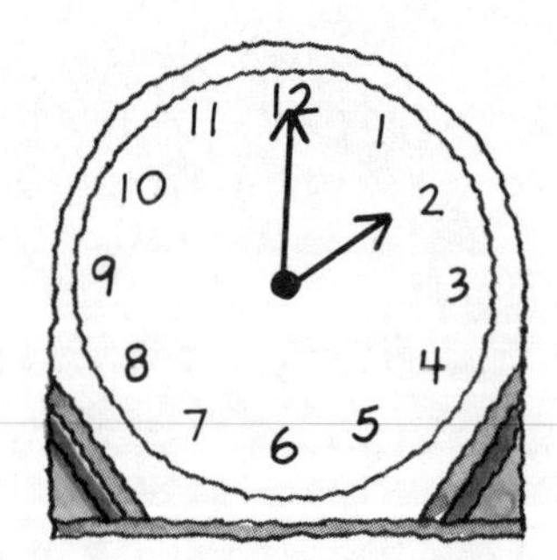

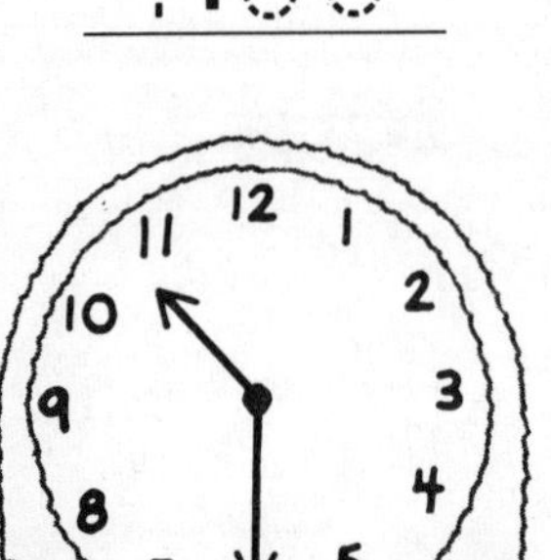

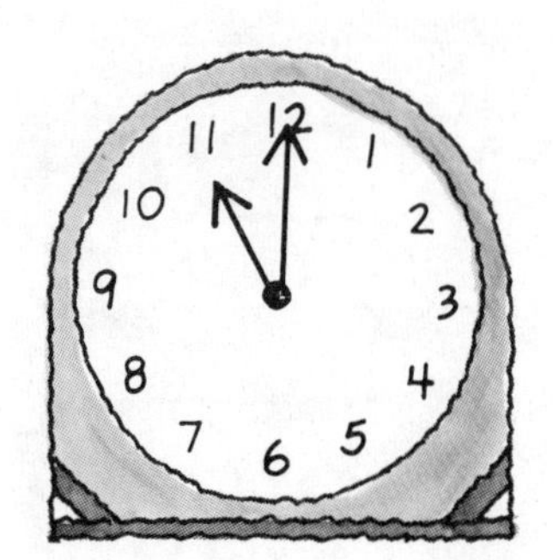

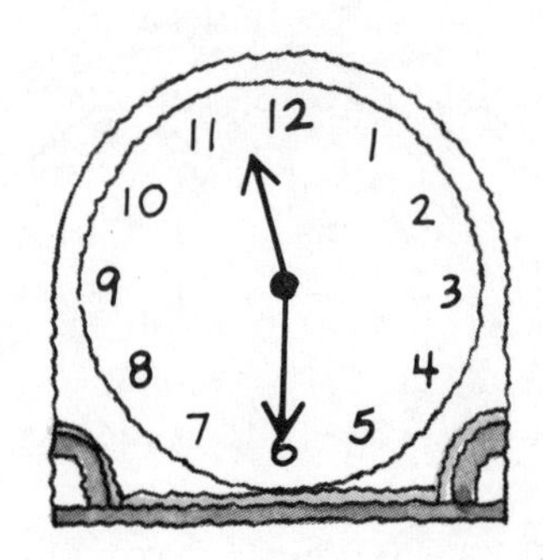

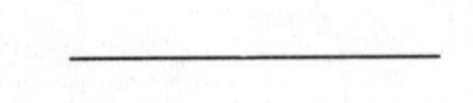

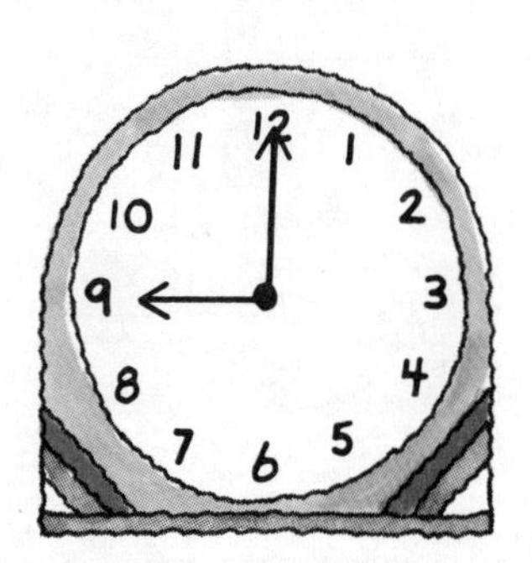

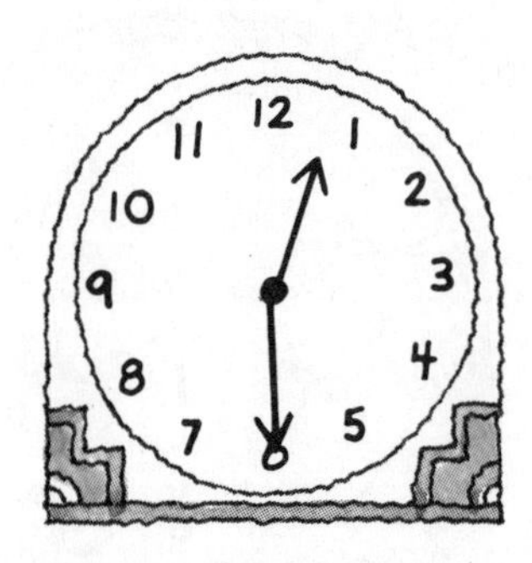

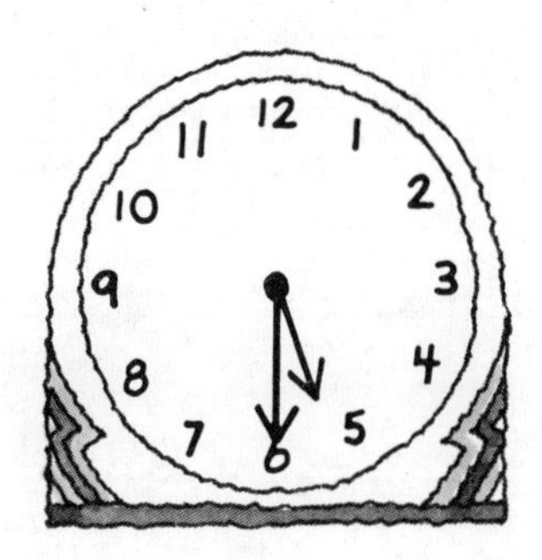

Name ____________________

January

Sunday	Monday	Tuesday	Wednesday	Thursday	Friday	Saturday
				1	2	3
4	5	6	7	8	9	10
11	12	13	14	15	16	17
18	19	20	21	22	23	24
25	26	27	28	29	30	31

Write the answers.

Which month is it? ____________

How many days in a week? ____

How many of each in this month?

Sundays ____ Mondays ____ Tuesdays ____

Wednesdays ____ Thursdays ____ Fridays ____

Saturdays ____

What is the date?

First Wednesday 7 Third Tuesday ____

Second Friday ____ Fourth Monday ____

New Year's day ____

Complete the calendar for this month.

Month				Year		
Sunday	Monday	Tuesday	Wednesday	Thursday	Friday	Saturday

Write the answers.

How many days in this month? ____

What date is the first Monday? ____

How many school days? ____

How many Saturdays? ____

How many Sundays? ____

What date is the third Saturday? ____

Name ______________________________

CHAPTER CHECKUP

Count the money.

___ ¢

___ ¢

___ ¢

___ ¢

Check the coins you need to buy the toy car.

How much is left? ___ ¢

Check the coins you need to buy the puppet.

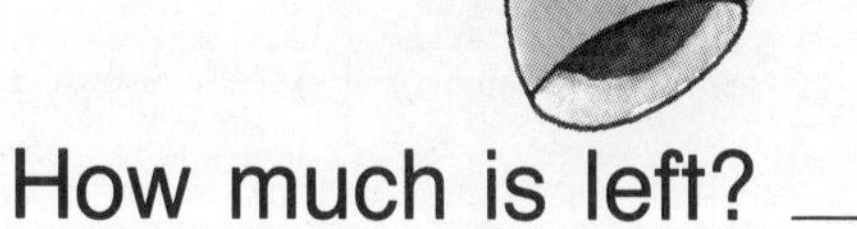

How much is left? ___ ¢

Write the times.

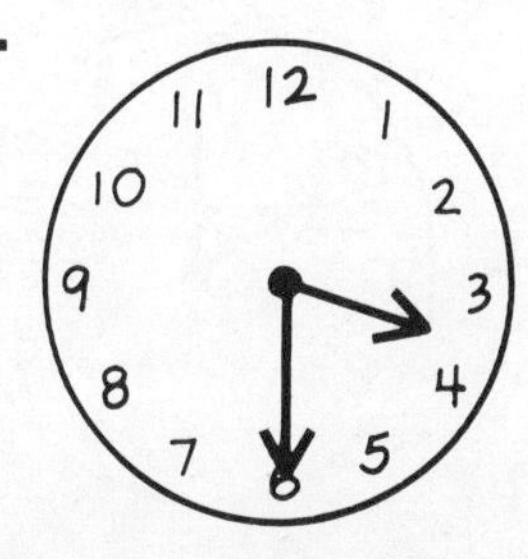

__________ __________

ROUNDUP REVIEW

Add or subtract.

$$\begin{array}{r} 5 \\ +7 \\ \hline \end{array} \quad \begin{array}{r} 9 \\ -3 \\ \hline \end{array} \quad \begin{array}{r} 15 \\ -\ 9 \\ \hline \end{array} \quad \begin{array}{r} 16 \\ -\ 8 \\ \hline \end{array} \quad \begin{array}{r} 7 \\ +6 \\ \hline \end{array} \quad \begin{array}{r} 5 \\ +9 \\ \hline \end{array} \quad \begin{array}{r} 17 \\ -\ 8 \\ \hline \end{array}$$

$$\begin{array}{r} 14 \\ -\ 7 \\ \hline \end{array} \quad \begin{array}{r} 5 \\ +8 \\ \hline \end{array} \quad \begin{array}{r} 12 \\ -\ 7 \\ \hline \end{array} \quad \begin{array}{r} 6 \\ +8 \\ \hline \end{array} \quad \begin{array}{r} 13 \\ -\ 5 \\ \hline \end{array} \quad \begin{array}{r} 15 \\ -\ 6 \\ \hline \end{array} \quad \begin{array}{r} 18 \\ -\ 9 \\ \hline \end{array}$$

How many?

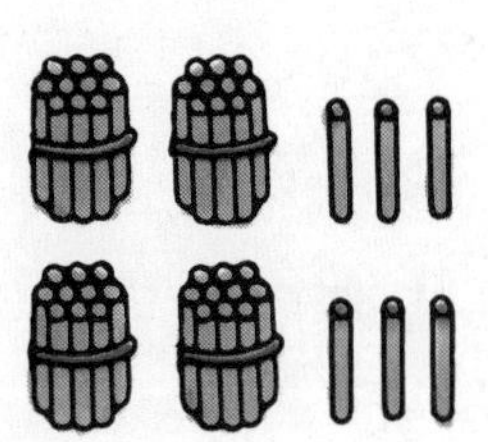

____

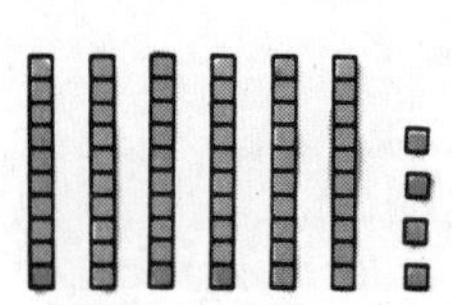

____

Count by fives.

5, 10, ____, ____, ____, ____, ____, ____, ____

How much money?

____ ¢

Write the time.

____ o'clock

____

Name ______________________________

BASIC FACTS, SUMS THROUGH 18

Add.

4 +2	5 +3	2 +2	4 +6	7 +1	3 +3	5 +0
8 +2	3 +1	3 +7	4 +3	1 +1	7 +2	1 +7
2 +8	3 +6	5 +5	6 +4	5 +1	1 +9	2 +4
7 +3	2 +5	4 +4	1 +5	6 +2	3 +4	2 +7

Solve.

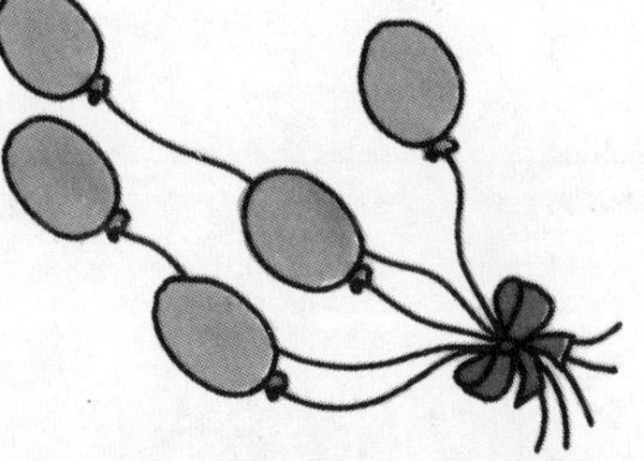

Lisa has 5 balloons.
Mark has 3 balloons.
How many in all?

____ balloons

Pete saw 3 cows.
Chris saw 7 cows.
How many in all?

____ cows

Subtract.

9 − 3	10 − 1	3 − 2	6 − 3	7 − 5	10 − 7	9 − 4
6 − 5	7 − 4	5 − 3	8 − 7	4 − 3	8 − 4	10 − 9
10 − 4	7 − 6	9 − 5	9 − 8	10 − 2	7 − 3	8 − 5
6 − 2	8 − 3	9 − 7	8 − 2	10 − 6	9 − 2	2 − 1

Solve.

Jerry saw 9 .
2 walked away.
How many
were left?

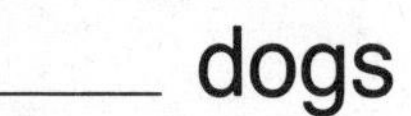

____ dogs

Mary Lou had 8 .
She gave Danny 3 .
How many
are left?

____ shells

Name ____________________

Add or subtract.

9	9	4	4	8	5	4
+1	+0	+1	−2	−1	−2	+5

2	7	6	3	6	6	9
+1	−2	−1	+5	−4	+3	−1

2	5	2	8	5	9	7
+6	+4	+3	−6	+2	−6	−1

FIELD TRIP

Add 3 to each number.

0	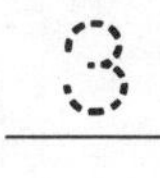
2	___
1	___
5	___
3	___
6	___
4	___
7	___

Subtract each number from 9.

6	3
2	___
5	___
3	___
7	___
1	___
4	___
8	___

Add or subtract.

$$\begin{array}{r}8\\+0\\\hline\end{array}\quad\begin{array}{r}6\\-2\\\hline\end{array}\quad\begin{array}{r}8\\-3\\\hline\end{array}\quad\begin{array}{r}10\\-\ 5\\\hline\end{array}\quad\begin{array}{r}7\\+0\\\hline\end{array}\quad\begin{array}{r}1\\+2\\\hline\end{array}$$

$$\begin{array}{r}1\\+4\\\hline\end{array}\quad\begin{array}{r}10\\-\ 3\\\hline\end{array}\quad\begin{array}{r}5\\-5\\\hline\end{array}\quad\begin{array}{r}6\\+0\\\hline\end{array}\quad\begin{array}{r}10\\-\ 8\\\hline\end{array}\quad\begin{array}{r}6\\+4\\\hline\end{array}$$

Complete the tables.

Add 4	
2	6
1	
3	
6	
5	

Subtract 3	
5	2
7	
10	
8	
6	

Add 5	
1	
3	
5	
4	
2	

Subtract 2	
8	
5	
7	
6	
4	

Solve.

Mike picked 7.
He ate 2.
How many are left?

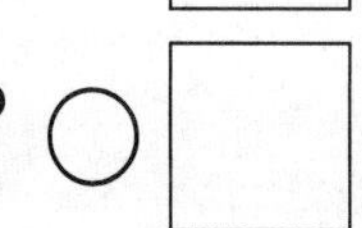

____ apples

Diana had 6.
She bought 4 more.
How many does she have now?

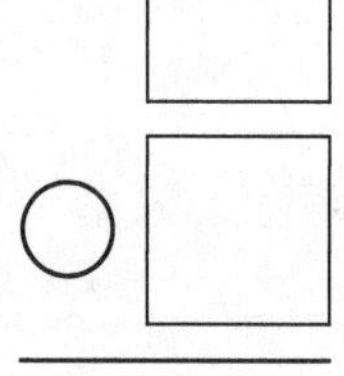

____ cars

Name ______________________________

Add.

4 +7	8 +5	7 +7	9 +4	8 +3	8 +7	7 +4
7 +9	2 +9	8 +8	7 +5	3 +8	9 +3	7 +6
5 +8	9 +9	4 +9	9 +6	8 +6	6 +6	9 +5
3 +9	8 +9	9 +8	4 +8	7 +8	9 +7	6 +8

Solve.

Lanny picked 6 oranges.
Kim picked 5 oranges.
How many oranges
in all?

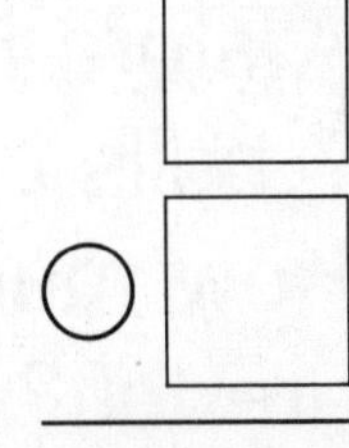

____ oranges

Pam had 8 boats.
She bought
6 more boats.
How many

in all?

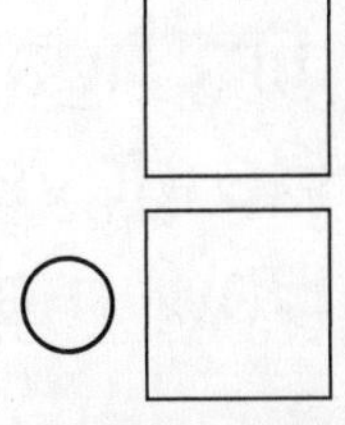

____ boats

Subtract.

$$\begin{array}{r}13\\-\ 7\\\hline\end{array}\quad\begin{array}{r}15\\-\ 6\\\hline\end{array}\quad\begin{array}{r}11\\-\ 9\\\hline\end{array}\quad\begin{array}{r}16\\-\ 8\\\hline\end{array}\quad\begin{array}{r}14\\-\ 5\\\hline\end{array}\quad\begin{array}{r}15\\-\ 7\\\hline\end{array}\quad\begin{array}{r}13\\-\ 8\\\hline\end{array}$$

$$\begin{array}{r}17\\-\ 9\\\hline\end{array}\quad\begin{array}{r}15\\-\ 9\\\hline\end{array}\quad\begin{array}{r}11\\-\ 6\\\hline\end{array}\quad\begin{array}{r}13\\-\ 9\\\hline\end{array}\quad\begin{array}{r}18\\-\ 9\\\hline\end{array}\quad\begin{array}{r}11\\-\ 5\\\hline\end{array}\quad\begin{array}{r}12\\-\ 7\\\hline\end{array}$$

$$\begin{array}{r}13\\-\ 5\\\hline\end{array}\quad\begin{array}{r}12\\-\ 5\\\hline\end{array}\quad\begin{array}{r}17\\-\ 8\\\hline\end{array}\quad\begin{array}{r}13\\-\ 6\\\hline\end{array}\quad\begin{array}{r}14\\-\ 8\\\hline\end{array}\quad\begin{array}{r}11\\-\ 4\\\hline\end{array}\quad\begin{array}{r}14\\-\ 6\\\hline\end{array}$$

$$\begin{array}{r}11\\-\ 8\\\hline\end{array}\quad\begin{array}{r}11\\-\ 7\\\hline\end{array}\quad\begin{array}{r}16\\-\ 9\\\hline\end{array}\quad\begin{array}{r}12\\-\ 8\\\hline\end{array}\quad\begin{array}{r}16\\-\ 7\\\hline\end{array}\quad\begin{array}{r}15\\-\ 8\\\hline\end{array}\quad\begin{array}{r}14\\-\ 9\\\hline\end{array}$$

Solve.

Jim had 11 .
He gave Sue 2 .
How many cars
are left?

____ cars

A store had 14 .
7 balls are sold.
How many balls
are left?

____ balls

Name ____________________

Add or subtract.

11	5	11	15	5	6	13
− 7	+7	− 3	− 8	+9	+7	− 5

9	8	16	8	13	9	17
+7	+5	− 8	+9	− 7	+6	− 8

18	9	15	7	4	13	7
− 9	+8	− 9	+8	+9	− 6	+9

Complete the wheels.

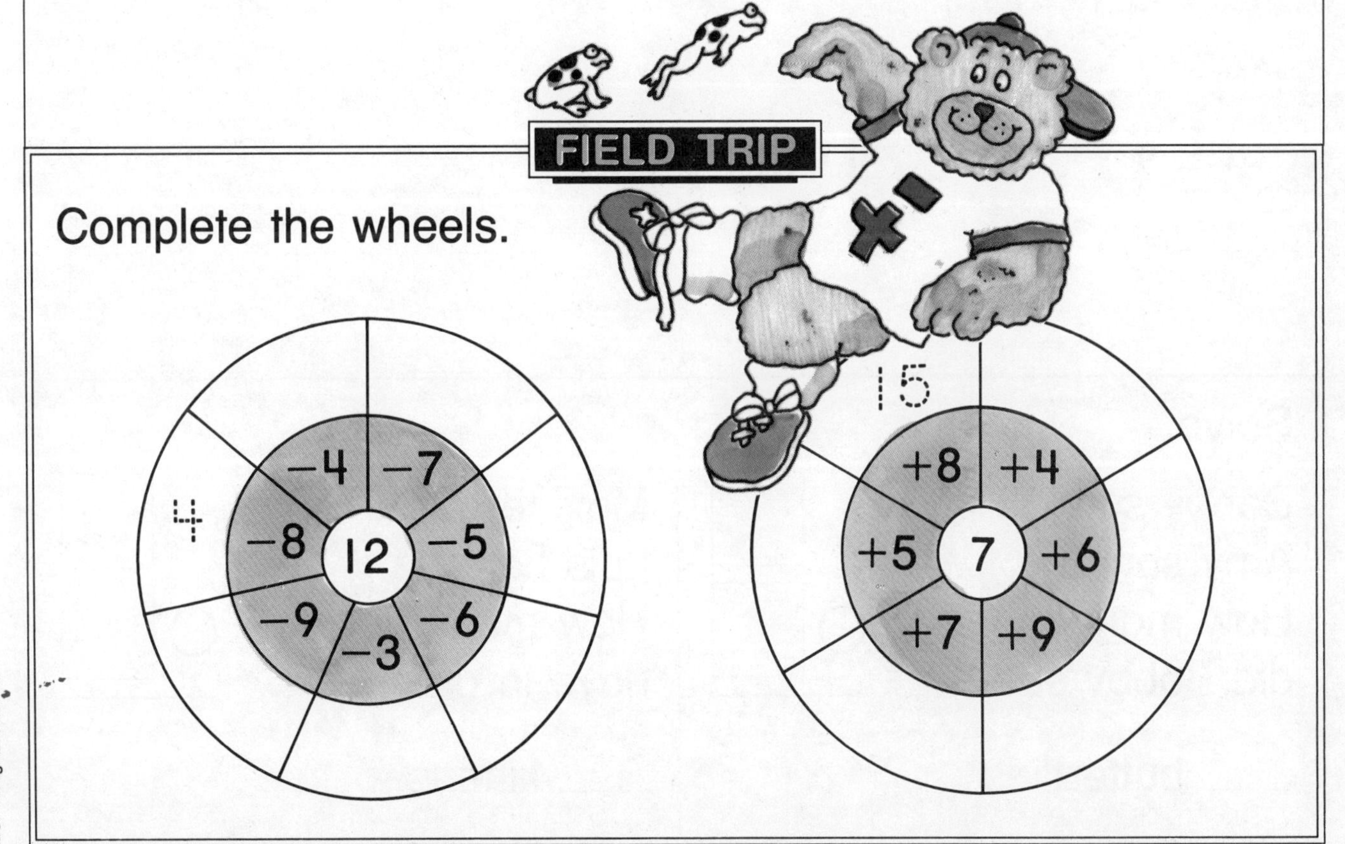

Complete the tables.

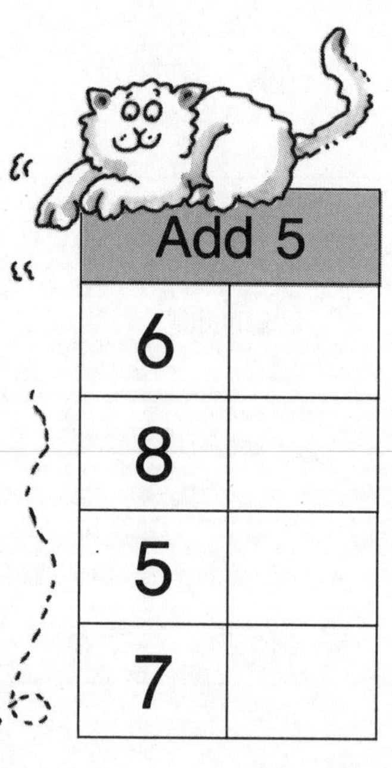

Add 4	
6	10
9	
8	
5	

Subtract 6	
11	5
14	
15	
13	

Add 5	
6	
8	
5	
7	

Add or subtract.

6 +7	13 − 4	14 − 9	9 +9	8 +6	8 +7	14 − 8
11 − 7	5 +8	16 − 9	4 +7	15 − 7	12 − 8	9 +2

Solve.

Bobby saw 15 butterflies.
Amy saw 8 butterflies.
How many more did Bobby see?

____ butterflies

Maxine has 6 kittens.
Luis has 7 kittens.
How many do they have in all?

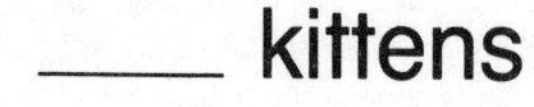

____ kittens

Name ____________________

Add.

1¢	7¢	8¢	9¢	8¢	3¢
+1¢	+3¢	+4¢	+2¢	+8¢	+3¢
¢	¢	¢	¢	¢	¢

4¢	5¢	2¢	6¢	1¢	9¢
+9¢	+5¢	+2¢	+6¢	+5¢	+9¢
¢	¢	¢	¢	¢	¢

6¢	5¢	3¢	7¢	7¢	4¢
+8¢	+7¢	+7¢	+7¢	+5¢	+4¢
¢	¢	¢	¢	¢	¢

Subtract.

6¢	10¢	12¢	8¢	16¢	9¢
−5¢	− 4¢	− 5¢	−3¢	− 7¢	−5¢
¢	¢	¢	¢	¢	¢

11¢	13¢	14¢	15¢	8¢	14¢
− 3¢	− 4¢	− 6¢	− 8¢	−6¢	− 7¢
¢	¢	¢	¢	¢	¢

12¢	17¢	10¢	14¢	13¢	11¢
− 8¢	− 9¢	− 7¢	− 9¢	− 7¢	− 6¢
¢	¢	¢	¢	¢	¢

Ed had 10¢.
He bought a ___.
How much was left?

	10	¢
−	7	¢
	3	¢

3 ¢

Rafer has 8¢.
Karen has 9¢.
How much in all?

	8	¢
+	9	¢
	17	¢

17 ¢

Solve.

Liz had 8¢.
She found 7¢.
How much in all?

	☐	¢
○	☐	¢
		¢

___ ¢

Joan had 17¢.
She bought a ___.
How much was left?

	☐	¢
○	☐	¢
		¢

___ ¢

Mei Ling has 7¢.
Randy has 5¢.
How much in all?

	☐	¢
○	☐	¢
		¢

___ ¢

Leah had 9¢.
Uncle Phil gave her 6¢.
How much in all?

	☐	¢
○	☐	¢
		¢

___ ¢

Fran had 15¢.
She bought a ___.
How much is left?

	☐	¢
○	☐	¢
		¢

___ ¢

Linda has 9¢.
Ro has 9¢.
How much in all?

	☐	¢
○	☐	¢
		¢

___ ¢

Name ______

Gina drew 4 pictures. Then she drew 5 more. How many in all?

4
+ 5

9

9 pictures

Greg had 15 rabbits. He gave Tony 7 rabbits. How many were left?

15
− 7

8

8 rabbits

Solve.

Lana found 8 cans. Pedro found 9 cans. How many in all?

____ cans

Lanny ran 6 blocks. Then he ran 7 more. How many blocks did he run in all?

____ blocks

12 bees were on a flower. 5 flew away. How many were left?

____ bees

There are 7 beetles and 8 beetles. How many in all?

____ beetles

Marta saw 5 horses. Then she saw 6 more. How many in all?

____ horses

There were 14 apples. 6 apples were eaten. How many are left?

____ apples

Color by answers.

6 purple 8 brown 11 blue 13 yellow 15 green

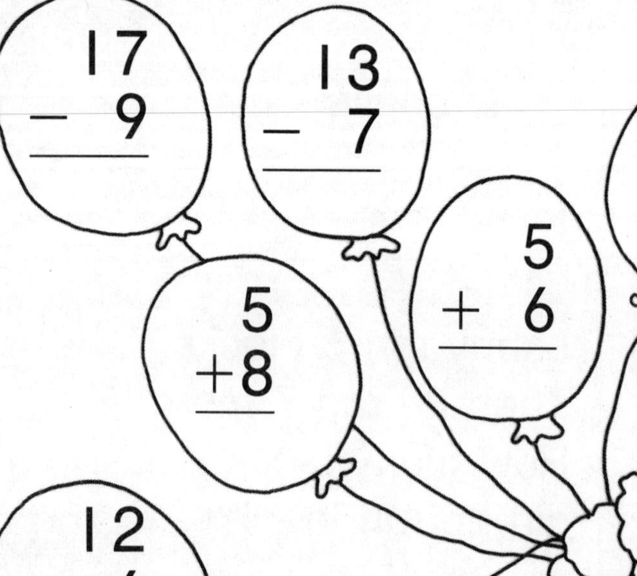

$\begin{array}{r} 17 \\ -\ 9 \\ \hline \end{array}$ $\begin{array}{r} 13 \\ -\ 7 \\ \hline \end{array}$ $\begin{array}{r} 6 \\ +7 \\ \hline \end{array}$ $\begin{array}{r} 15 \\ -\ 9 \\ \hline \end{array}$

$\begin{array}{r} 5 \\ +8 \\ \hline \end{array}$ $\begin{array}{r} 5 \\ +\ 6 \\ \hline \end{array}$

$\begin{array}{r} 12 \\ -\ 4 \\ \hline \end{array}$

$\begin{array}{r} 12 \\ -\ 6 \\ \hline \end{array}$

$\begin{array}{r} 14 \\ -\ 8 \\ \hline \end{array}$

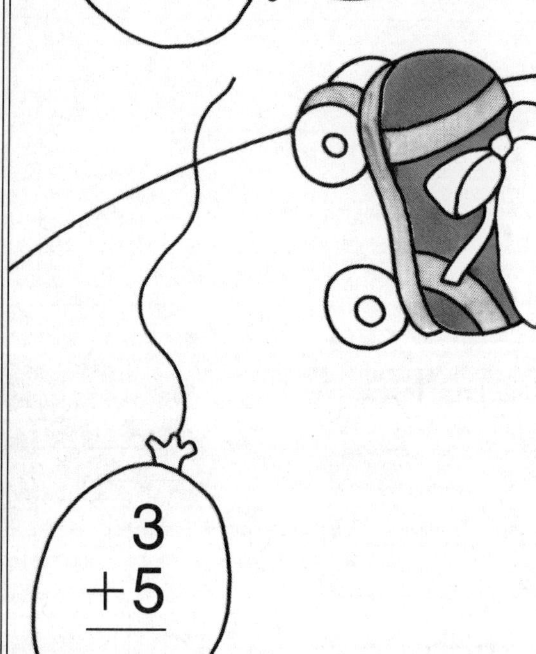

$\begin{array}{r} 2 \\ +6 \\ \hline \end{array}$ $\begin{array}{r} 14 \\ -\ 6 \\ \hline \end{array}$

$\begin{array}{r} 3 \\ +5 \\ \hline \end{array}$ $\begin{array}{r} 4 \\ +9 \\ \hline \end{array}$ $\begin{array}{r} 6 \\ +9 \\ \hline \end{array}$

Name ______________________________

CHAPTER CHECKUP

Add or subtract.

5	6	6	3	4	9	13
−1	−3	+3	+7	−2	−6	− 7
5	2	8	4	7	17	8
+2	+4	−5	+5	−2	− 8	+2
1	12	16	7	11	7	9
+6	− 9	− 8	+8	− 4	+6	−2
6	10	7	9	14	8	9
+7	− 5	+4	+8	− 7	+7	+5

Solve.

Jenny had 15¢. She bought a hat for 8¢. How much was left?

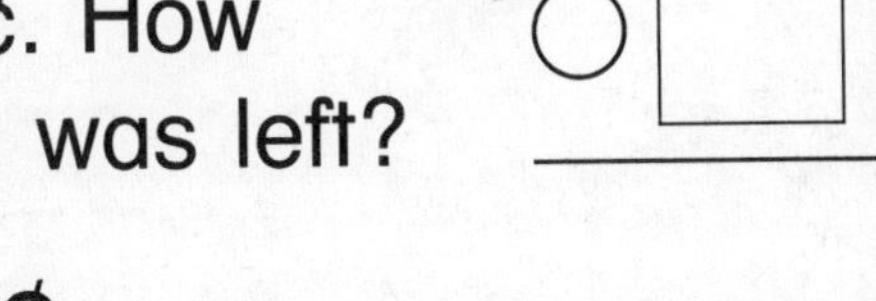

☐ ¢
◯ ☐ ¢
_____ ¢

_____ ¢

Stacey ran 5 blocks. Then she ran 6 more. How many blocks did she run in all?

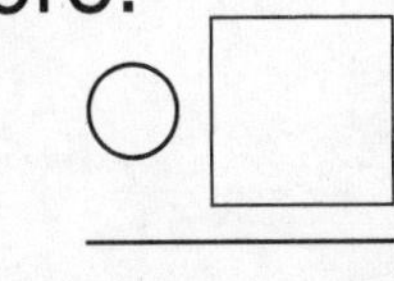

☐
◯ ☐
_____

_____ blocks

ROUNDUP REVIEW

Write the missing numbers.

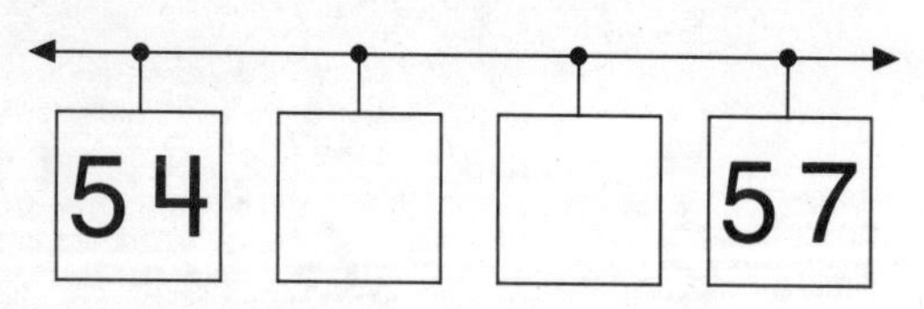

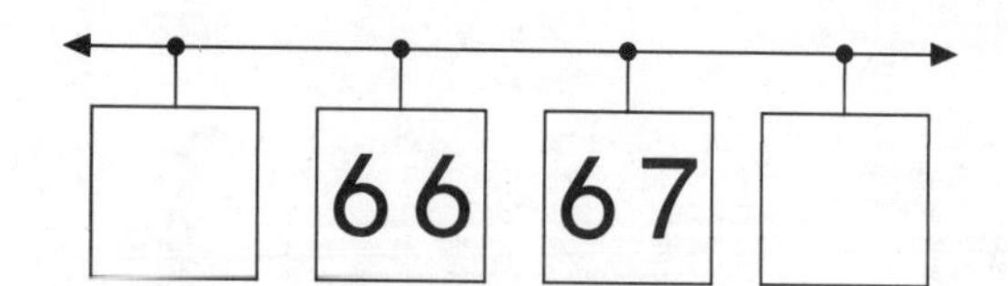

How many?

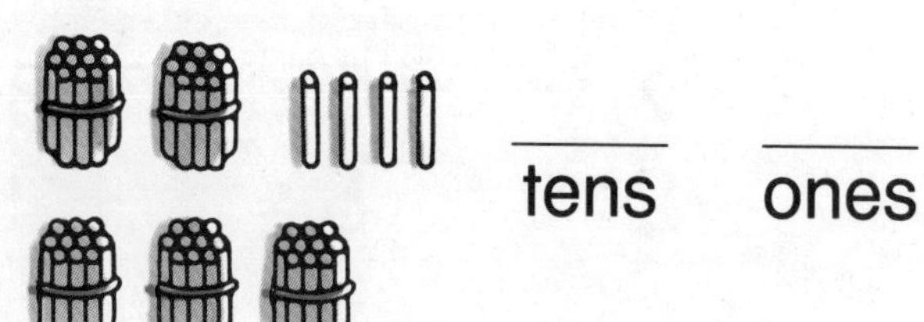

____ tens ____ ones

____

Circle the number that is less.

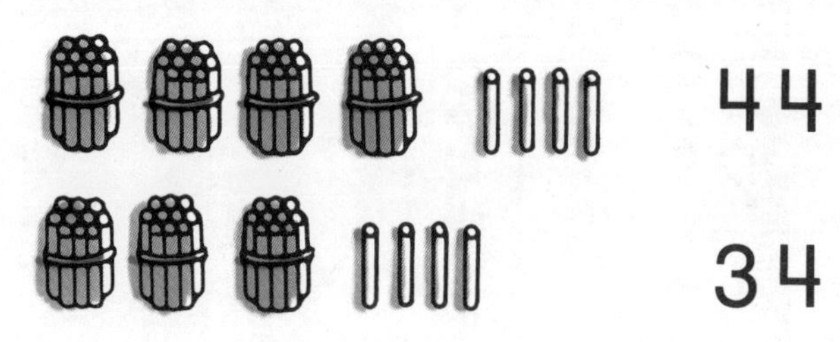

44

34

Add or subtract.

$\begin{array}{r} 3 \\ +6 \\ \hline \end{array}$ $\begin{array}{r} 9 \\ -7 \\ \hline \end{array}$ $\begin{array}{r} 5 \\ +6 \\ \hline \end{array}$ $\begin{array}{r} 12 \\ -\ 6 \\ \hline \end{array}$ $\begin{array}{r} 15 \\ -\ 8 \\ \hline \end{array}$ $\begin{array}{r} 9 \\ +6 \\ \hline \end{array}$

Circle the third bear.

How much?

____ ¢

Write the times.

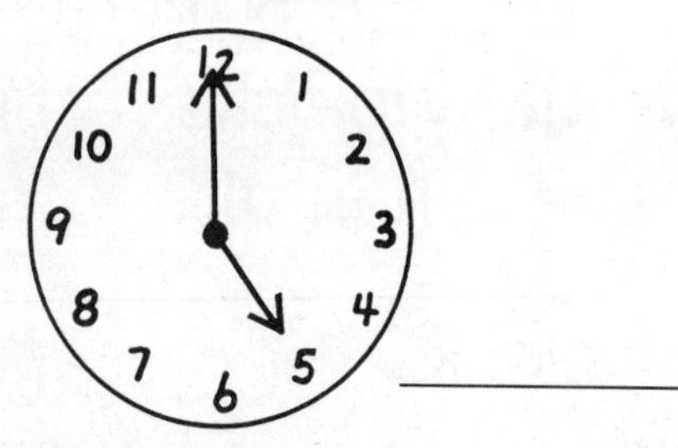

____

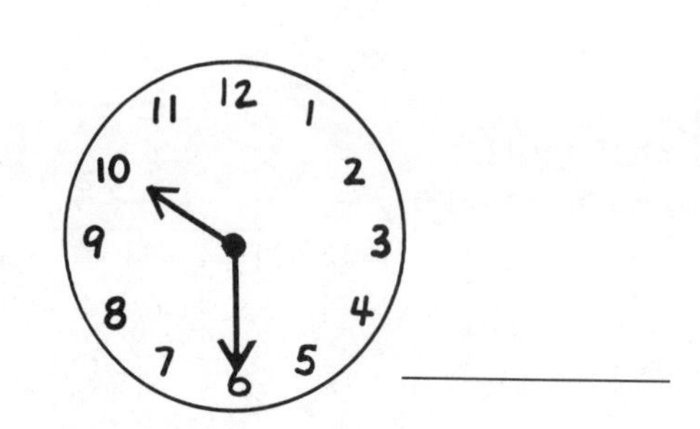

____

Name ______________________________

10 ADDITION, 2-AND 1-DIGIT NUMBERS

How many?

  10 ten

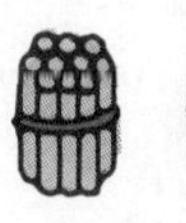 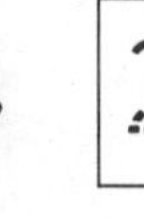 20 twenty

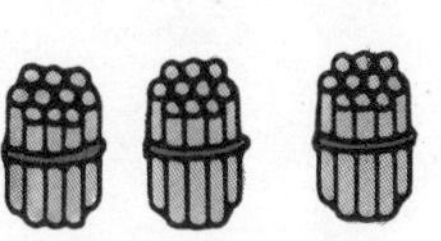  thirty

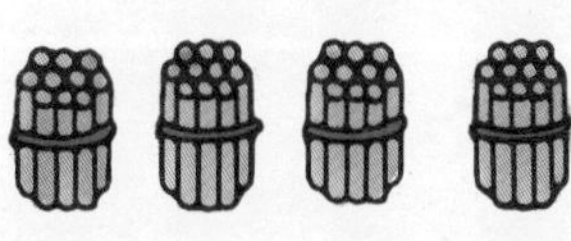 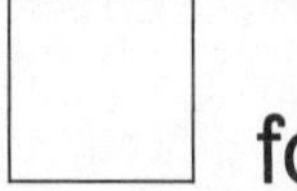 forty

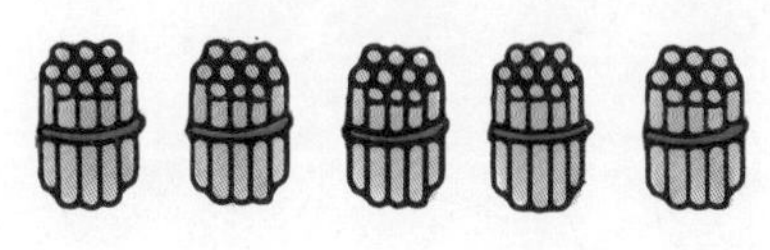  fifty

   sixty

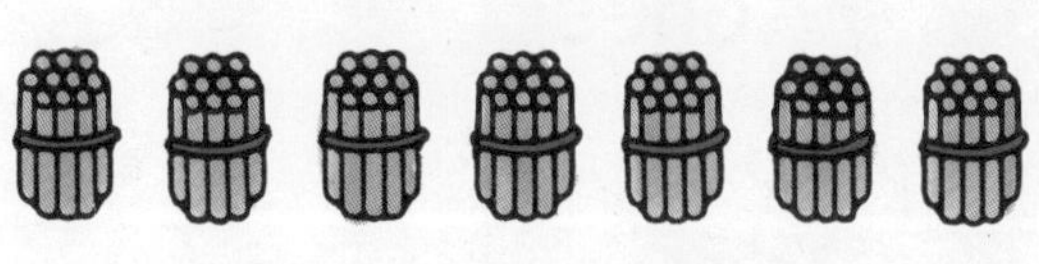  seventy

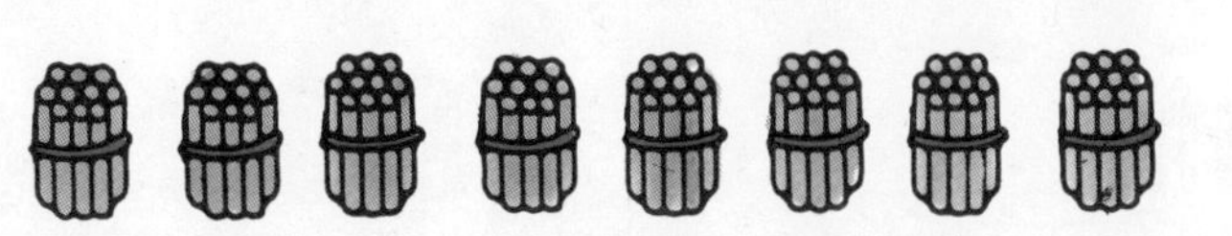  eighty

  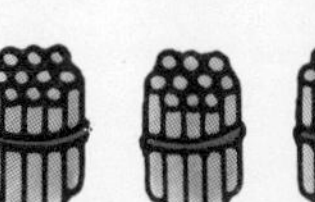 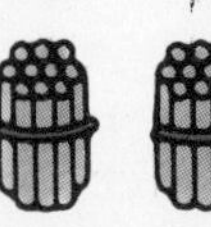 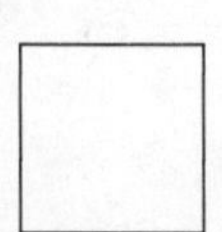 ninety

Match the numbers and number names.

5 groups of ten	40	forty
4 tens	50	fifty
seventy	60	7 tens
sixty	70	ninety
9 groups of ten	80	eighty
8 tens	90	6 groups of ten

How many?

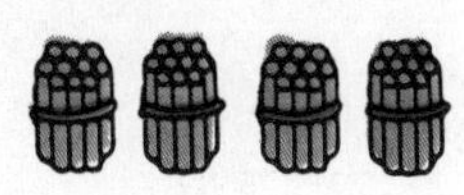

4 tens 0 ones

40

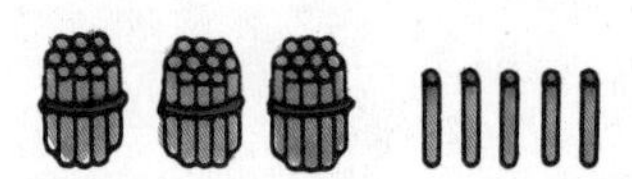

____ tens ____ ones

____

____ tens ____ ones

____

____ tens ____ ones

____

____ tens ____ ones

____

____ tens ____ ones

____

Name ______________________________

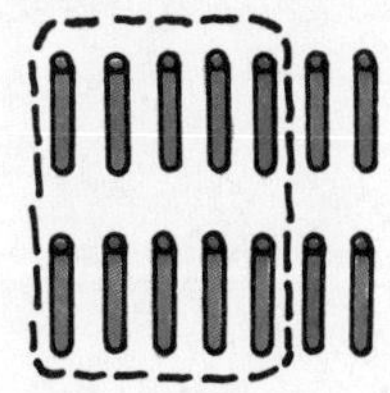

→ 1 tens 4 ones → 14

Circle groups of 10. How many?

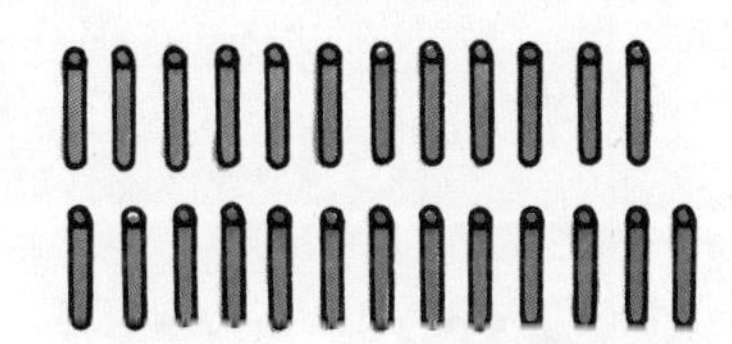

→ ____ tens ____ ones → ____

→ ____ tens ____ ones → ____

Write the numbers.

twenty-two 22

thirty-five ____

sixty-seven ____

ninety-seven ____

fifty ____

forty-three ____

seventy-one ____

eighty-four ____

Write the missing numbers.

4 tens 7 ones → 47

6 tens 2 ones → ____

9 tens 9 ones → ____

5 tens 2 ones → ____

5 tens 5 ones → 55

____ tens ____ ones → 69

____ tens ____ ones → 34

____ tens ____ ones → 26

Write the missing numbers.

1	2	3							10
11							18		
		23							30
				35				39	
41			44						
	52					57			
				65				69	
		73					78		
	82				86				
			94					99	

FIELD TRIP

Write the missing numbers.

35, 36, 37, 38, ___, ___, ___, ___, ___, ___, ___, 45

61, 62, 63, 64, ___, ___, ___, ___, ___, 70

2, 4, 6, 8, ___, ___, ___, ___, ___, ___, 22

10, 20, 30, 40, ___, ___, ___, ___, 90

5, 10, 15, 20, ___, ___, ___, ___, ___, ___, 55

Name ______________________________

tens	ones
2	3
+	4
2	7

23, 24, 25, 26, 27

Count on to add.

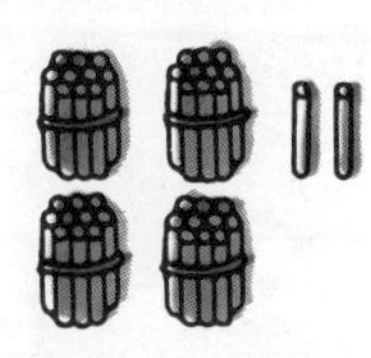

tens	ones
4	2
+	5

____, ____, ____, ____, ____, ____

tens	ones
4	4
+	5

tens	ones
3	2
+	6

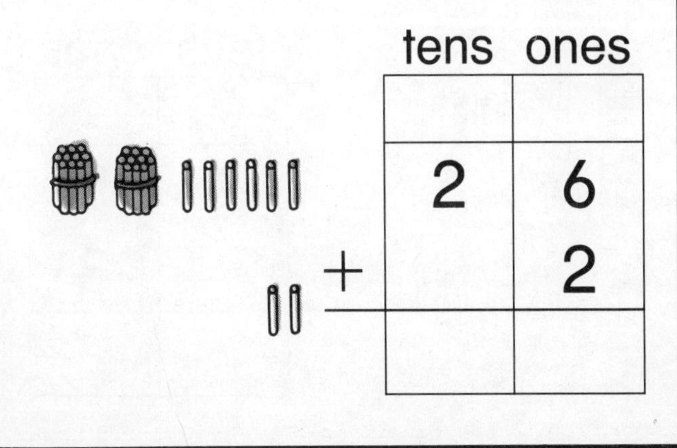

tens	ones
2	6
+	2

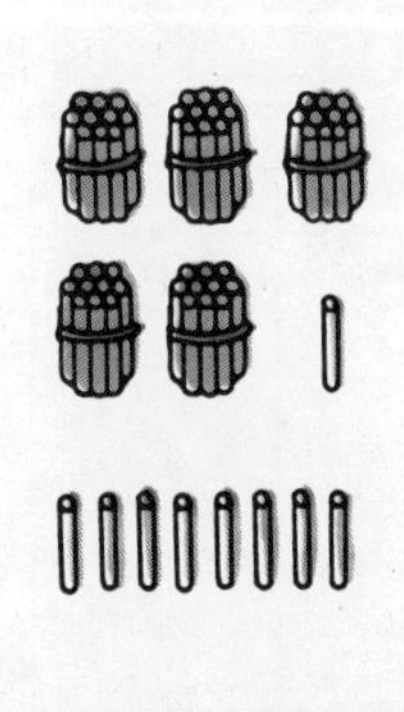

tens	ones
5	1
+	8

Add. Remember to add the ones first.

	tens	ones
	1	5
+		2
	1	7

	tens	ones
	3	3
+		3

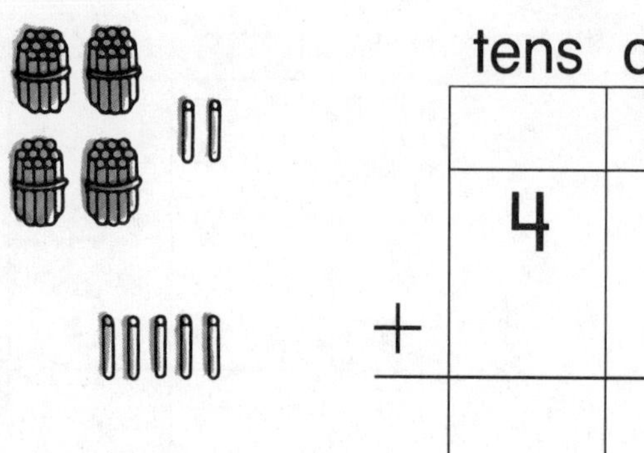
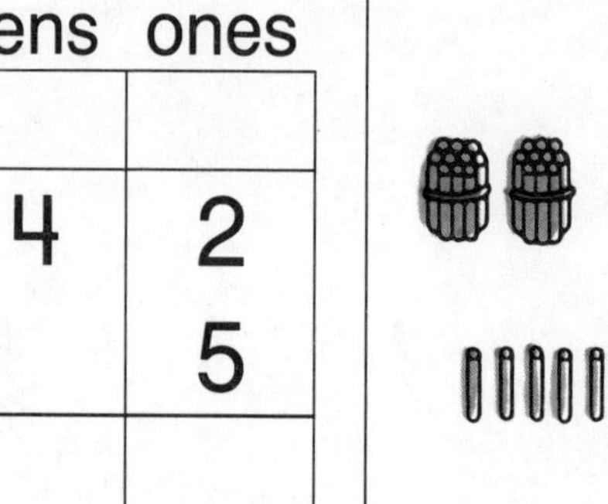

	tens	ones
	4	2
+		5

	tens	ones
	2	1
+		6

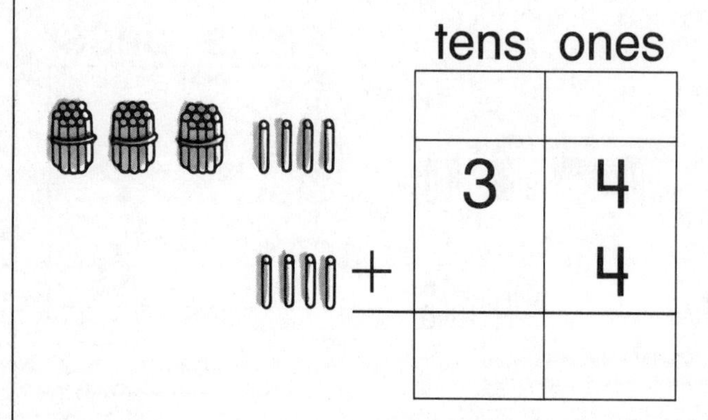

	tens	ones
	3	4
+		4

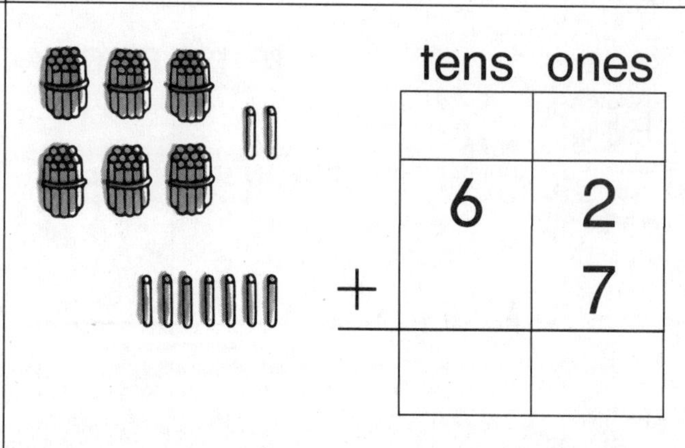

	tens	ones
	6	2
+		7

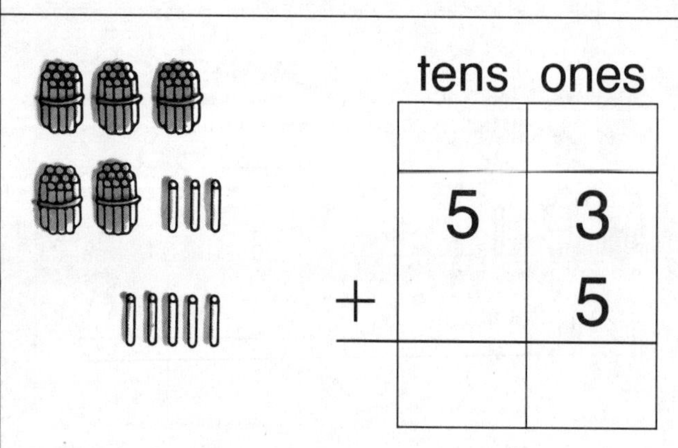

	tens	ones
	5	3
+		5

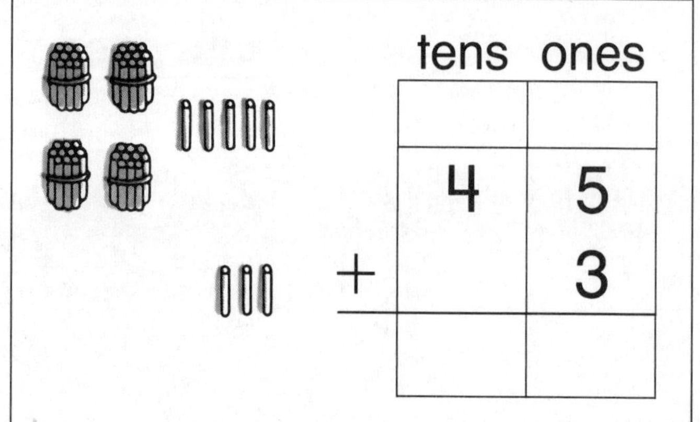

	tens	ones
	4	5
+		3

Name ______________________

Add.

9 +1	6 +6	7 +7	8 +8	9 +9	5 +6	6 +7
7 +8	4 +7	8 +9	9 +2	2 +8	6 +5	4 +9
9 +4	7 +5	8 +3	1 +9	9 +3	9 +8	5 +7
3 +8	9 +7	8 +5	4 +6	9 +5	8 +3	6 +8
2 +9	8 +7	7 +4	8 +2	9 +6	3 +9	5 +8
4 +7	8 +6	7 +9	5 +9	4 +8	6 +9	7 +6

16, 17, 18, 19, 20, 21 $16 + 5 = 21$

Count on to add.

___, ___, ___, ___, ___ $27 + 4 =$ ___

___, ___, ___, ___, ___, ___ $25 + 5 =$ ___

___, ___, ___, ___, ___ $38 + 4 =$ ___

___, ___, ___, ___, ___, ___ $56 + 5 =$ ___

Name ______________________________

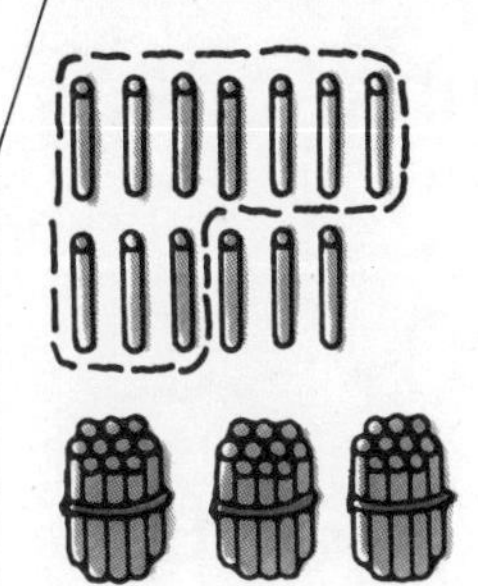

How many ones? 13

How many tens? 3

Write a 3 in ones place.
Write a 1 in tens place.
Now how many tens? 4

	tens	ones
	1	
	3	6
+		7
	4	3

Circle 10 ones. Add.

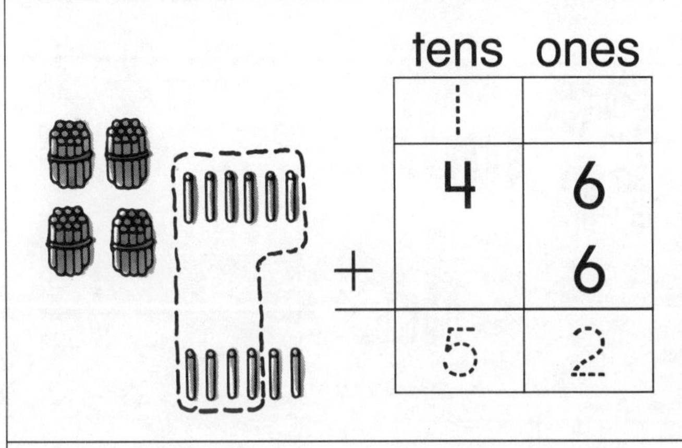

	tens	ones
	1	
	4	6
+		6
	5	2

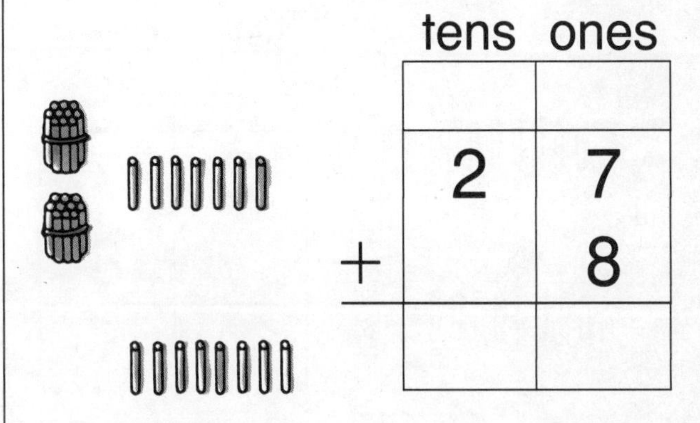

	tens	ones
	2	7
+		8

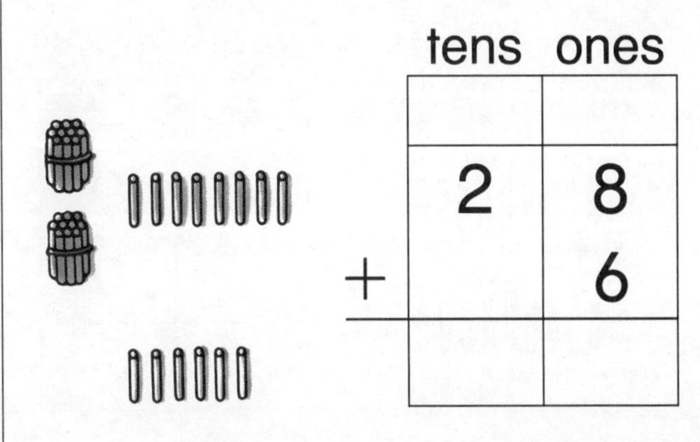

	tens	ones
	2	8
+		6

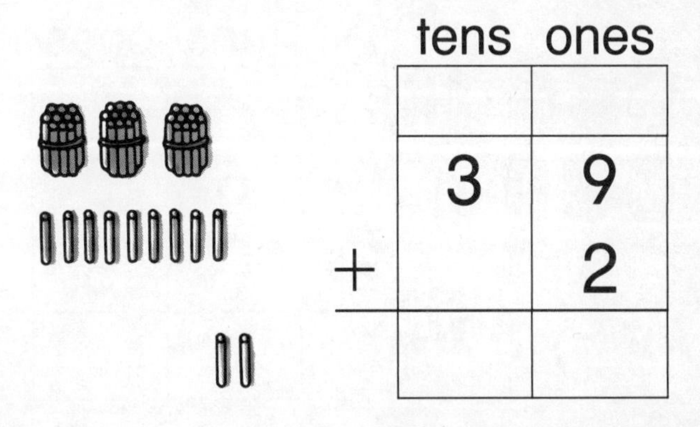

	tens	ones
	3	9
+		2

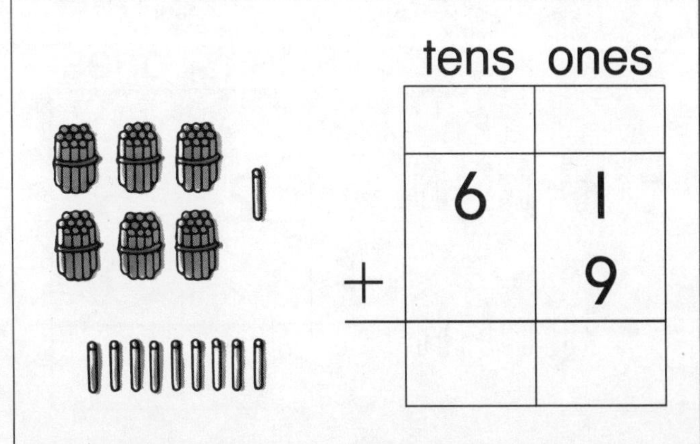

	tens	ones
	6	1
+		9

	tens	ones
	4	8
+		5

	tens	ones
	1	
	3	3
+		7
	4	0

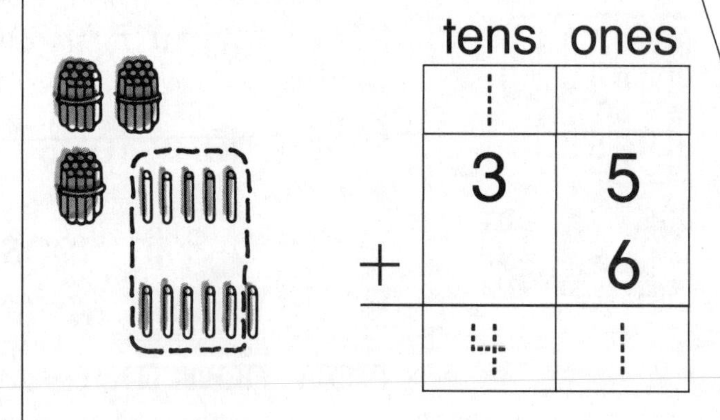

	tens	ones
	1	
	3	5
+		6
	4	1

Circle 10 ones. Add.

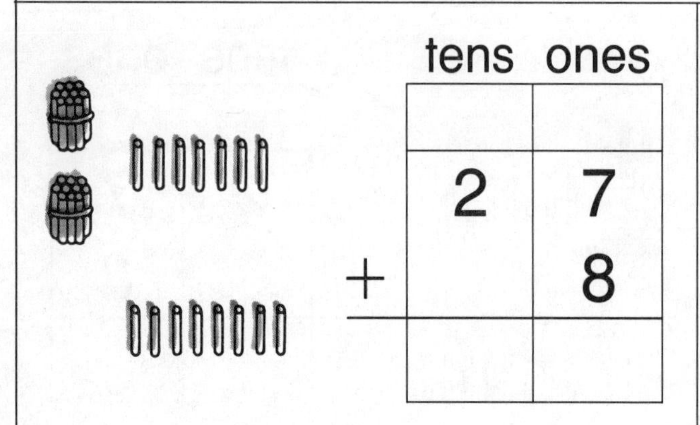

	tens	ones
	2	7
+		8

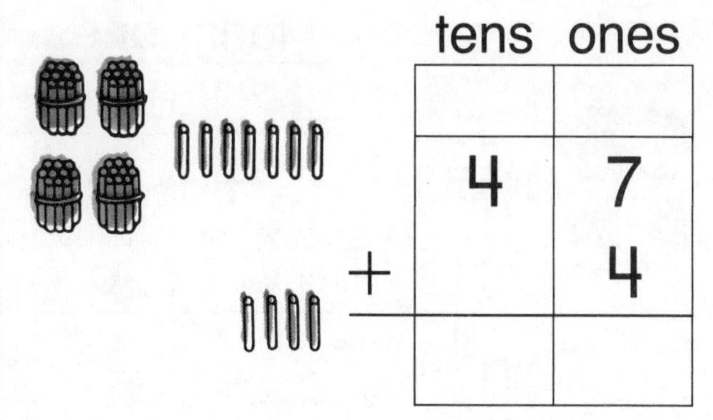

	tens	ones
	4	7
+		4

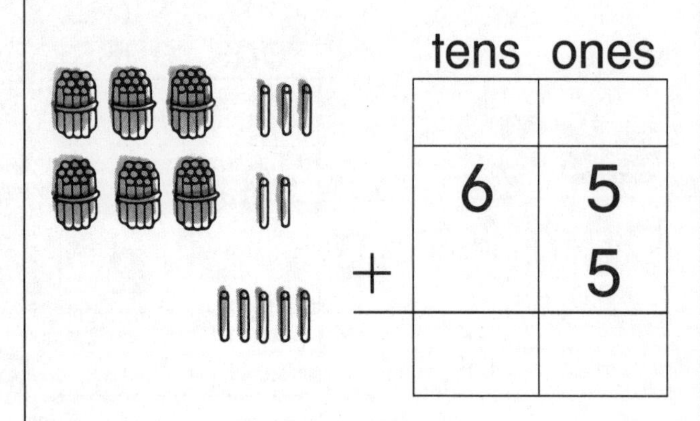

	tens	ones
	6	5
+		5

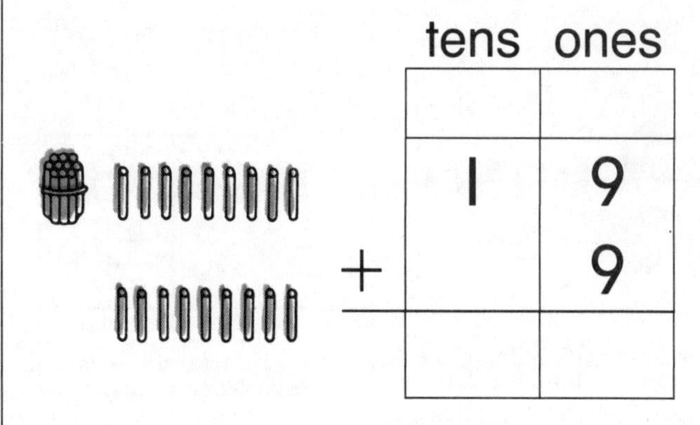

	tens	ones
	1	9
+		9

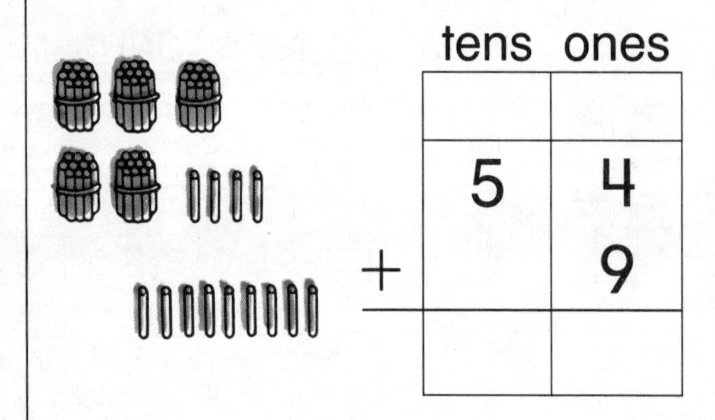

	tens	ones
	5	4
+		9

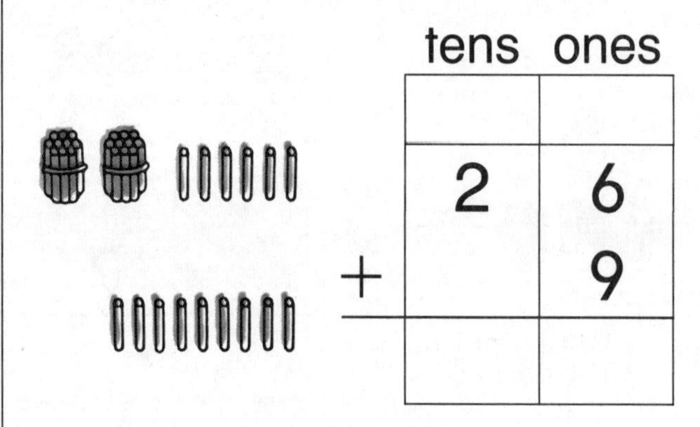

	tens	ones
	2	6
+		9

Name ______________________________

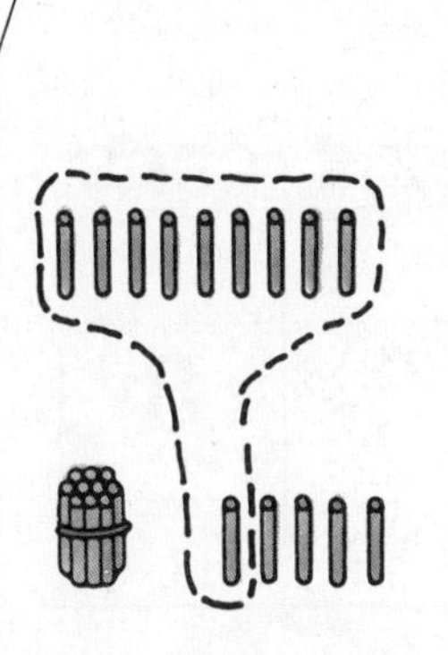

	tens	ones
	1	
		9
+	1	5
	2	4

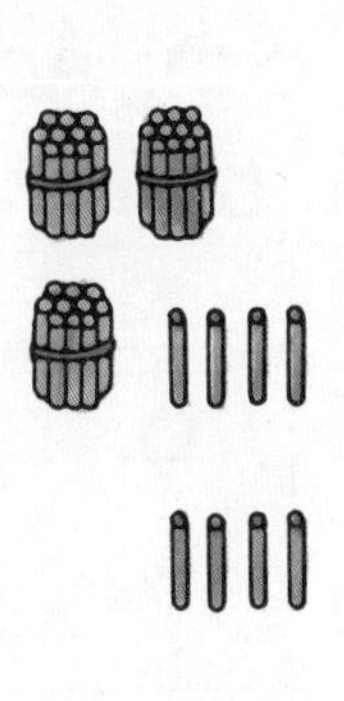

	tens	ones
	3	4
+		4
	3	8

Circle 10 ones if you can. Add.

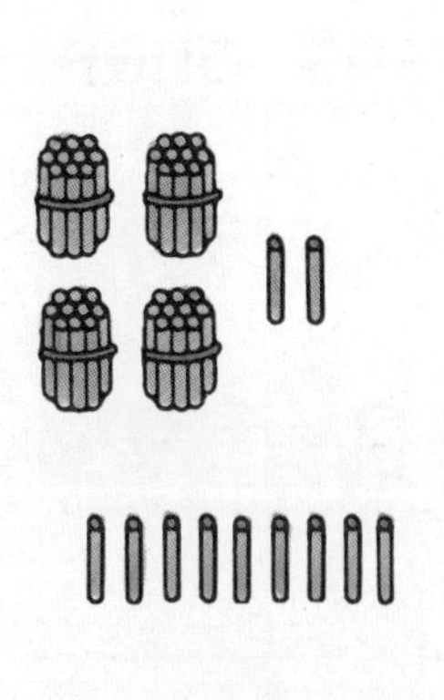

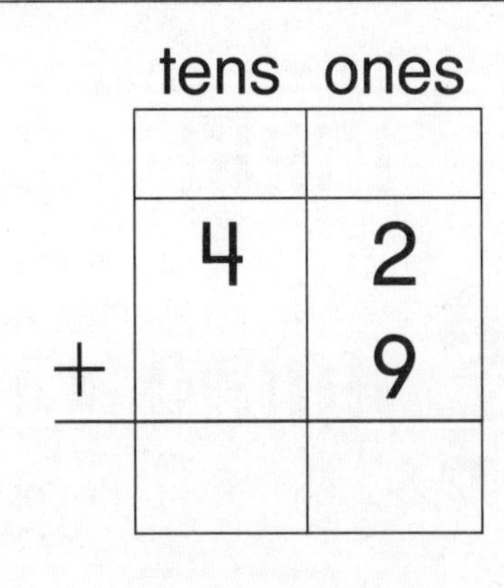

	tens	ones
	4	2
+		9

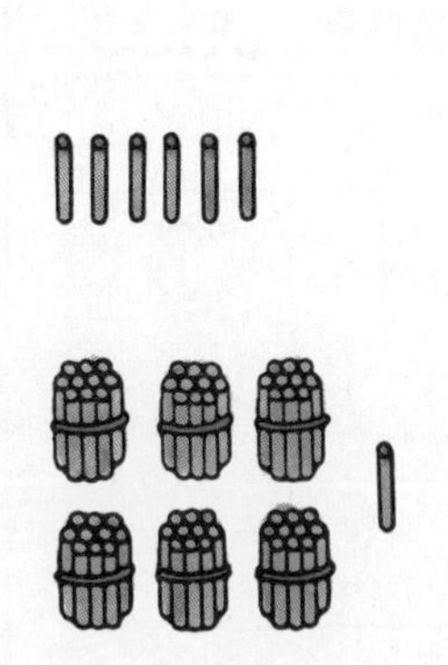

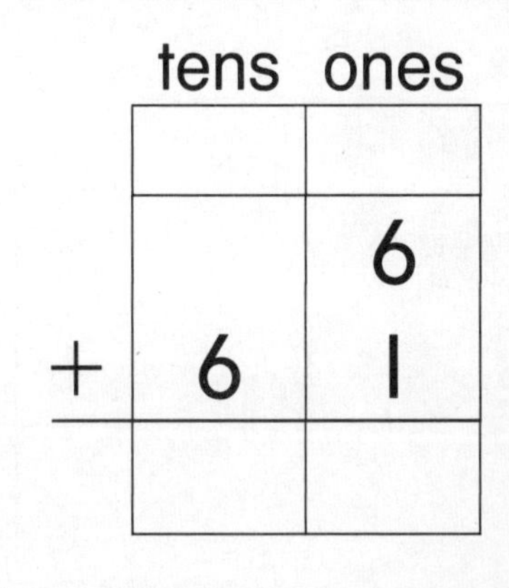

	tens	ones
		6
+	6	1

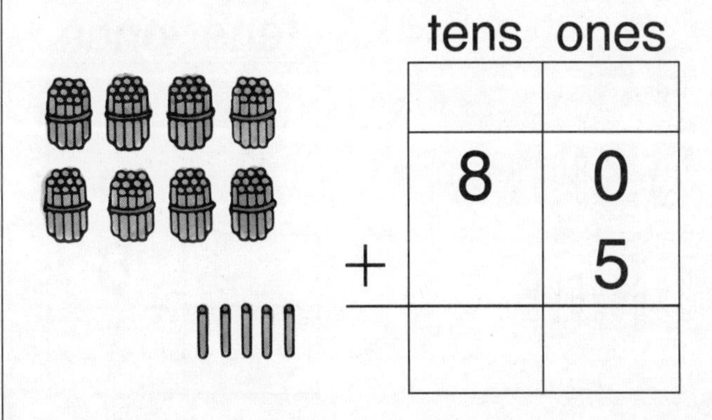

	tens	ones
	8	0
+		5

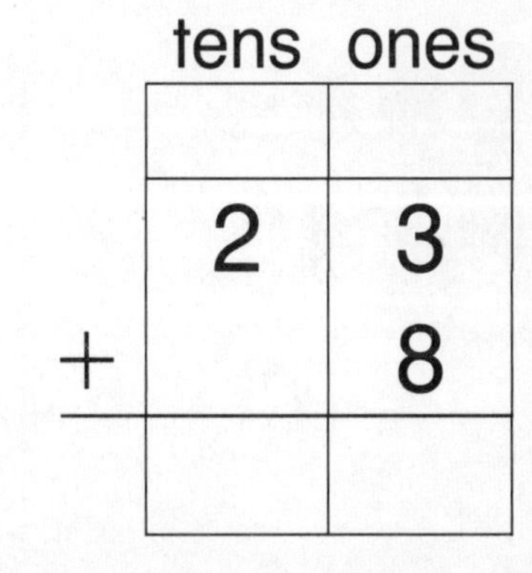

	tens	ones
	2	3
+		8

	tens	ones
	4	6
+		6

	tens	ones
	5	5
+		8

Circle 10 ones if you can. Add.

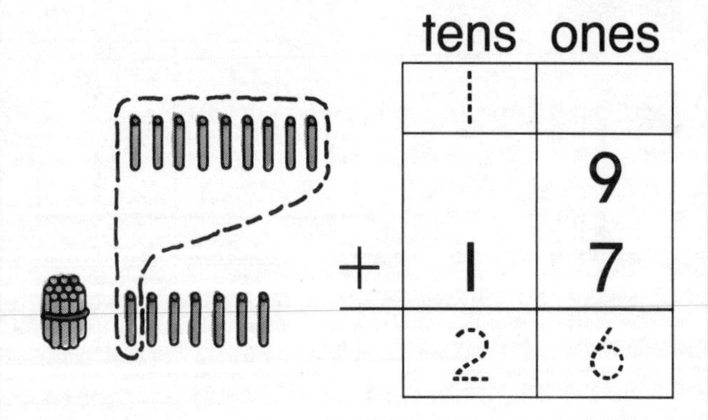

	tens	ones
	1	
		9
+	1	7
	2	6

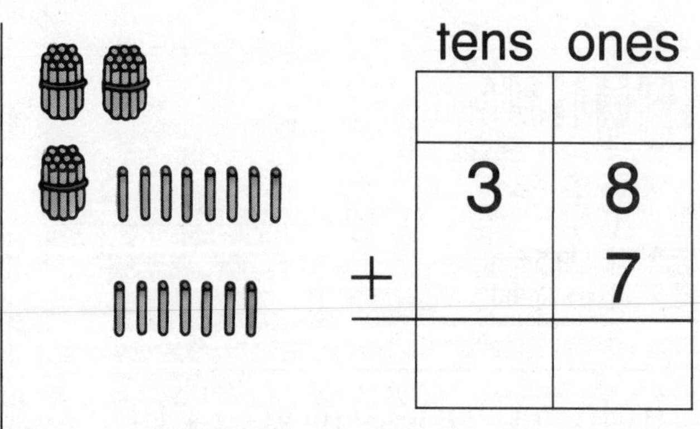

	tens	ones
	3	8
+		7

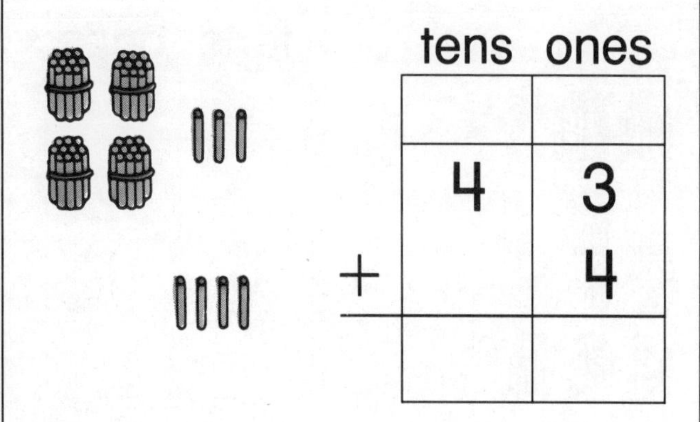

	tens	ones
	4	3
+		4

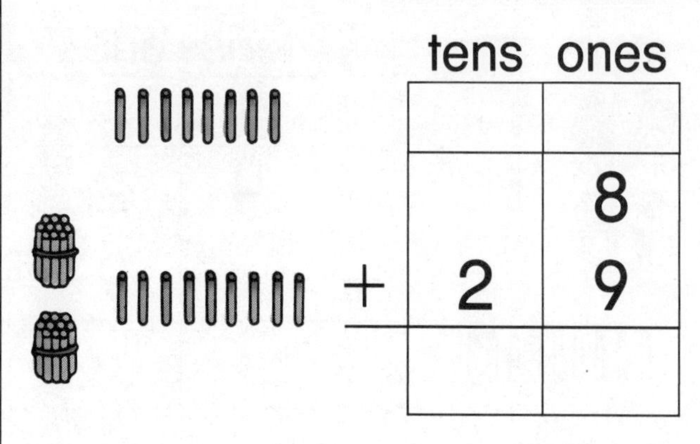

	tens	ones
		8
+	2	9

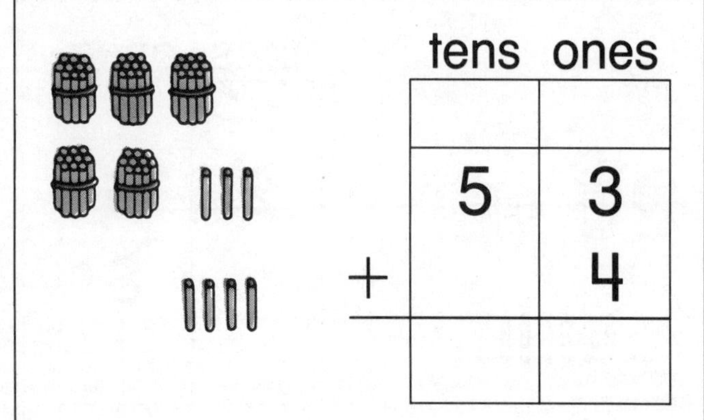

	tens	ones
	5	3
+		4

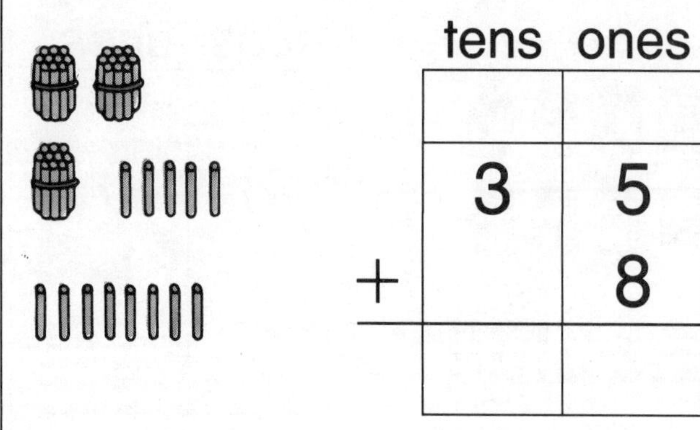

	tens	ones
	3	5
+		8

Solve.

Jerry had 22 baseball cards.
Joey gave him 5 more.
How many does Jerry have now?

____ baseball cards

	tens	ones
○		

Name ____________________

Circle 10 ones if you can. Add.

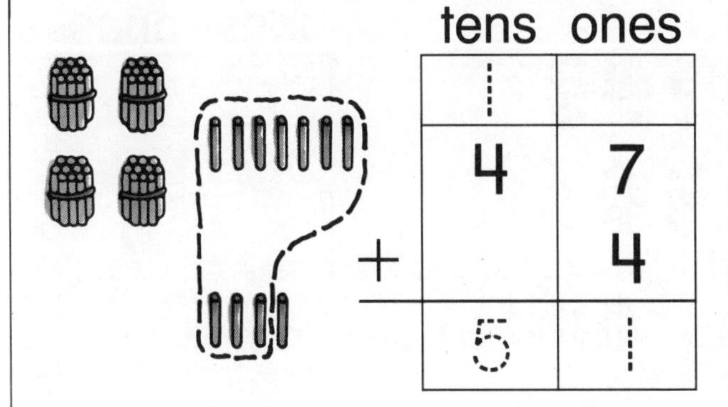

	tens	ones
	1	
	4	7
+		4
	5	1

	tens	ones
		9
+	2	1

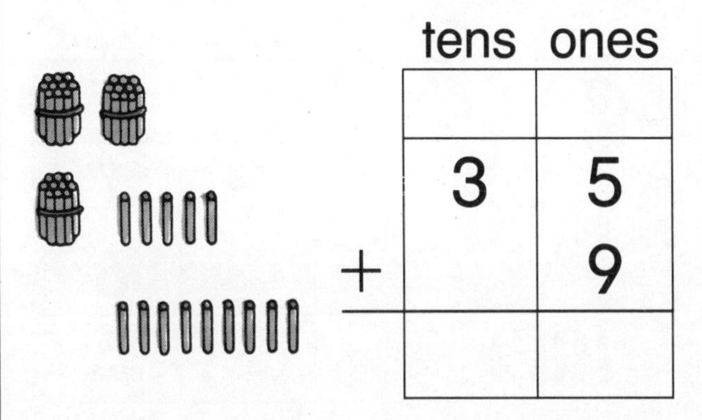

	tens	ones
	3	5
+		9

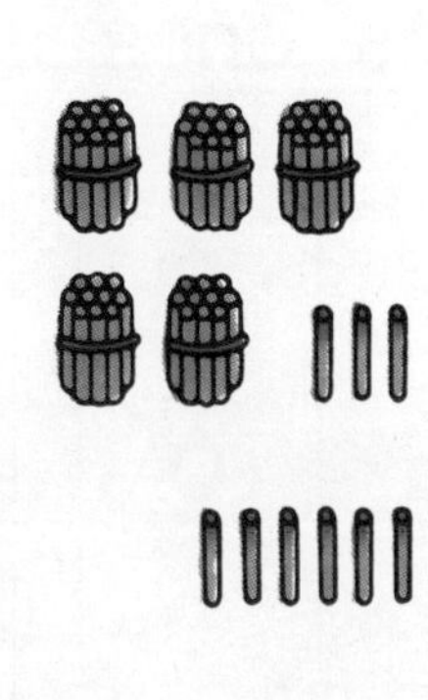

	tens	ones
	5	3
+		6

	tens	ones
		6
+	1	8

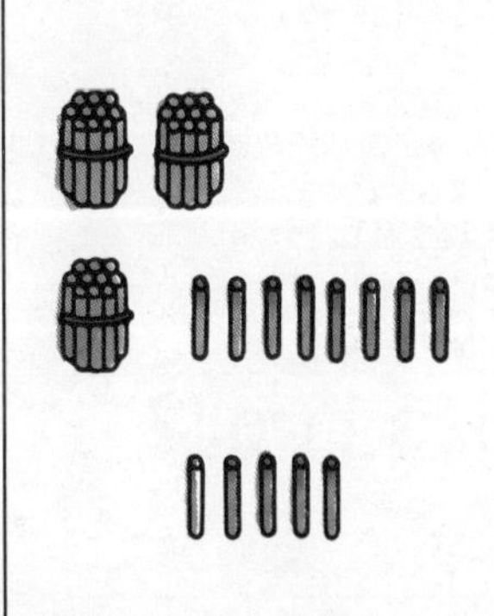

	tens	ones
	3	8
+		5

Solve.

Ted saw 17 birds.
Jan saw 5 birds.
How many birds in all?

____ birds

	tens	ones
◯		

Circle 10 ones if you can. Add.

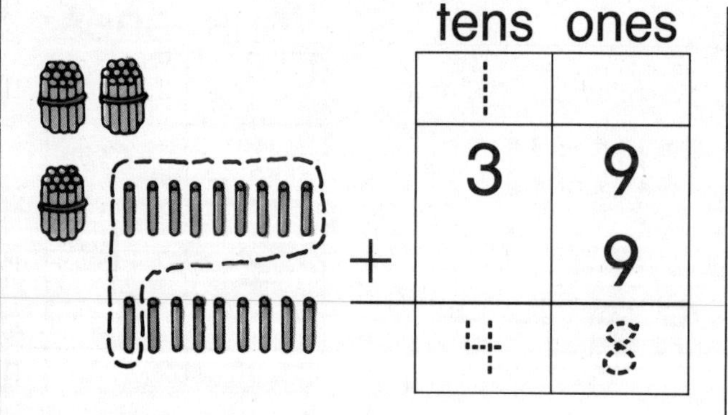

	tens	ones
	1	
	3	9
+		9
	4	8

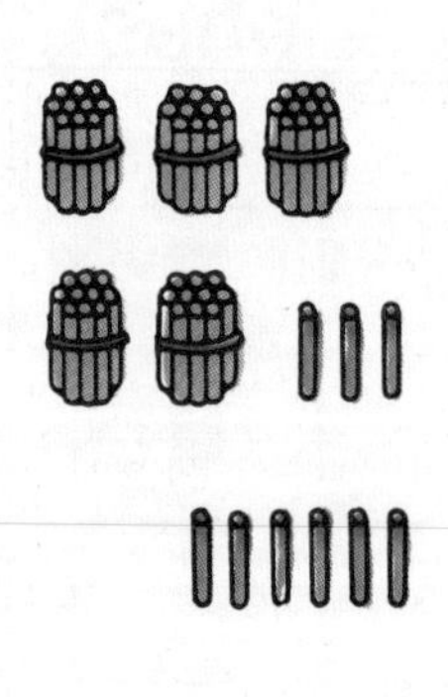

	tens	ones
	5	3
+		6

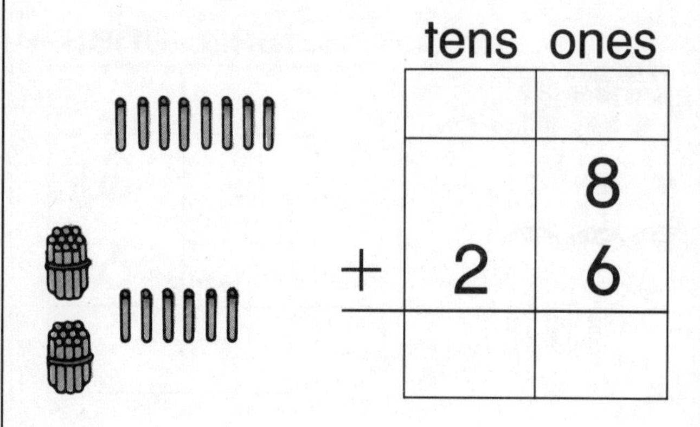

	tens	ones
		8
+	2	6

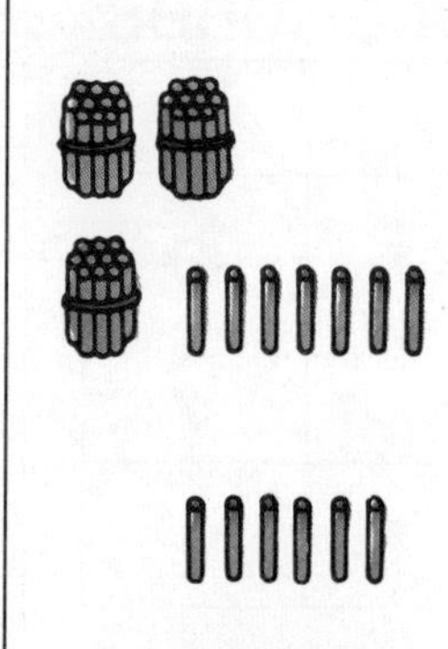

	tens	ones
	3	7
+		6

Solve.

Jenny has 25 marbles.
Ralph has 8 marbles.
How many marbles in all?

____ marbles

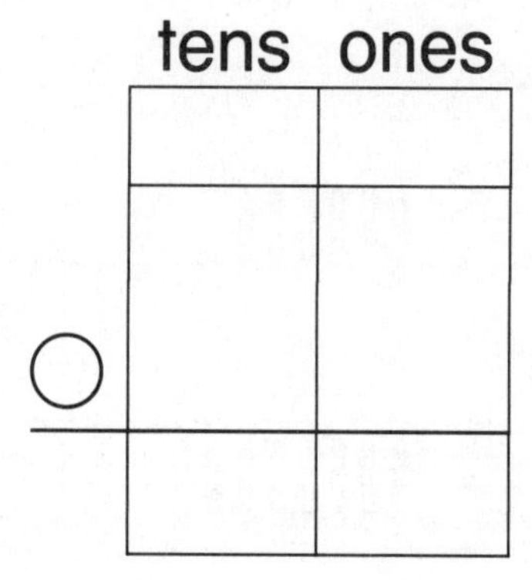

Alex counted 32 chicks.
He then counted 7 more.
How many chicks in all?

____ chicks

	tens	ones
○		

Name ______________________________

	10¢	1¢	
	1		
	1	3	¢
+		8	¢
	2	1	¢

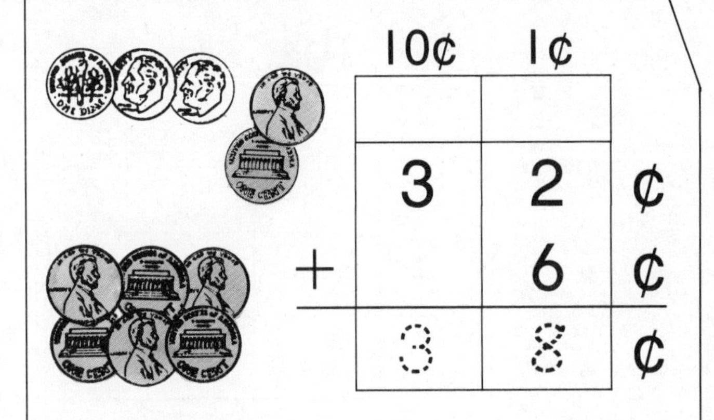

	10¢	1¢	
	3	2	¢
+		6	¢
	3	8	¢

Add.

	10¢	1¢	
	2	9	¢
+		7	¢
			¢

	10¢	1¢	
	3	3	¢
+		5	¢
			¢

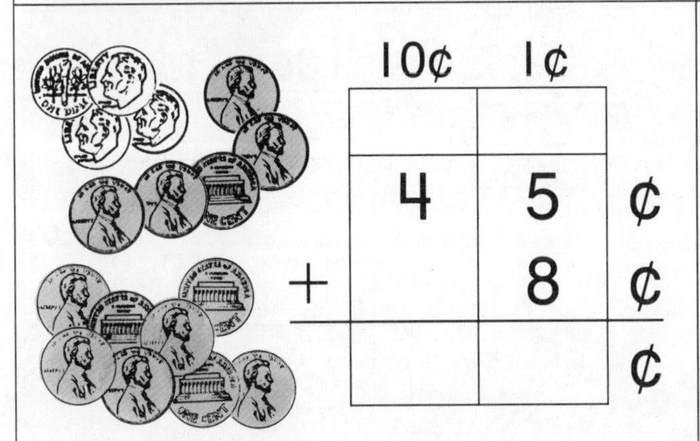

	10¢	1¢	
	4	5	¢
+		8	¢
			¢

	10¢	1¢	
	3	9	¢
+		4	¢
			¢

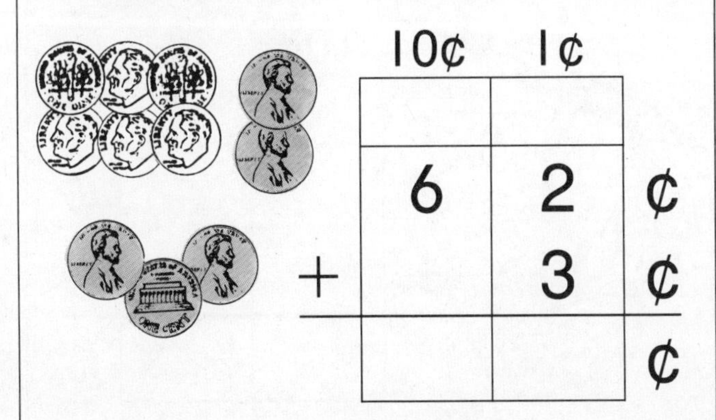

	10¢	1¢	
	6	2	¢
+		3	¢
			¢

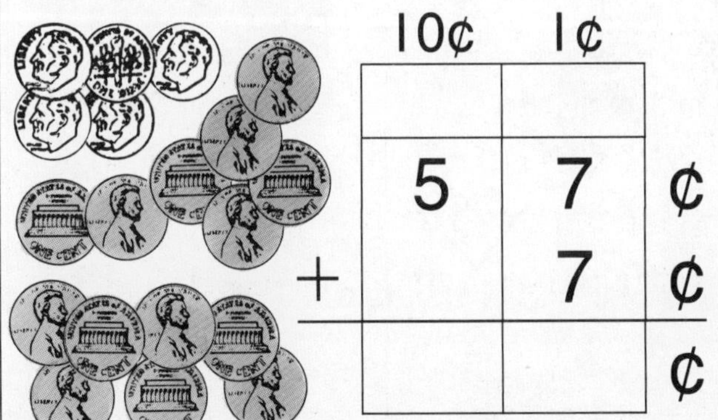

	10¢	1¢	
	5	7	¢
+		7	¢
			¢

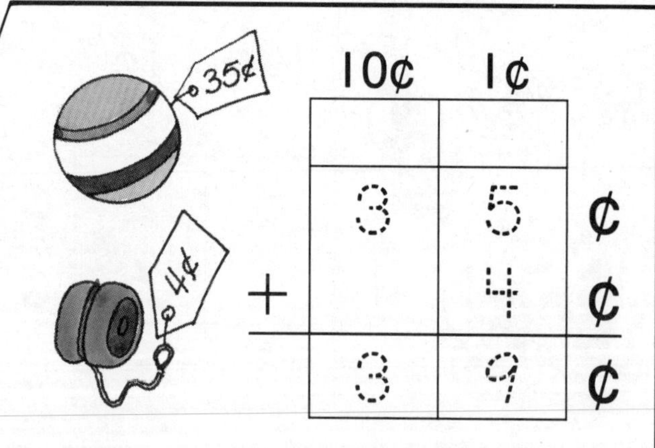

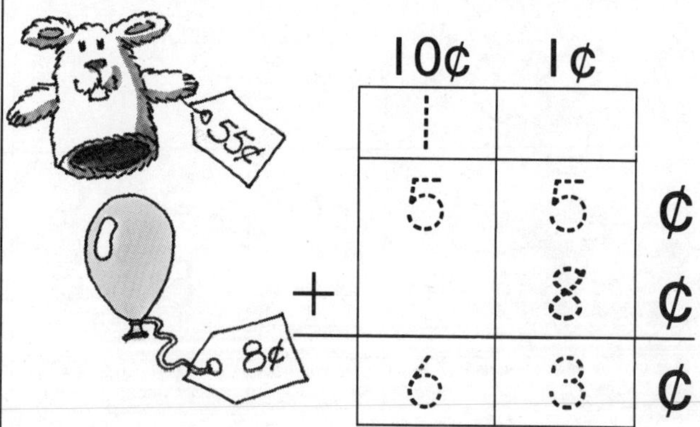

How much for both?

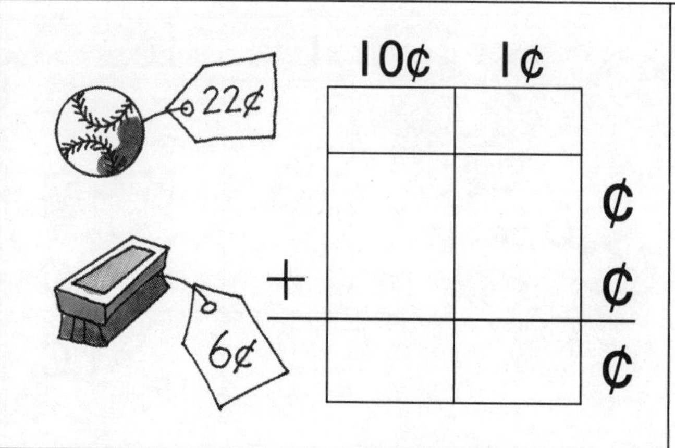

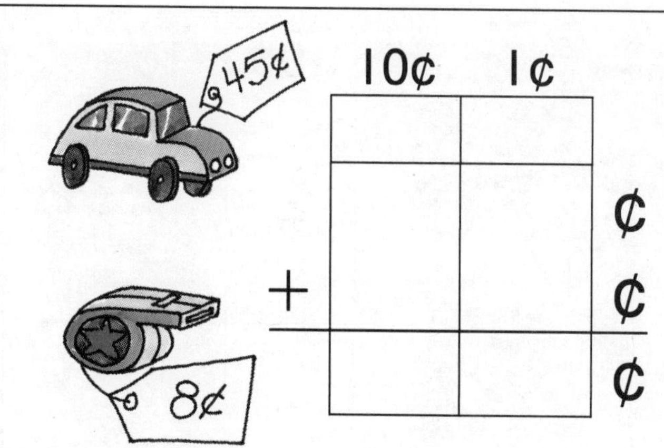

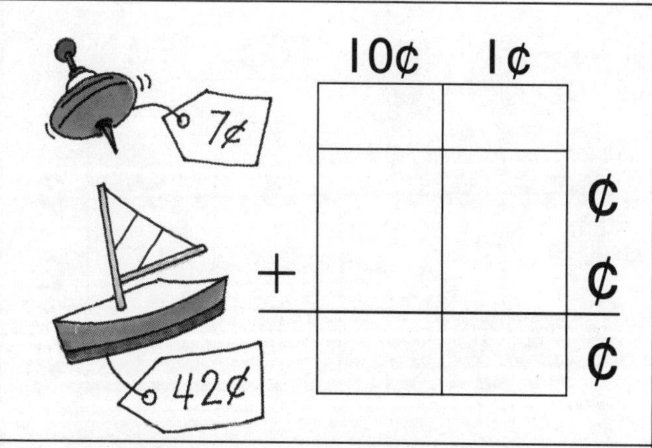

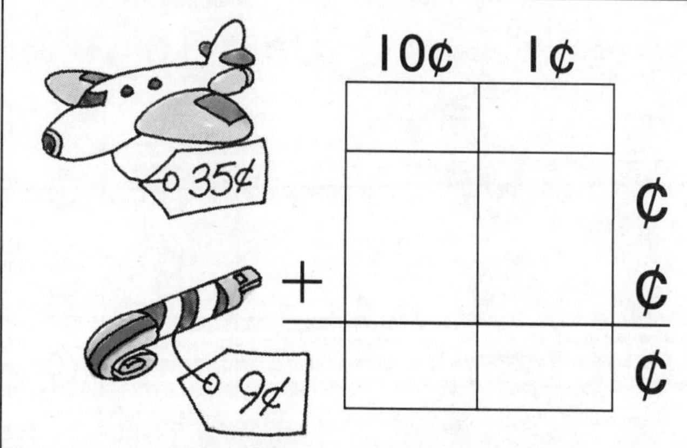

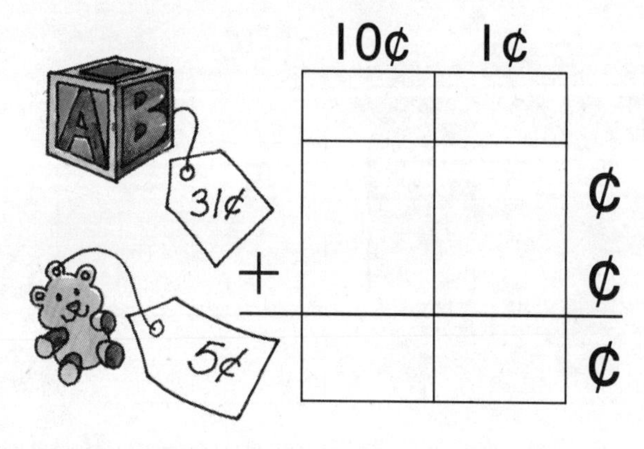

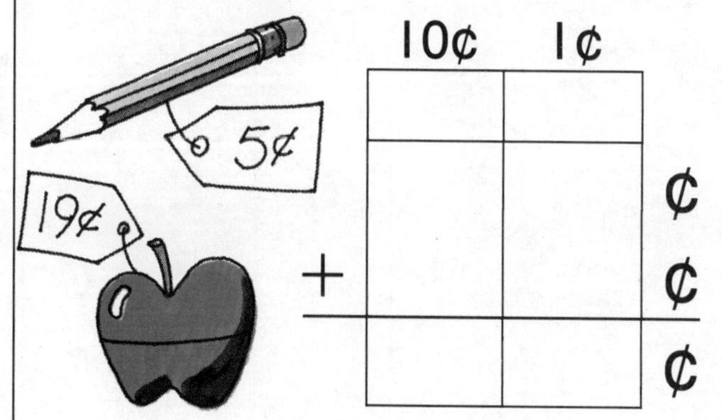

Name ______________________________

Add.

23 + 6 29	15 + 8 23	27 + 5	33 + 4	55 + 9	42 + 7
86 + 7	91 + 6	47 + 8	75 + 5	12 + 3	29 + 2
48 + 1	73 + 3	38 + 5	64 + 9	89 + 3	17 + 7
37 + 2	81 + 8	55 + 6	78 + 2	44 + 4	63 + 8
91 + 4	28 + 9	67 + 4	95 + 4	38 + 6	58 + 7

Solve.

Cory counted 18 birds.
She saw 7 more.
How many birds in all?

$$\begin{array}{r} 18 \\ + \quad 7 \\ \hline 25 \end{array}$$

25 birds

Vince found 42 leaves.
He found 6 more.
How many in all?

____ leaves

Ms. Li picked 19 flowers.
She picked 8 more.
How many flowers in all?

____ flowers

Katy rode 25 miles.
She rode 4 more miles. How many miles in all?

____ miles

Roscoe found 28 shells.
He found 9 more.
How many shells in all?

____ shells

Betty counted 32 butterflies.
She counted 6 more.
How many in all?

____ butterflies

David has 25 pencils.
Jaime has 5.
How many in all?

____ pencils

Toni has 34 spools.
Mickey has 5.
How many in all?

____ spools

Name ______________________________

CHAPTER CHECKUP

How many?

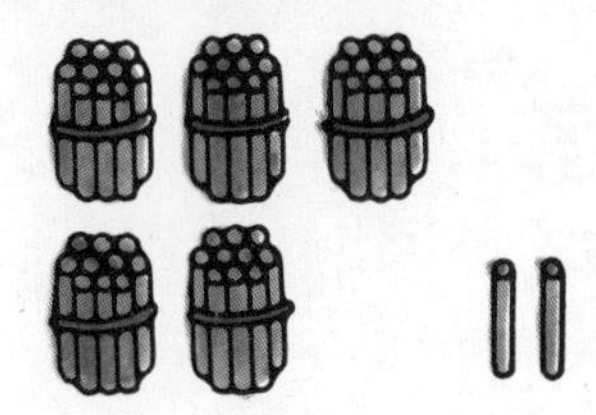

____ tens ____ ones

____

8 tens 5 ones ____

thirty-five ____

67 is ____ tens ____ ones.

Write the missing numbers.

36, 37, ____, ____, ____, ____, ____, ____, ____, 45

72, 73, ____, ____, ____, ____, ____, ____, ____, ____

Add.

$$\begin{array}{r} 3 \\ +5 \\ \hline \end{array} \quad \begin{array}{r} 9 \\ +6 \\ \hline \end{array} \quad \begin{array}{r} 6 \\ +7 \\ \hline \end{array} \quad \begin{array}{r} 7 \\ +8 \\ \hline \end{array} \quad \begin{array}{r} 6 \\ +4 \\ \hline \end{array} \quad \begin{array}{r} 9 \\ +7 \\ \hline \end{array} \quad \begin{array}{r} 4 \\ +9 \\ \hline \end{array}$$

Add.

	tens	ones
	5	2
+		6

	tens	ones
	3	4
+		7

	10¢	1¢	
	3	8	¢
+		5	¢
			¢

ROUNDUP REVIEW

Add or subtract.

$$\begin{array}{r} 14 \\ -\ 8 \\ \hline \end{array} \quad \begin{array}{r} 17 \\ -\ 9 \\ \hline \end{array} \quad \begin{array}{r} 5 \\ +9 \\ \hline \end{array} \quad \begin{array}{r} 14 \\ -\ 6 \\ \hline \end{array} \quad \begin{array}{r} 7 \\ +5 \\ \hline \end{array} \quad \begin{array}{r} 9 \\ +7 \\ \hline \end{array} \quad \begin{array}{r} 8 \\ +5 \\ \hline \end{array}$$

How much for both?

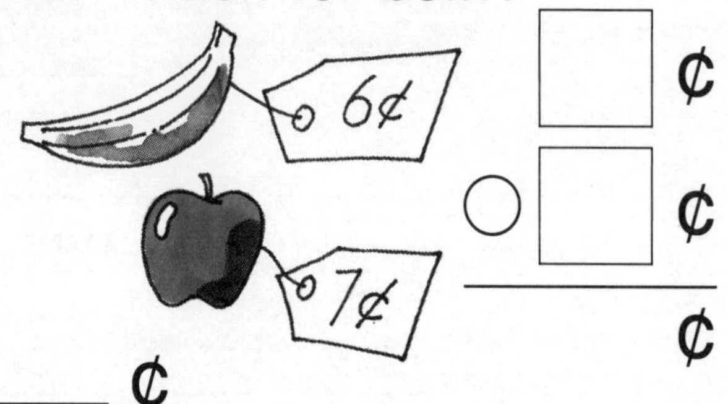

☐ ¢

○ ☐ ¢

______ ¢

____ ¢

Solve.

Sharon had 17¢.
She spent 9¢.
How much does Sharon have left?

☐ ¢

○ ☐ ¢

______ ¢

____ ¢

How many?

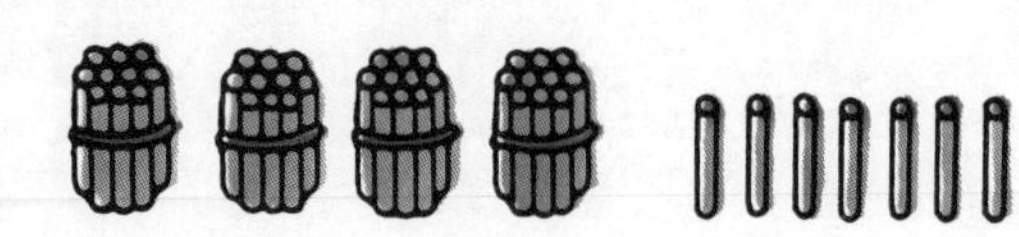

____

Write the number.

8 tens 8 ones is ____.

74 is ____ tens ____ ones.

Sixty-three is ____.

Add.

$$\begin{array}{r} 42 \\ +\ 6 \\ \hline \end{array} \qquad \begin{array}{r} 54 \\ +\ 8 \\ \hline \end{array}$$

How much for both?

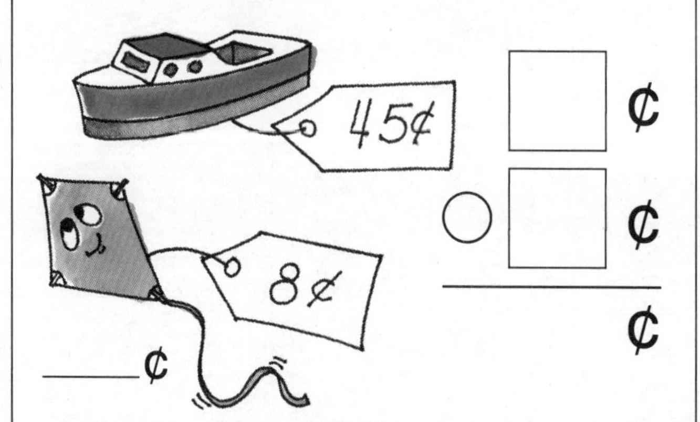

☐ ¢

○ ☐ ¢

______ ¢

____¢

Name ____________________

11 SUBTRACTION, 2- AND 1-DIGITS

Match the numbers with their names.

thirteen	99	1 ten 3 ones
ninety-nine	13	9 tens 9 ones
forty-four	35	4 tens 4 ones
fifty-eight	44	3 tens 5 ones
thirty-five	58	8 tens 6 ones
eighty-six	77	5 tens 8 ones
seventy-seven	86	7 tens 7 ones

Draw a line to the number before and the number after.

Number Before		Number After
44	23	57
55	45	24
22	56	35
33	17	46
16	34	71
69	30	31
29	70	18

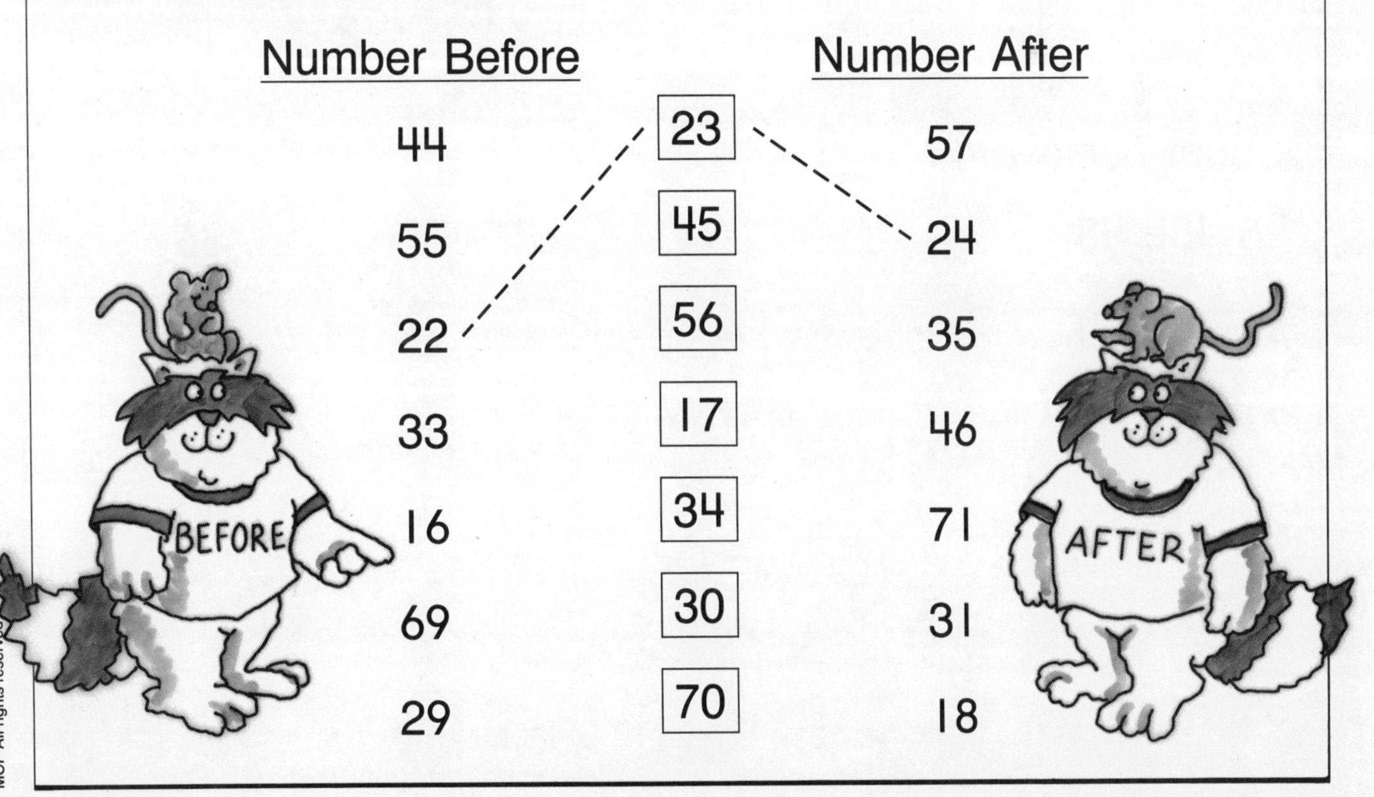

Count backwards.

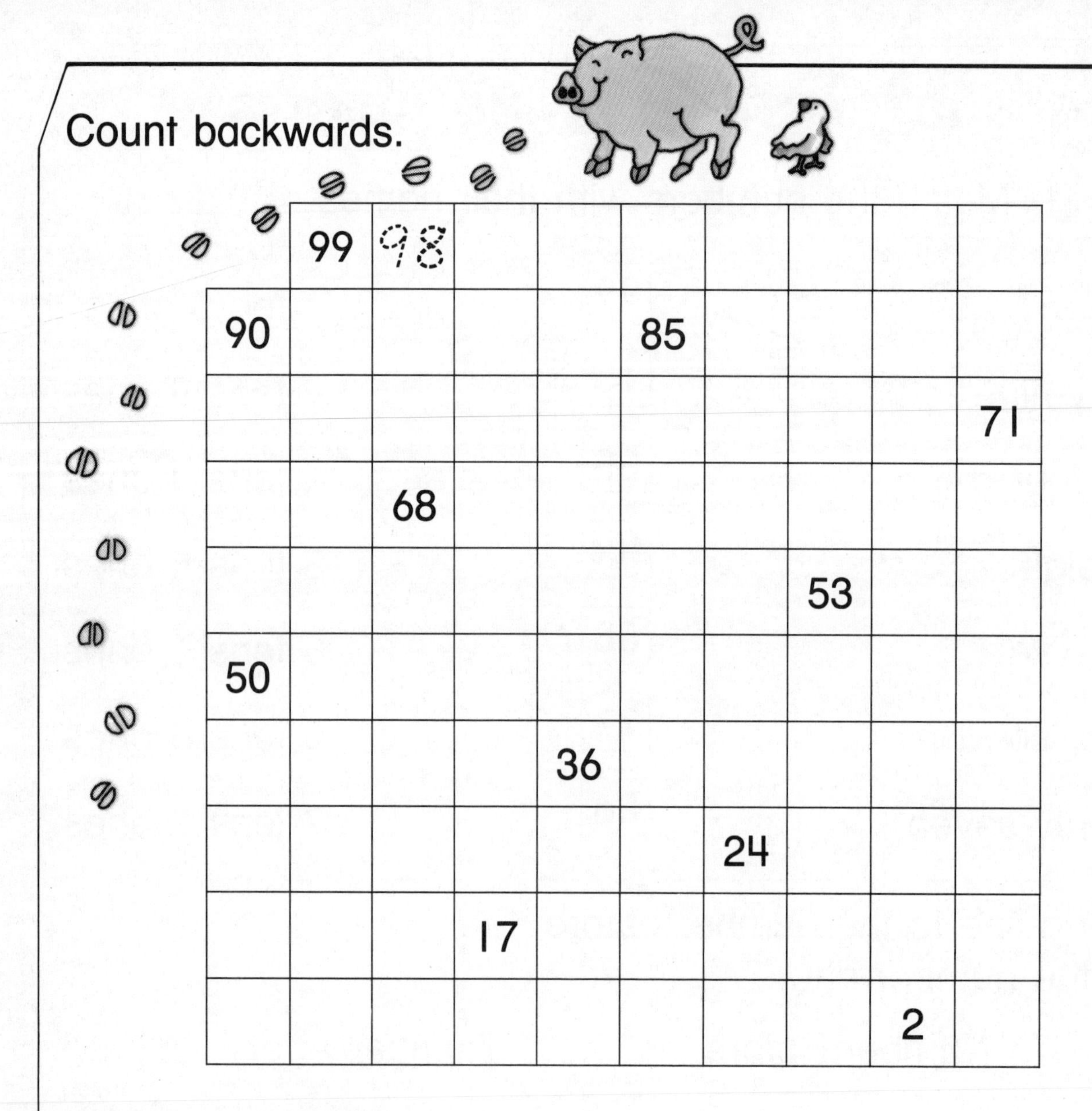

	99	98							
90					85				
									71
		68							
							53		
50									
				36					
						24			
			17						
								2	

Count backwards.

45, 44, 43, 42, ____, ____, ____, ____, ____, 36

96, 95, 94, 93, ____, ____, ____, ____, ____, 87

71, 70, ____, ____, ____, ____, ____, ____, 63

22, 20, 18, ____, ____, ____, ____, ____, ____, 4

90, 80, ____, ____, ____, ____, ____, ____, 10

55, 50, ____, ____, ____, ____, ____, ____, ____, 10

Name ____________________

Subtract.

8	9	8	8	7	6	9
−2	−4	−8	−3	−6	−6	−3

9	5	8	7	6	9	7
−8	−1	−1	−2	−4	−9	−1

7	6	9	6	5	9	8
−7	−5	−2	−1	−5	−1	−7

4	5	8	9	4	7	6
−3	−2	−0	−6	−1	−3	−0

FIELD TRIP

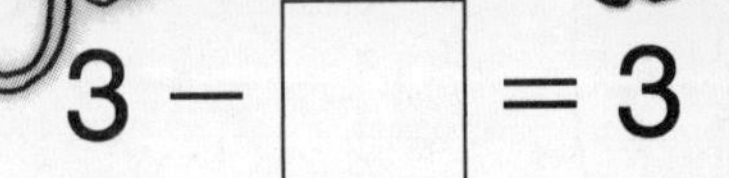

Write the missing number.

7 − [5] = 2 | 5 − [ ] = 3 | 3 − [ ] = 3

6 − [ ] = 3 | 8 − [ ] = 4 | 9 − [ ] = 2

4 − [ ] = 4 | 5 − [ ] = 4 | 7 − [ ] = 3

Subtract.

$11 - 2$	$12 - 6$	$14 - 7$	$10 - 2$	$12 - 3$	$16 - 8$	$13 - 6$
$16 - 7$	$13 - 5$	$15 - 6$	$11 - 7$	$17 - 8$	$12 - 9$	$10 - 3$
$11 - 8$	$15 - 7$	$14 - 5$	$10 - 6$	$12 - 5$	$14 - 8$	$11 - 4$
$15 - 8$	$11 - 6$	$13 - 4$	$11 - 9$	$17 - 9$	$10 - 5$	$12 - 8$

FIELD TRIP

Write the missing numbers.

$6 - \boxed{4} = 2$	$8 - \boxed{} = 2$	$9 - \boxed{} = 4$
$9 - \boxed{} = 3$	$2 - \boxed{} = 2$	$8 - \boxed{} = 3$
$7 - \boxed{} = 4$	$4 - \boxed{} = 3$	$6 - \boxed{} = 4$

Name ______________________________

Take away 4.
How many left?

tens	ones
3	6
−	4
3	2

Cross out and subtract.

Take away 6.
How many left?

tens	ones
4	8
−	6

Take away 4.
How many left?

tens	ones
1	9
−	4

Take away 3.
How many left?

tens	ones
2	5
−	3

Take away 2.
How many left?

tens	ones
3	8
−	2

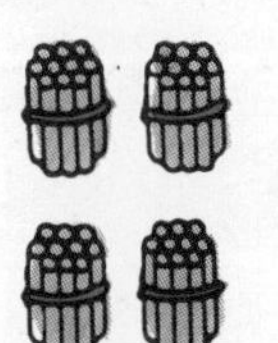

Take away 4.
How many left?

tens	ones
4	5
−	4

Take away 7.
How many left?

tens	ones
2	7
−	7

Cross out and subtract.

Take away 6.

	tens	ones
	4	9
−		6
	4	3

How many left?

Take away 3.

	tens	ones
	3	5
−		3

How many left?

Take away 2.

	tens	ones
	2	7
−		2

How many left?

Take away 5.

	tens	ones
	1	6
−		5

How many left?

Take away 4.

	tens	ones
	4	8
−		4

How many left?

Take away 4.

	tens	ones
	3	4
−		4

How many left?

Take away 5.

	tens	ones
	4	7
−		5

How many left?

Take away 7.

	tens	ones
	3	8
−		7

How many left?

Name ______________________________

tens	ones
0	12
1	2

1 ten 2 ones → 0 tens 12 ones

Trade 1 ten for 10 ones.

tens	ones

____ ten ____ ones → ____ tens ____ ones

tens	ones

____ tens ____ ones → ____ ten ____ ones

tens	ones

____ tens ____ ones → ____ tens ____ ones

tens	ones

____ tens ____ ones → ____ tens ____ ones

Trade 1 ten for 10 ones.

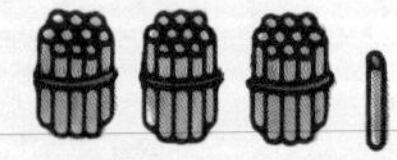

tens	ones
2	11
3	1

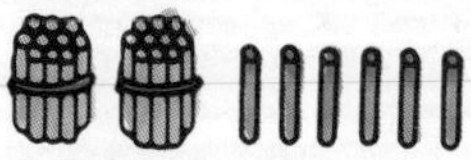

tens	ones
2	6

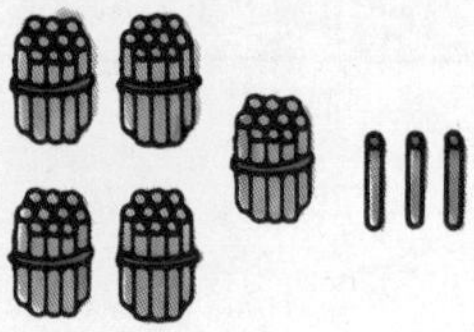

tens	ones
5	3

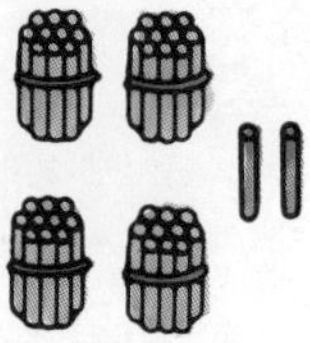

tens	ones
4	2

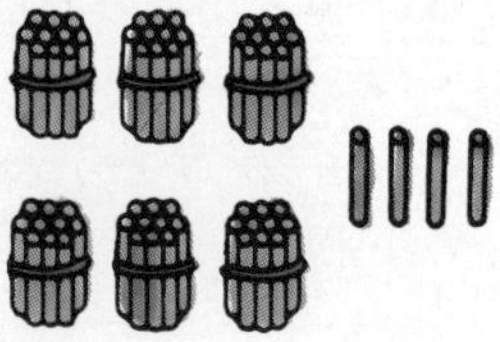

tens	ones
6	4

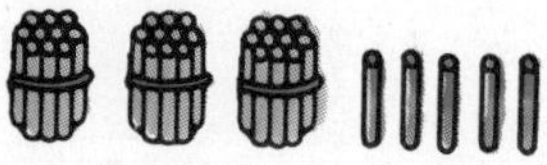

tens	ones
3	5

tens	ones
2	7

tens	ones
7	3

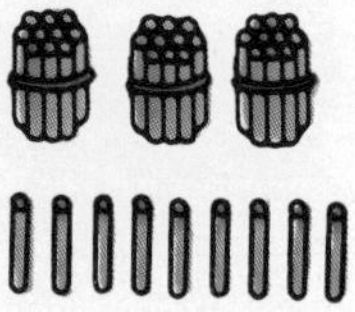

tens	ones
3	9

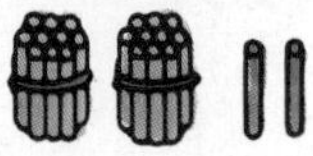

tens	ones
2	2

Name ______________________________

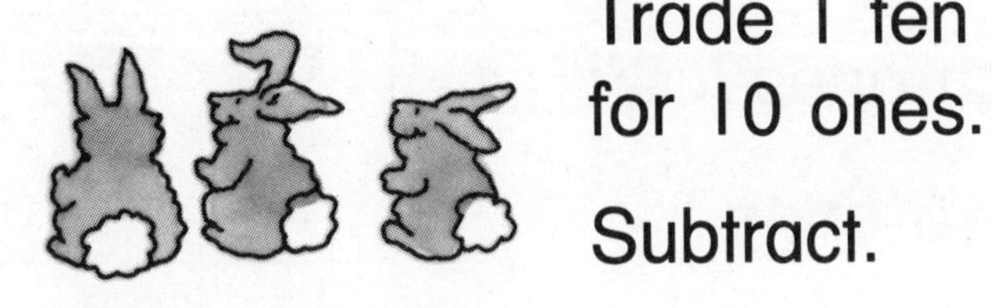

Are there enough ones? No

Trade 1 ten for 10 ones.

Subtract.

	tens	ones
	3	14
	~~4~~	~~4~~
−		7
	3	7

Trade 1 ten for 10 ones if needed. Subtract.

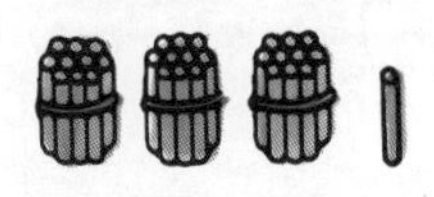

	tens	ones
	3	1
−		6

Enough ones? ____

	tens	ones
	5	2
−		9

Enough ones? ____

	tens	ones
	5	8
−		4

Enough ones? ____

	tens	ones
	2	5
−		8

Enough ones? ____

	tens	ones
	3	5
−		6

Enough ones? ____

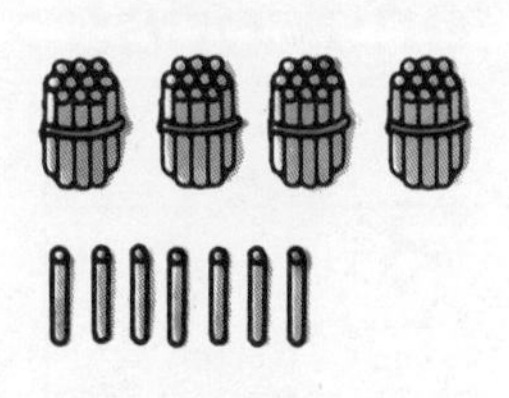

	tens	ones
	4	7
−		5

Enough ones? ____

Are there enough ones? No

Trade 1 ten for 10 ones.

Subtract.

	tens	ones
	4	10
	~~5~~	~~0~~
−		3
	4	7

Trade 1 ten for 10 ones if needed. Subtract.

	tens	ones
	4	1
−		6

Enough ones? ____

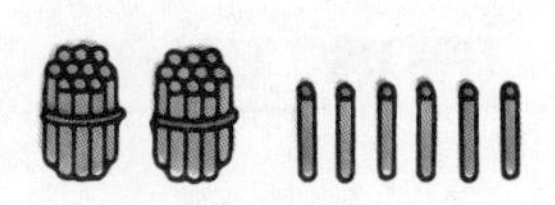

	tens	ones
	2	6
−		3

Enough ones? ____

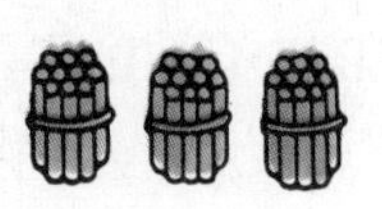

	tens	ones
	3	0
−		9

Enough ones? ____

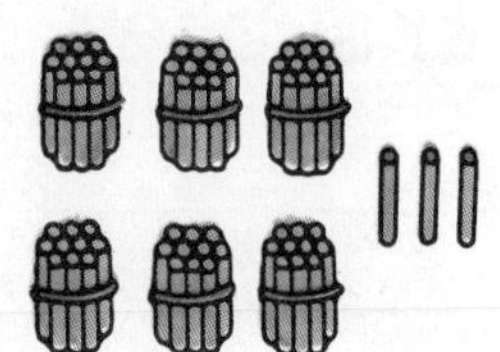

	tens	ones
	6	3
−		4

Enough ones? ____

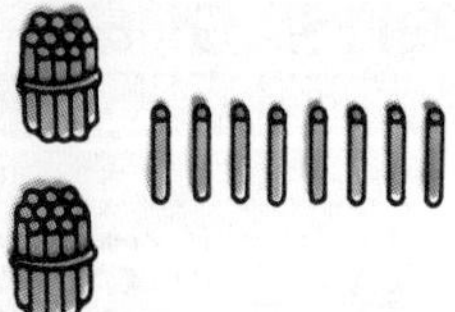

	tens	ones
	2	8
−		7

Enough ones? ____

	tens	ones
	4	8
−		9

Enough ones? ____

Name ____________________

Are there enough ones? No

Trade 1 ten for 10 ones.

Subtract.

tens	ones
3	13
~~4~~	~~3~~
−	7
3	6

Trade 1 ten for 10 ones if needed. Subtract.

tens	ones
5	4
−	4

Enough ones? ____

tens	ones
7	2
−	8

Enough ones? ____

tens	ones
3	5
−	8

Enough ones? ____

tens	ones
4	1
−	5

Enough ones? ____

tens	ones
3	9
−	5

Enough ones? ____

tens	ones
6	4
−	6

Enough ones? ____

Trade 1 ten for 10 ones if needed. Subtract.

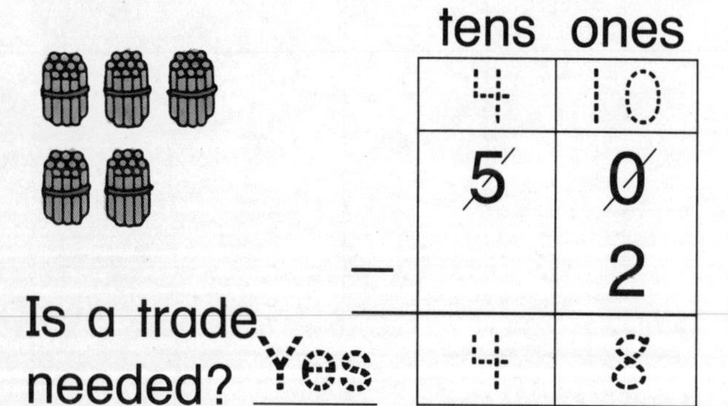

	tens	ones
	4	10
	~~5~~	~~0~~
−		2
	4	8

Is a trade needed? Yes

	tens	ones
	4	1
−		7

Is a trade needed? ____

	tens	ones
	3	9
−		8

Is a trade needed? ____

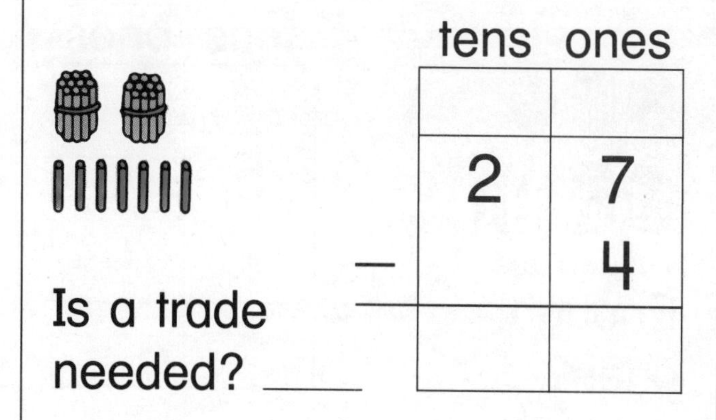

	tens	ones
	2	7
−		4

Is a trade needed? ____

	tens	ones
	5	2
−		3

Is a trade needed? ____

	tens	ones
	4	0
−		6

Is a trade needed? ____

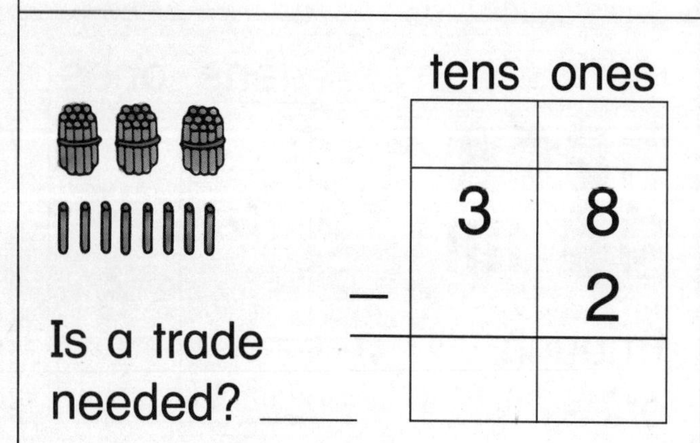

	tens	ones
	3	8
−		2

Is a trade needed? ____

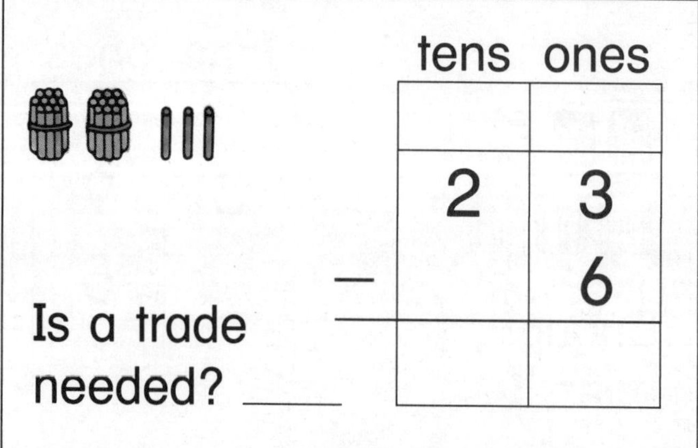

	tens	ones
	2	3
−		6

Is a trade needed? ____

Name ______________________________

Trade 1 ten for 10 ones if needed. Subtract.

	tens	ones
	2	17
	~~3~~	~~7~~
−		8
	2	9

Is a trade needed? Yes

	tens	ones
	1	9
−		8

Is a trade needed? ____

	tens	ones
	4	6
−		9

Is a trade needed? ____

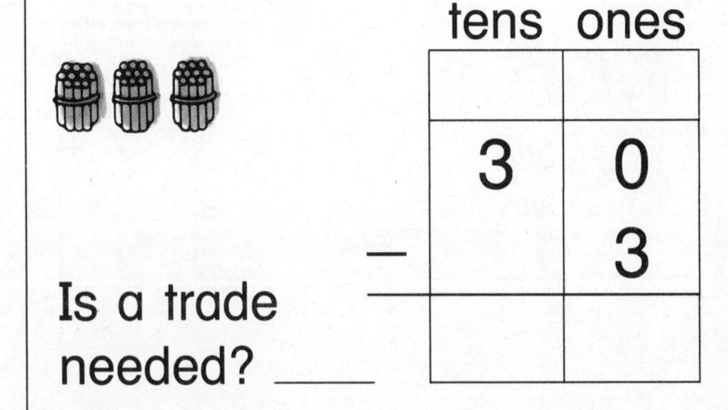

	tens	ones
	3	0
−		3

Is a trade needed? ____

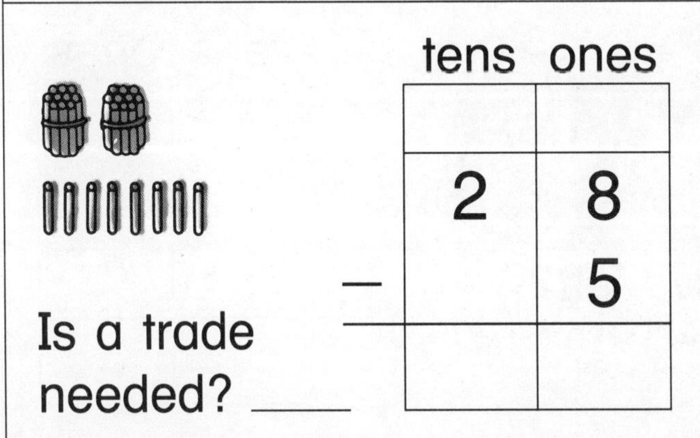

	tens	ones
	2	8
−		5

Is a trade needed? ____

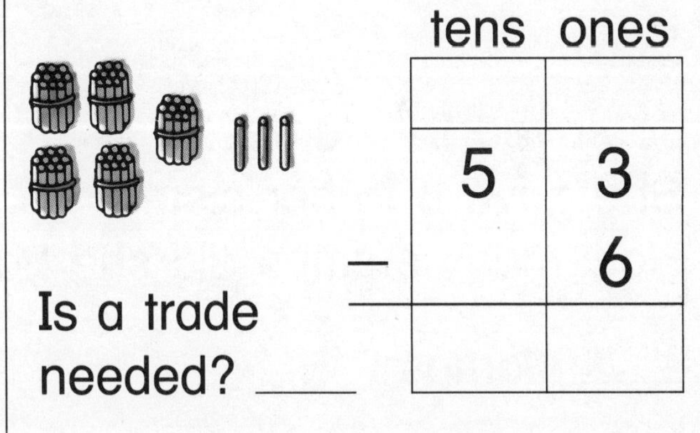

	tens	ones
	5	3
−		6

Is a trade needed? ____

Solve.

Beth saw 25 birds on a fence.
Then she saw 8 birds fly away.
How many were left?

____ birds

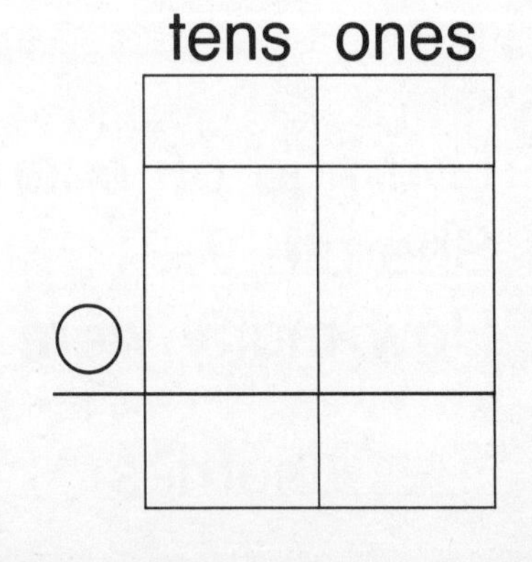

	tens	ones
○		

Trade if needed. Subtract.

	tens	ones
	4	2
−		7

	tens	ones
	2	9
−		5

	tens	ones
	6	7
−		4

	tens	ones
	7	4
−		6

Solve.

Jo saved 31 stamps.
She gave 8 to her sister.
How many stamps did she have left?

____ stamps

	tens	ones
○		

Lori had 66 cherries.
She ate 9.
How many were left?

____ cherries

	tens	ones
○		

Name ______________________________

2 dimes 3 pennies → 1 dime 13 pennies

Trade 1 dime for 10 pennies.

Is a trade needed to take away 7¢? Yes

Trade 1 dime for 10 pennies.

Subtract pennies first.

	10¢	1¢	
	2	12	
	~~3~~	~~2~~	¢
−		7	¢
	2	5	¢

Trade 1 dime for 10 pennies if needed. Subtract.

	10¢	1¢	
	2	6	¢
−		3	¢
			¢

Is a trade needed? ____

	10¢	1¢	
	3	1	¢
−		9	¢
			¢

Is a trade needed? ____

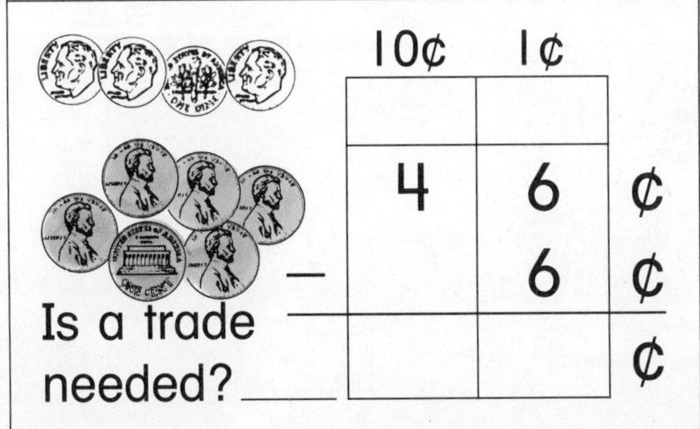

	10¢	1¢	
	4	6	¢
−		6	¢
			¢

Is a trade needed? ____

	10¢	1¢	
	2	3	¢
−		7	¢
			¢

Is a trade needed? ____

Trade if needed. Subtract.

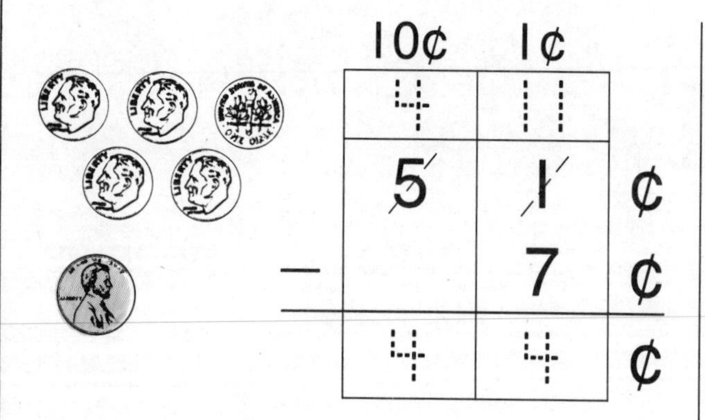

	10¢	1¢	
	4	11	
	5	1	¢
−		7	¢
	4	4	¢

	10¢	1¢	
	1	9	¢
−		6	¢
			¢

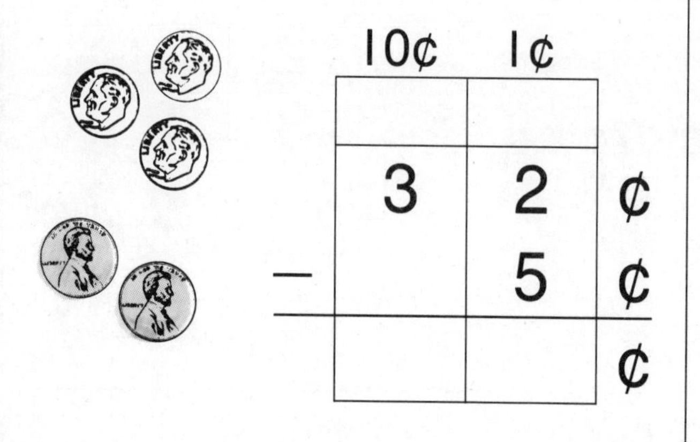

	10¢	1¢	
	3	2	¢
−		5	¢
			¢

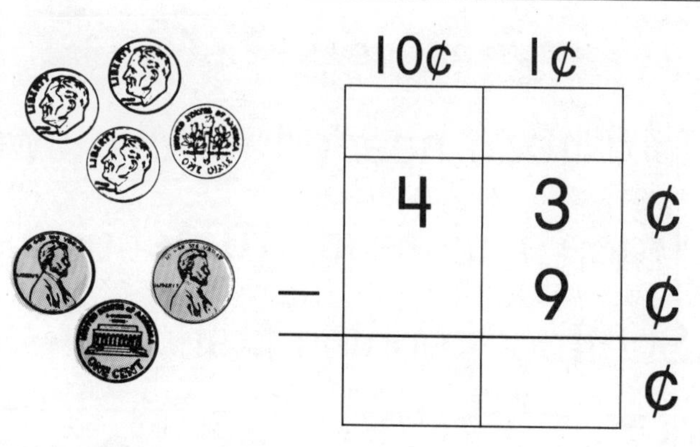

	10¢	1¢	
	4	3	¢
−		9	¢
			¢

Solve.

Martha had 42¢.
She bought a

How much was left?

____ ¢

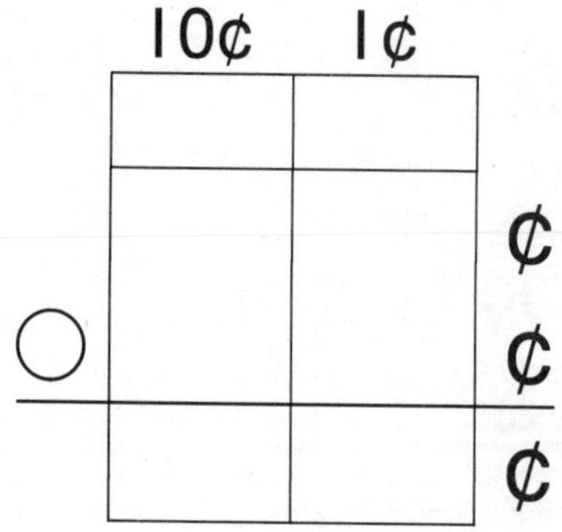

	10¢	1¢	
			¢
○			¢
			¢

Barb had 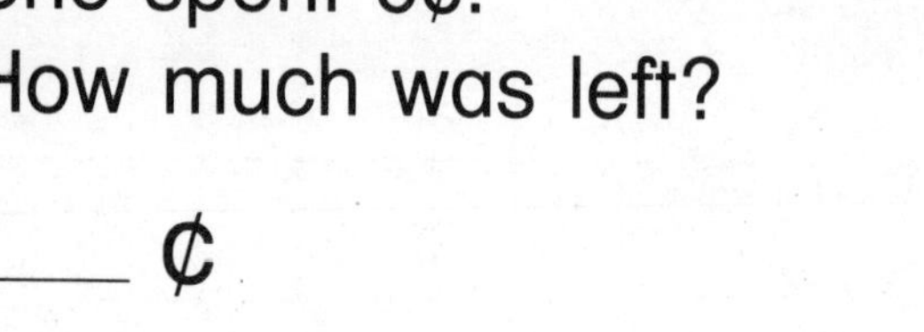.
She spent 6¢.
How much was left?

____ ¢

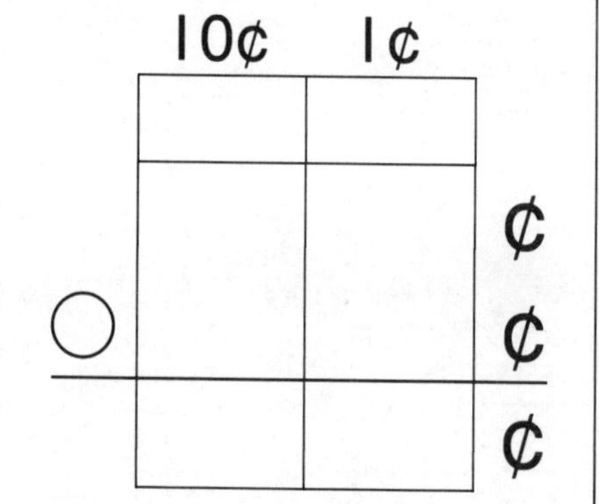

	10¢	1¢	
			¢
○			¢
			¢

Name ______________________________

Trade if needed. Subtract.

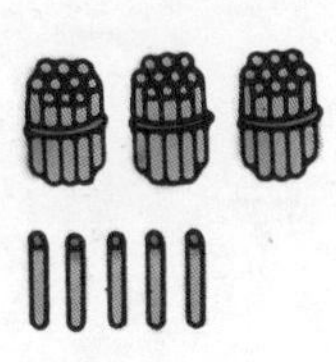

	tens	ones
	3	5
−		7

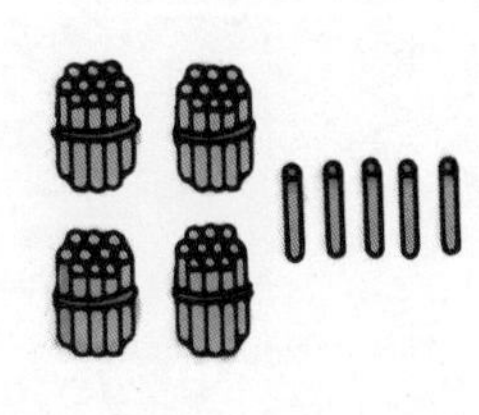

	tens	ones
	4	5
−		3

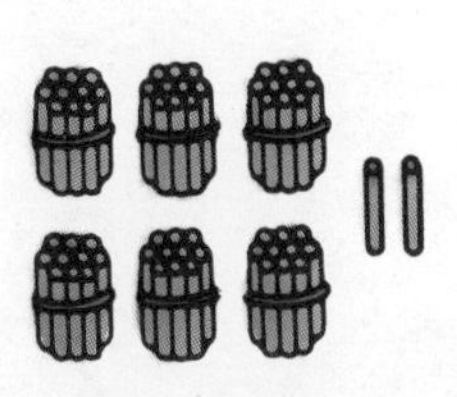

	tens	ones
	6	2
−		8

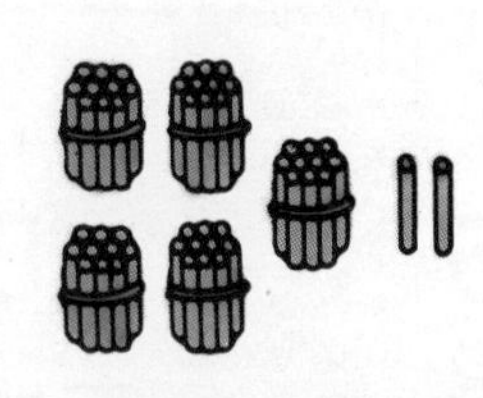

	tens	ones
	5	2
−		4

Solve.

Cal had 85¢.
He bought a drink for 8¢.
How much was left?

____ ¢

	10¢	1¢	
			¢
◯			¢
			¢

32 elephants were in a field.
9 joined the circus.
How many were left?

____ elephants

	tens	ones
◯		

Trade if needed. Subtract.

35	71	29	84	67
− 3	− 6	− 3	− 9	− 5
32	65			

87	56	41	73	34
− 6	− 4	− 7	− 5	− 8

18	45	52	38	95
− 3	− 8	− 9	− 5	− 7

Solve.

Chuck had 32 .
He gave 6 to Molly.
How many did he
have left?

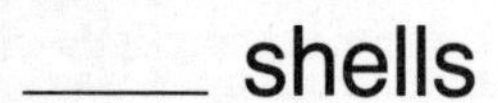

____ shells

Patsy had 28 .
She sold 4 of them.
How many were
left?

____ cards

Abby had 82¢.
She spent 8¢.
How much was
left?

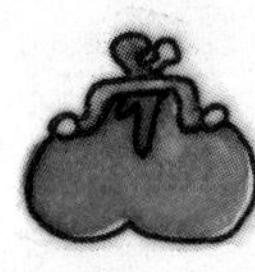

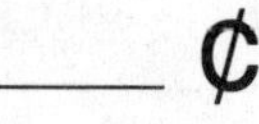

____ ¢

Larry had 35 .
He ate 9 of them.
How many were
left?

____ peanuts

Name ______________________________

CHAPTER CHECKUP

Trade if needed. Subtract.

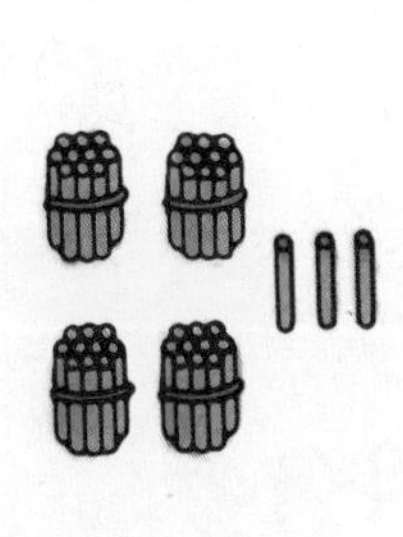

tens	ones
3	7
−	2

tens	ones
2	1
−	2

tens	ones
4	3
−	8

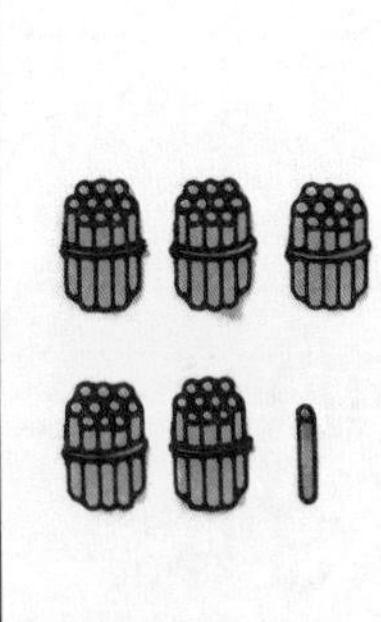

tens	ones
5	1
−	4

tens	ones
6	3
−	9

10¢	1¢	
7	5	¢
−	3	¢
		¢

Solve.

Flo had 53¢.
She bought a 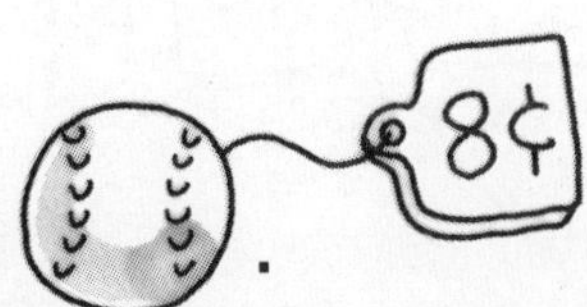

.

How much does she have left? ____ ¢

10¢	1¢	
		¢
○		¢
		¢

ROUNDUP REVIEW

Add or subtract.

5	10	13	8	15	8	12
+5	− 4	− 7	+8	− 7	+6	− 5

9	10	7	11	4	5	16
+9	− 2	+9	− 3	+9	+8	− 9

Circle the greater number.

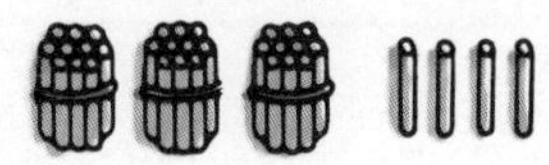 34  43

Add.

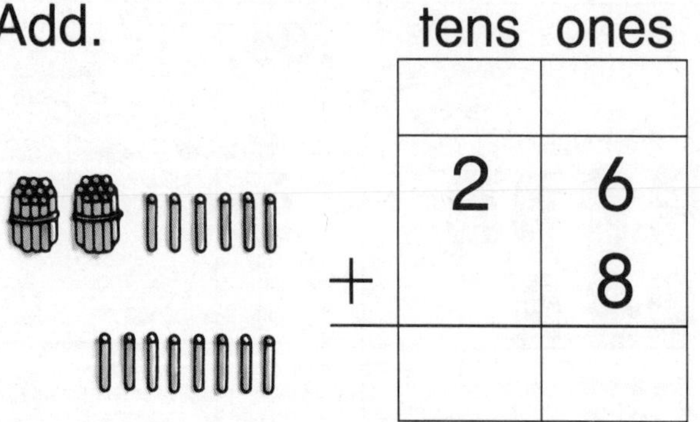

	tens	ones
	2	6
+		8

Subtract.

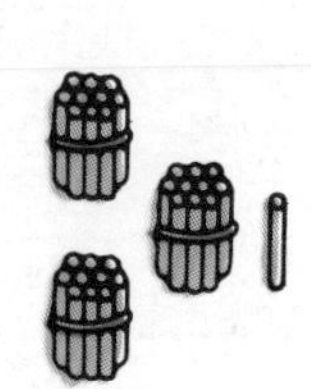

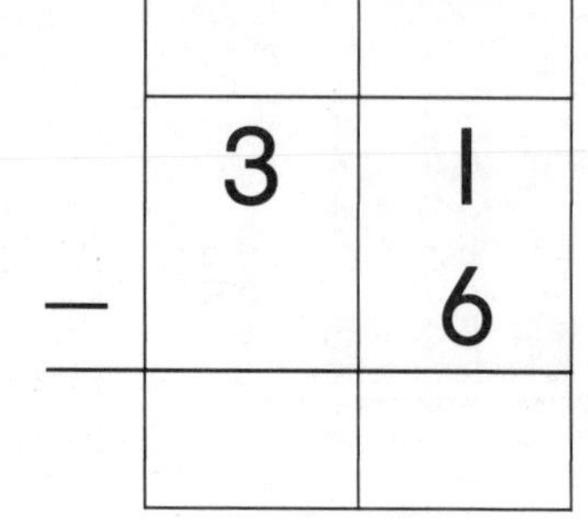

	tens	ones
	3	1
−		6

Solve.

How much for both? ____ ¢

	10¢	1¢	
			¢
○			¢
			¢

Name ______________________________

12 PLACE VALUE THROUGH 200

How many are there in all?

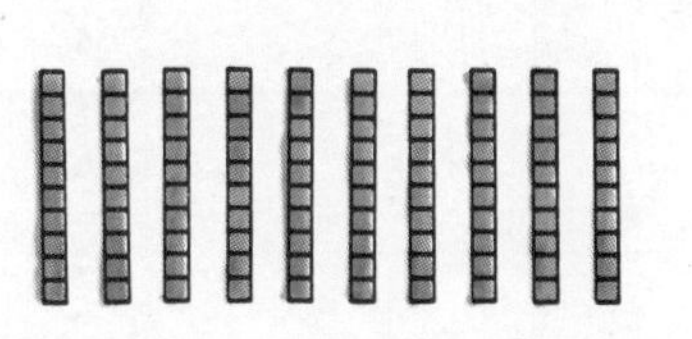

tens	ones
10	0

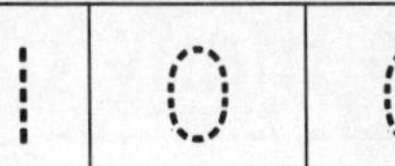

hundreds	tens	ones
1	0	0

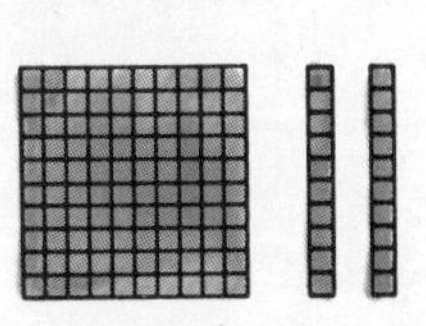

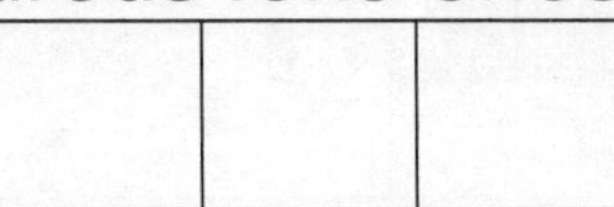

hundreds	tens	ones

______

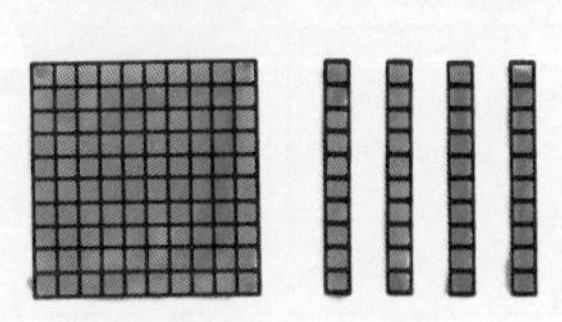

hundreds	tens	ones

______

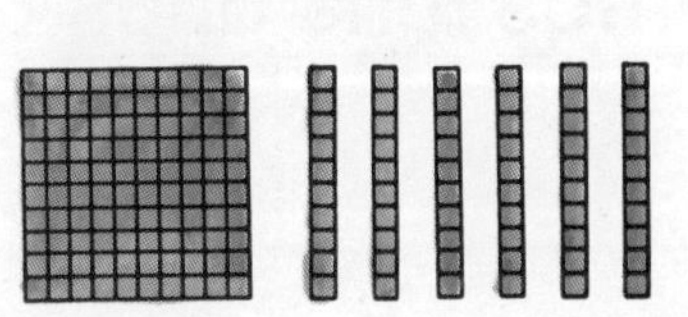

hundreds	tens	ones

______

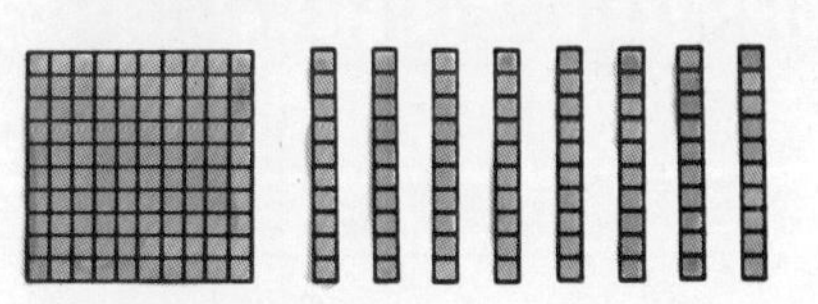

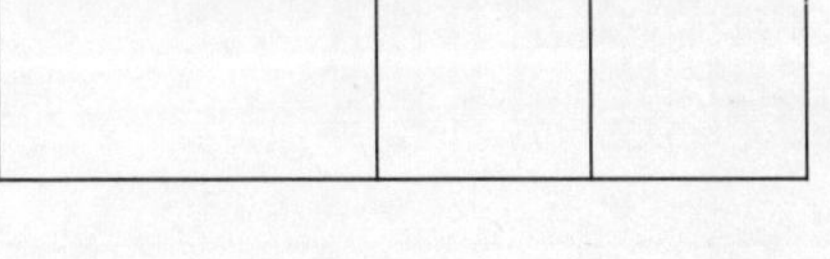

hundreds	tens	ones

______

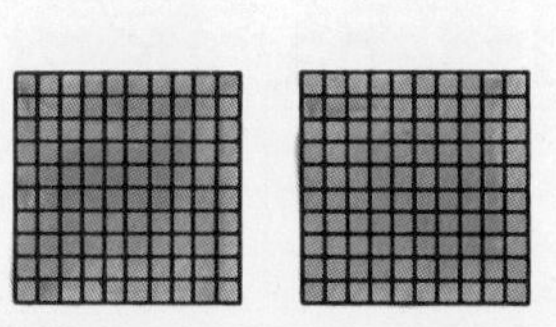

hundreds	tens	ones

______

hundreds	tens	ones
1	3	0

130

How many are there in all?

hundreds	tens	ones

hundreds	tens	ones

hundreds	tens	ones

hundreds	tens	ones

hundreds	tens	ones

Name ______________________

1 hundred 2 tens 3 ones

123

How many are there in all?

____ hundreds ____ tens ____ ones

______

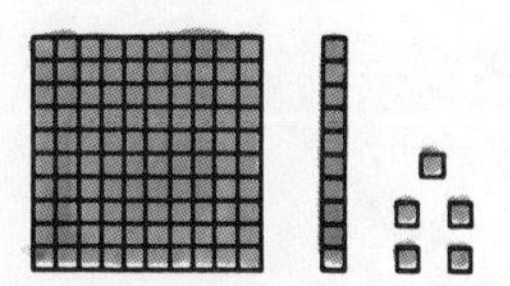

____ hundreds ____ tens ____ ones

______

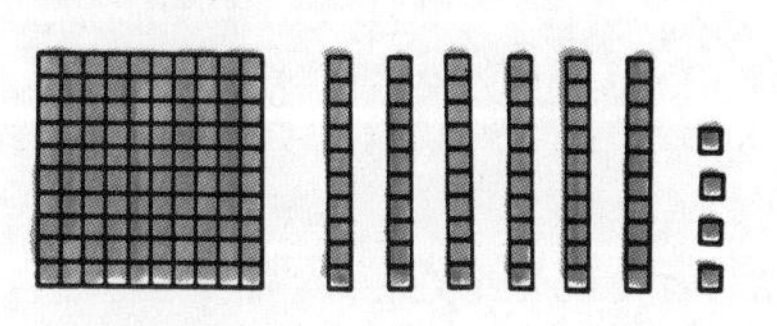

____ hundreds ____ tens ____ ones

______

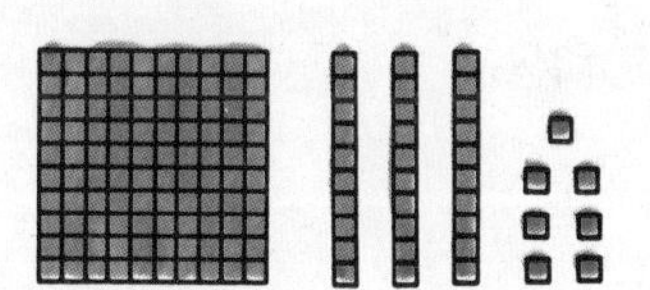

____ hundreds ____ tens ____ ones

______

____ hundreds ____ tens ____ ones

______

How many are there in all?

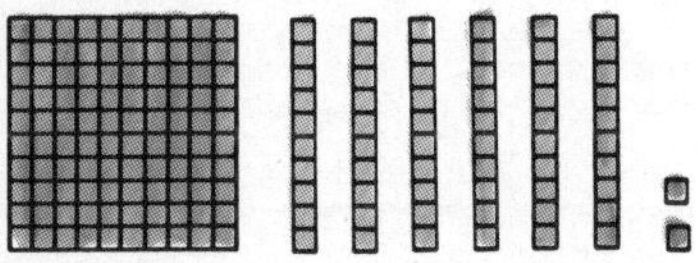

____ hundreds ____ tens ____ ones

______

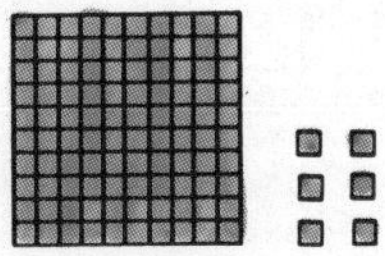

____ hundreds ____ tens ____ ones

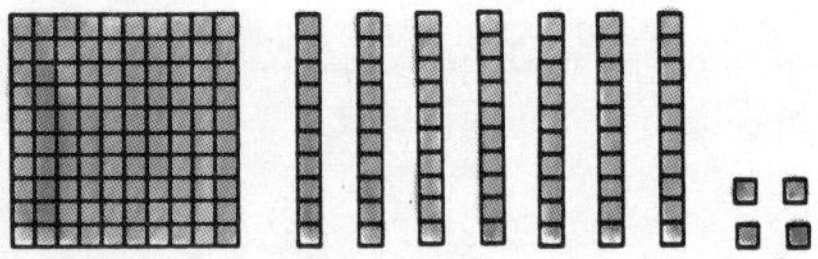

______

____ hundreds ____ tens ____ ones

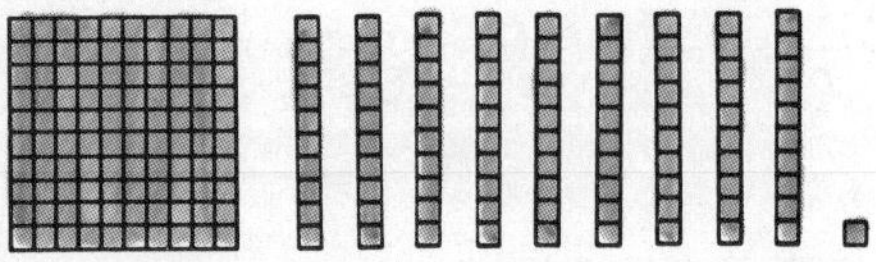

______

____ hundreds ____ tens ____ ones

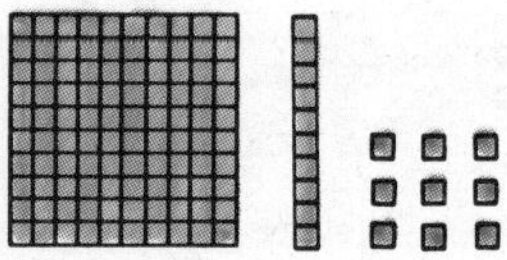

______

____ hundreds ____ tens ____ ones

______

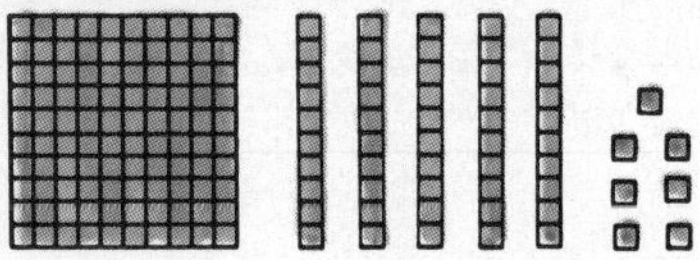

____ hundreds ____ tens ____ ones

______

Name ________________________________

Write the missing numbers.

91									100
				105					
111									
		128							
						137			
			144						150

Write the missing numbers.

94, 95, ____, ____, 98, ____, ____

101, 102, ____, ____, ____, ____, ____, ____

128, 129, ____, ____, ____, 133, ____, ____

FIELD TRIP

Count by tens.

80, 90, ____, ____, ____, ____, ____, ____

Count by fives.

95, 100, ____, ____, ____, ____, ____, ____

Count by twos.

100, 102, 104, 106, ____, ____, ____, ____, ____

Write the missing numbers.

151						157			
		163							
				175					
							188		
			194						200

Write the missing numbers.

161, 162, 163, ____, ____, ____, ____, ____

154, 155, ____, ____, ____, ____, ____, ____

177, 178, ____, ____, ____, ____, ____, ____

148, 149, ____, ____, ____, ____, ____, ____

FIELD TRIP

Count by tens.

100, 110, ____, ____, ____, ____, ____, ____, ____

Count by fives.

150, 155, ____, ____, ____, ____, ____, ____, ____

Count by twos.

160, 162, 164, ____, ____, ____, ____, ____, ____, ____

Name ______________________________

Match the numbers with their names.

forty-four	22	1 hundred 2 tens 2 ones
twenty-two	122	2 tens 2 ones
one hundred forty-four	44	4 tens 4 ones
one hundred twenty-two	103	1 hundred 4 tens 4 ones
one hundred three	144	1 hundred 0 tens 3 ones
seventy-two	35	3 tens 5 ones
thirty-five	72	7 tens 2 ones
one hundred twelve	112	1 hundred 1 ten 2 ones

FIELD TRIP

Find the number in the picture. Color it.

one hundred thirty-four
sixty-three
one hundred ninety-five
ninety-nine
one hundred fifty-five
fifty

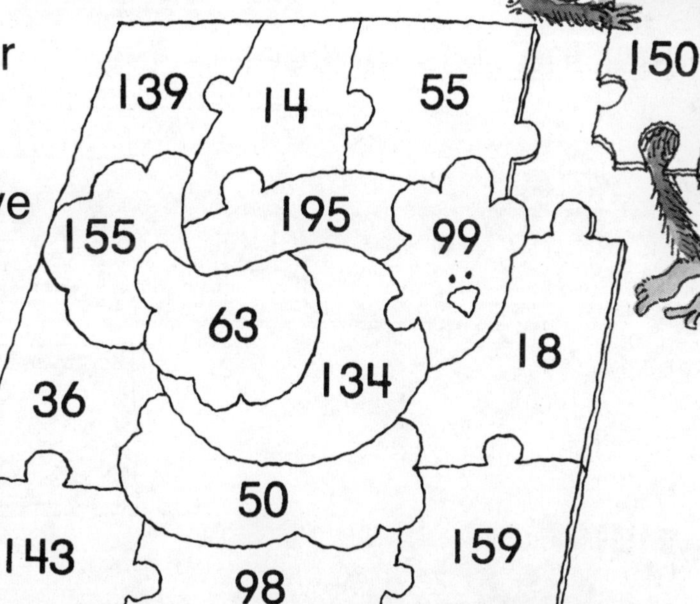

Draw a line to the number before and the number after.

Number Before		Number After
103	101	110
108	104	125
123	109	102
100	124	105
140	137	138
196	141	142
136	168	198
167	197	169

FIELD TRIP

Connect the dots in order.

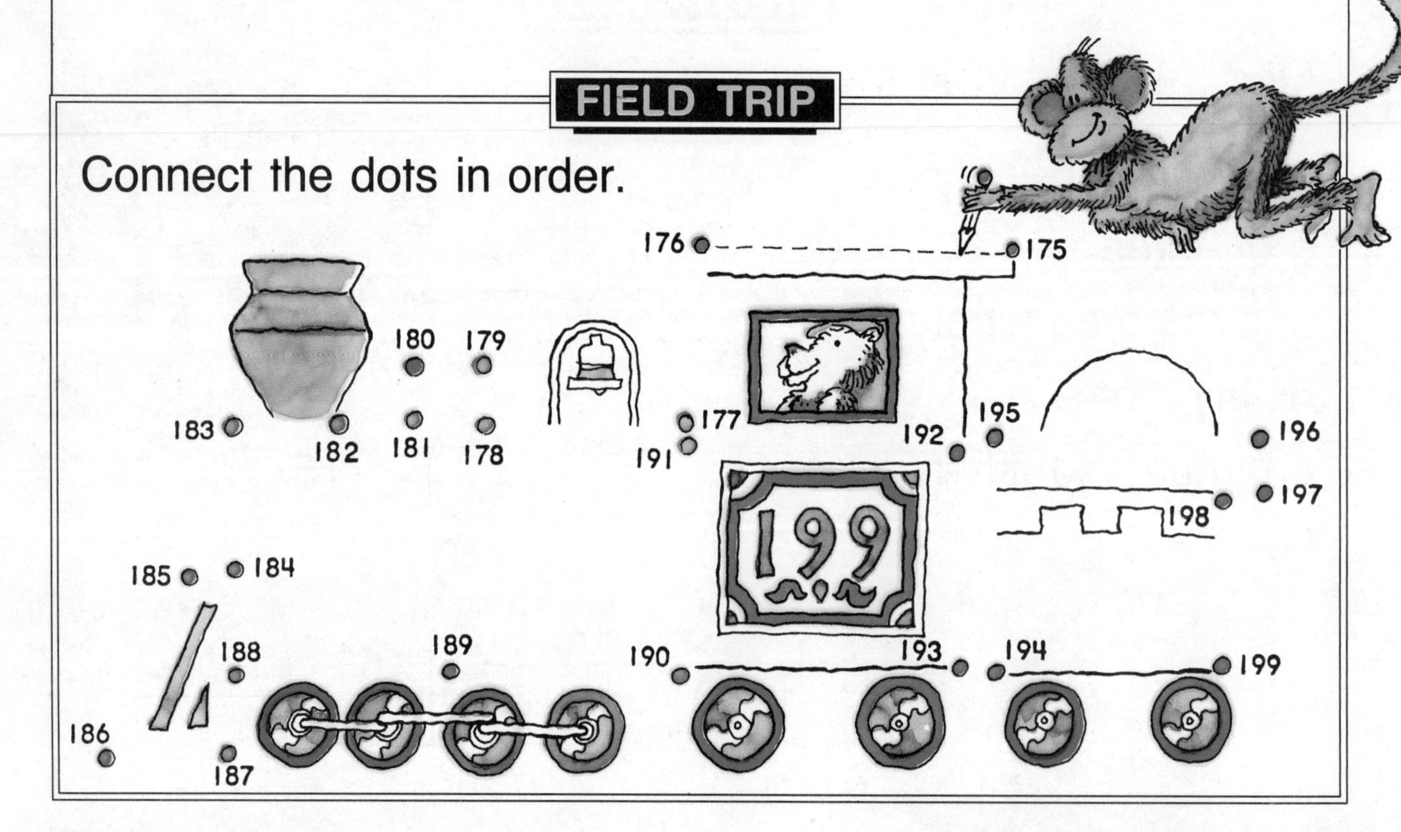

Name ______________________

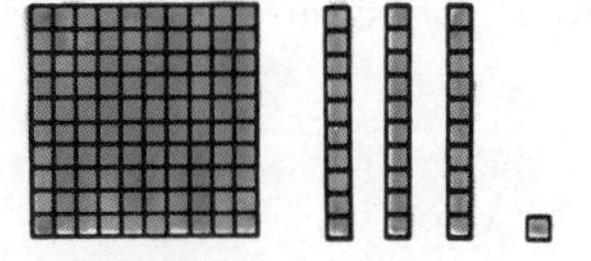

131

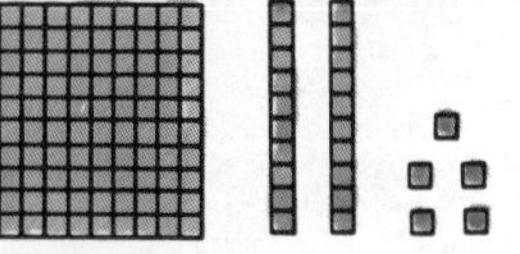

125

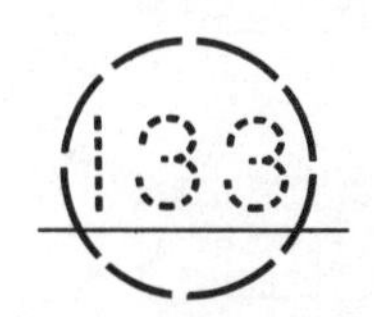

133

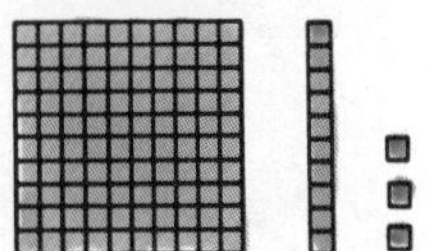

113

How many? Circle the number that is greater.

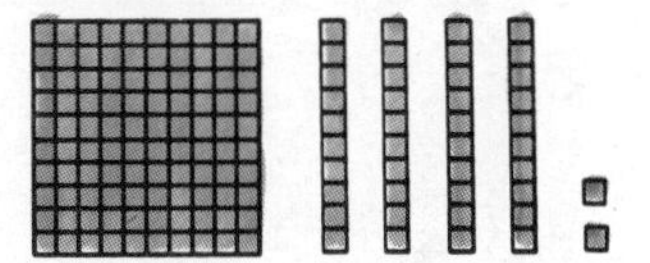

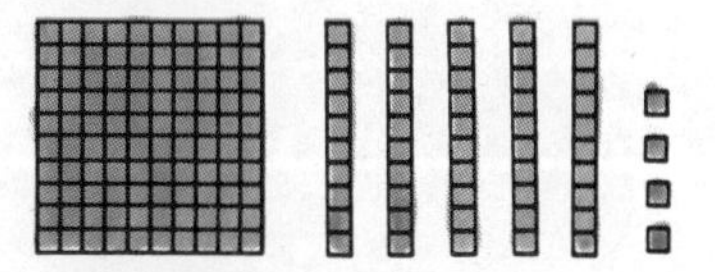

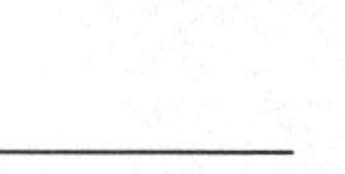

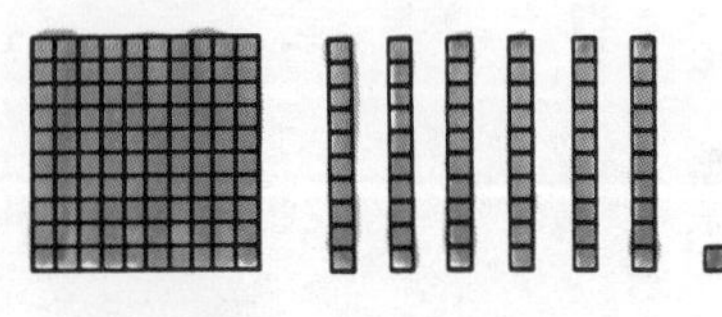

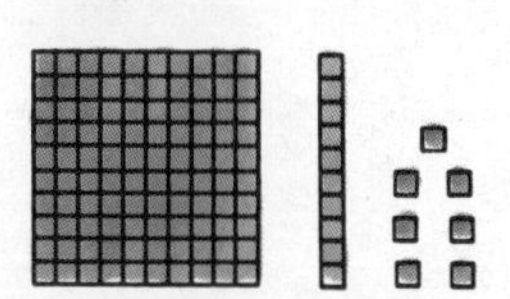

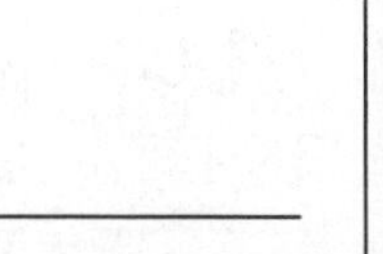

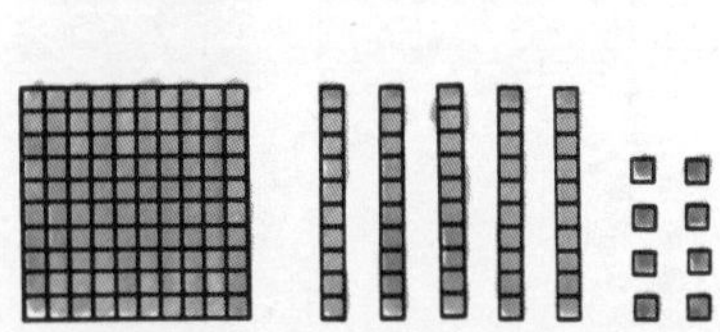

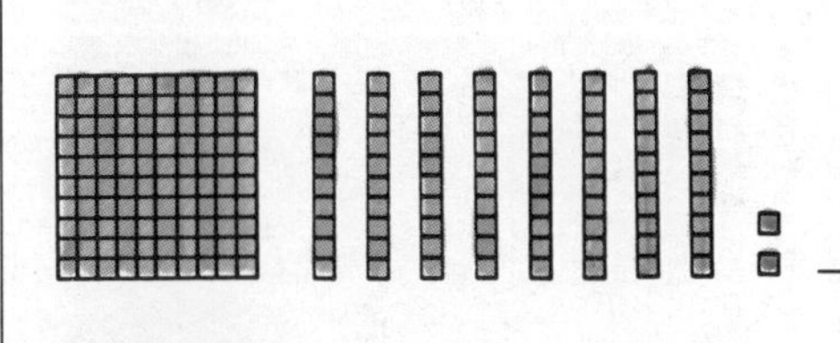

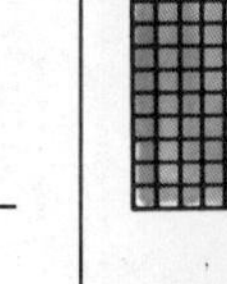

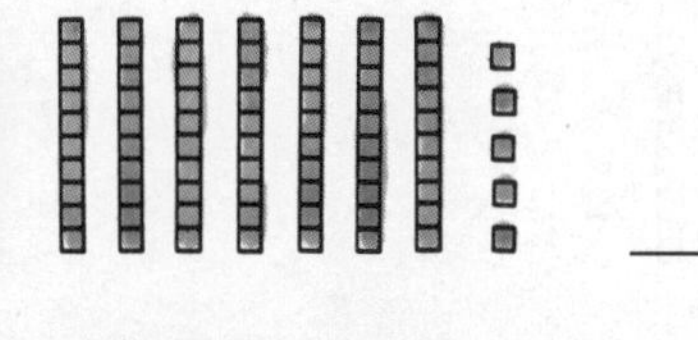

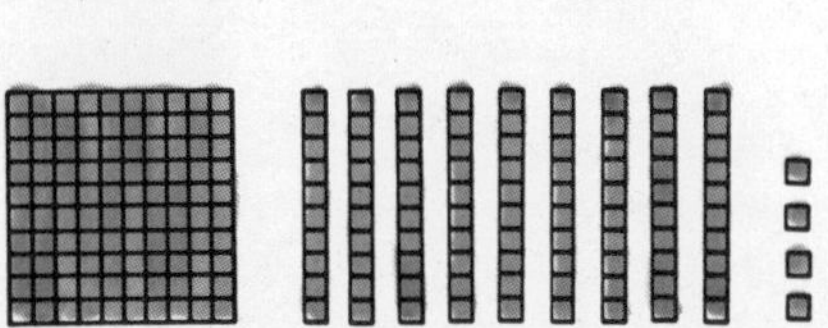

How many? Circle the number that is less.

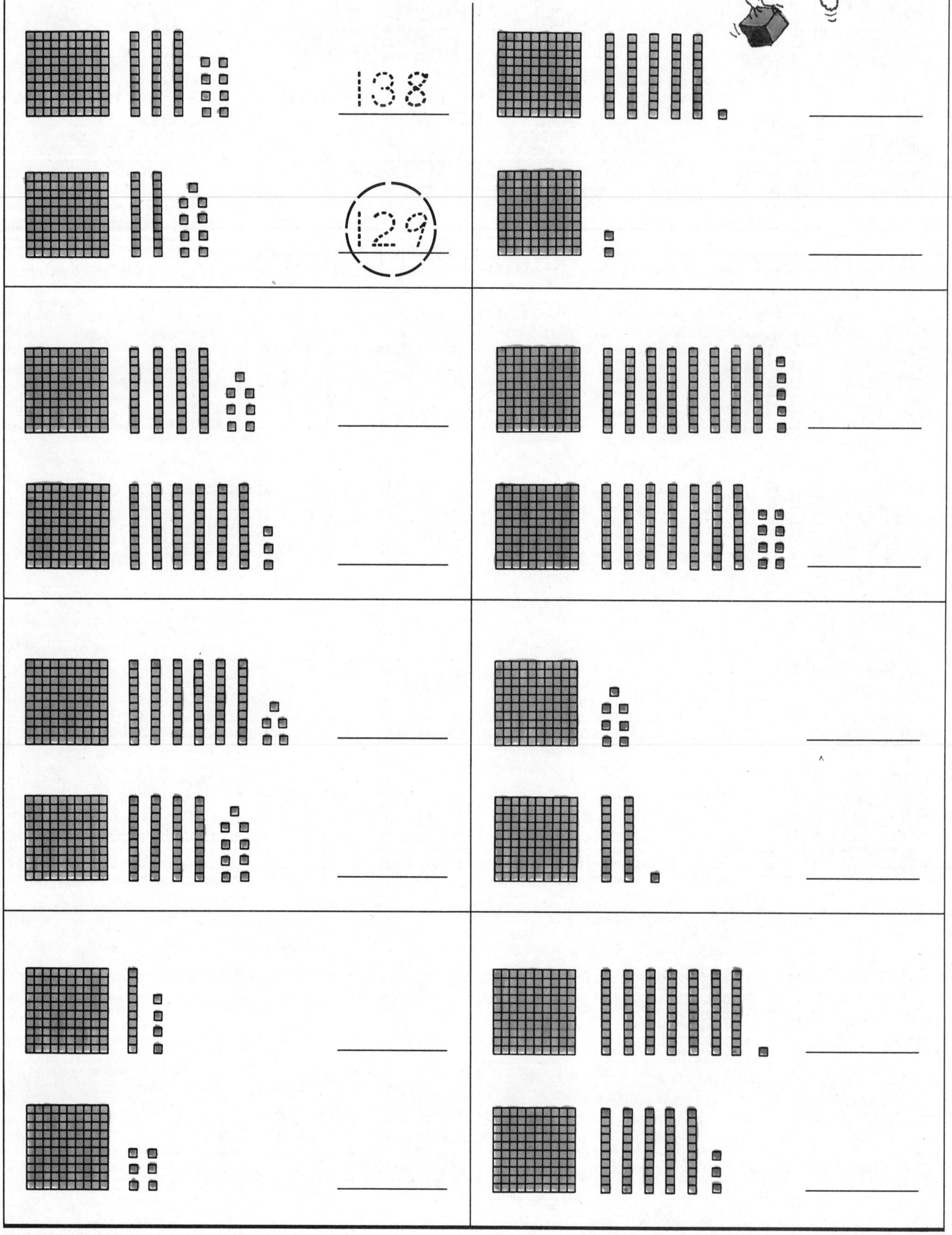

138

(129)

Name ______________________________

10¢	1¢
10	0

100 ¢

$1.00	10¢	1¢
1	0	0

$ 1.00

How much?

$1.00	10¢	1¢

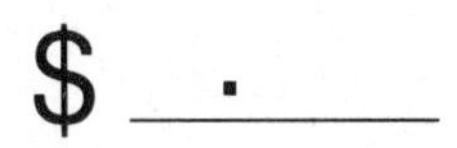

$ ___ . ___

$1.00	10¢	1¢

$ ___ . ___

$1.00	10¢	1¢

$ ___ . ___

$1.00	10¢	1¢

$ ___ . ___

How much?

$1.00	10¢	1¢

$ ___.___

$1.00	10¢	1¢

$ ___.___

$1.00	10¢	1¢

$ ___.___

$1.00	10¢	1¢

$ ___.___

$1.00	10¢	1¢

$ ___.___

Name ______________________________

How many points does each child have?

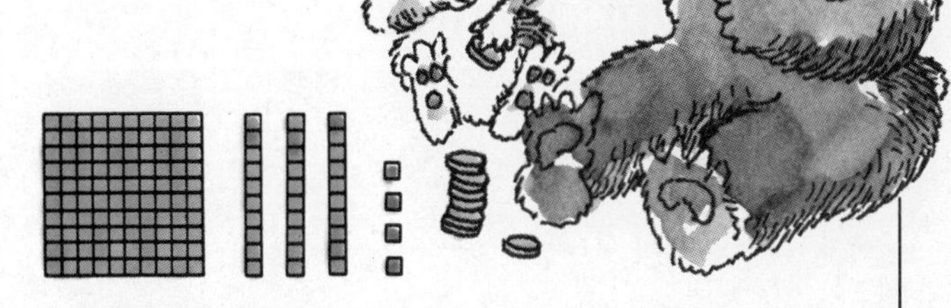

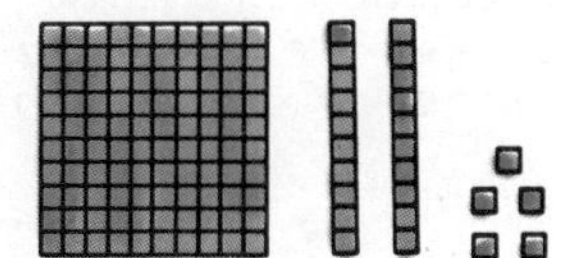

Al has ______.

Tina has ______.

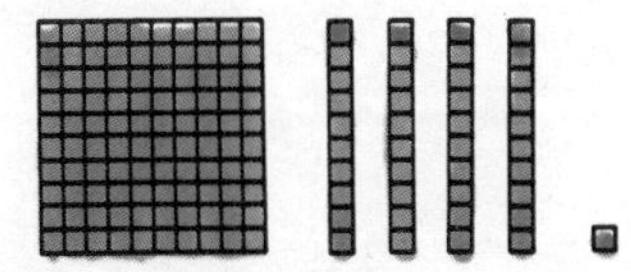

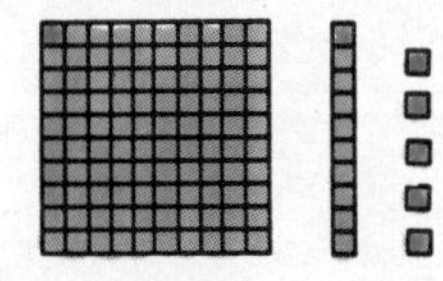

Lin has ______.

Donna has ______.

Who has more? ______.

Who has more? ______.

How much money does each child have?

Carol has $ __.____.

Scott has $ __.____.

Ling has $ __.____.

Chip has $ __.____.

Who has more? ______

Who has more? ______

Write the missing numbers before and after.

28, 29, 30

_____, 129, _____

_____, 99, _____

_____, 199, _____

_____, 100, _____

_____, 148, _____

_____, 169, _____

_____, 151, _____

_____, 110, _____

_____, 119, _____

Write the missing numbers.

46, 47, 48, 49

146, _____, _____, 149

83, _____, _____, 86

183, _____, _____, 186

129, _____, _____, 132

197, _____, _____, 200

160, _____, _____, 163

103, _____, _____, 106

112, _____, _____, 115

169, _____, _____, 172

FIELD TRIP

Count by tens.

10, 20, 30, _____, _____, _____, _____, 80

90, _____, _____, _____, _____, 140, _____

160, _____, _____, _____, _____

Name ______

CHAPTER CHECKUP

How many?

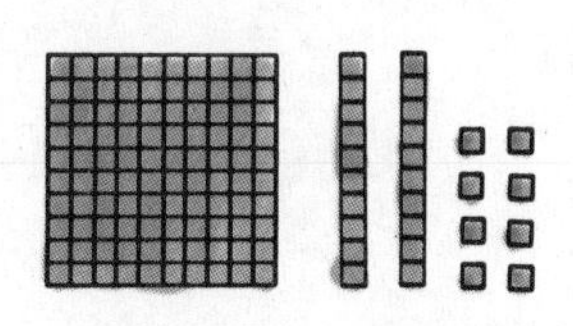

hundreds	tens	ones

______

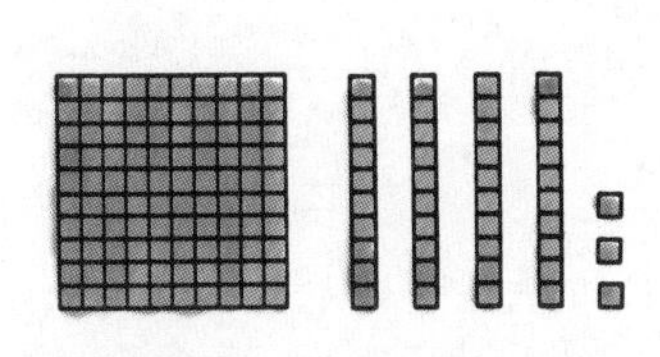

hundreds	tens	ones

______

Write the missing numbers.

96, 97, 98, ______, ______, ______, ______, ______

105, 106, 107, ______, ______, ______, ______, ______

173, 174, 175, ______, ______, ______, ______, ______

______, 107, 108, ______

136, 137, ______, ______, 140

______, 198, 199, ______

110, 111, ______, ______, 114

How much money?

	\$1.00	10¢	1¢
\$			

\$ ___ . ___

ROUNDUP REVIEW

Add or subtract.

$$\begin{array}{r} 5 \\ +5 \\ \hline \end{array} \quad \begin{array}{r} 6 \\ +6 \\ \hline \end{array} \quad \begin{array}{r} 7 \\ +7 \\ \hline \end{array} \quad \begin{array}{r} 8 \\ +8 \\ \hline \end{array} \quad \begin{array}{r} 9 \\ +9 \\ \hline \end{array} \quad \begin{array}{r} 10 \\ -\ 3 \\ \hline \end{array} \quad \begin{array}{r} 12 \\ -\ 5 \\ \hline \end{array}$$

$$\begin{array}{r} 15 \\ -\ 8 \\ \hline \end{array} \quad \begin{array}{r} 14 \\ -\ 9 \\ \hline \end{array} \quad \begin{array}{r} 12 \\ -\ 7 \\ \hline \end{array} \quad \begin{array}{r} 7 \\ +8 \\ \hline \end{array} \quad \begin{array}{r} 9 \\ +5 \\ \hline \end{array} \quad \begin{array}{r} 13 \\ -\ 4 \\ \hline \end{array} \quad \begin{array}{r} 17 \\ -\ 8 \\ \hline \end{array}$$

Add.

	tens	ones
	3	4
+		3

	tens	ones
	4	6
+		7

Subtract.

	tens	ones
	2	8
−		5

	tens	ones
	5	1
−		7

Name ______________________________

13 ADDITION, 2-DIGIT NUMBERS

Add. Trade if needed.

	tens	ones
	2	4
+		5
	2	9

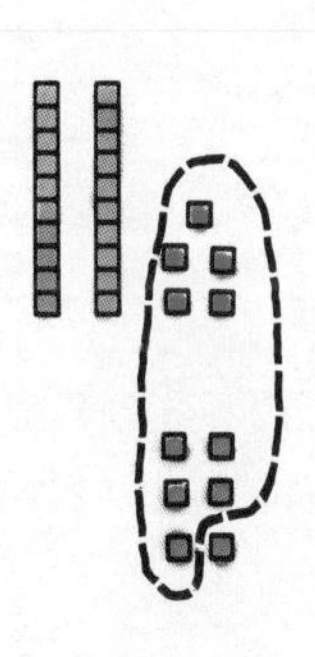

	tens	ones
	1	
	2	5
+		6
	3	1

	tens	ones
	7	3
+		4

	tens	ones
	4	6
+		8

	tens	ones
	6	4
+		9

	tens	ones
	8	2
+		8

Add. Trade if needed.

	tens	ones
	1	
	5	6
+		7
	6	3

	tens	ones
	3	8
+		7

	tens	ones
	1	6
+		9

	tens	ones
	3	2
+		6

	tens	ones
	6	5
+		5

	tens	ones
	2	7
+		6

	tens	ones
	7	3
+		9

	tens	ones
	5	6
+		5

	tens	ones
	9	1
+		7

	tens	ones
	4	7
+		8

	tens	ones
	2	9
+		5

	tens	ones
	4	9
+		8

Name ______________________________

How many ones? $2 + 3 =$ 5

Is a trade needed? No

How many tens? $4 + 2 =$ 6

	tens	ones
	4	2
+	2	3
	6	5

How many ones? $6 + 5 =$ 11

Is a trade needed? Yes

11 ones = 1 ten 1 one

How many tens? 1 $+ 3 + 5 =$ 9

	tens	ones
	1	
	3	6
+	5	5
	9	1

Add. Trade if needed.

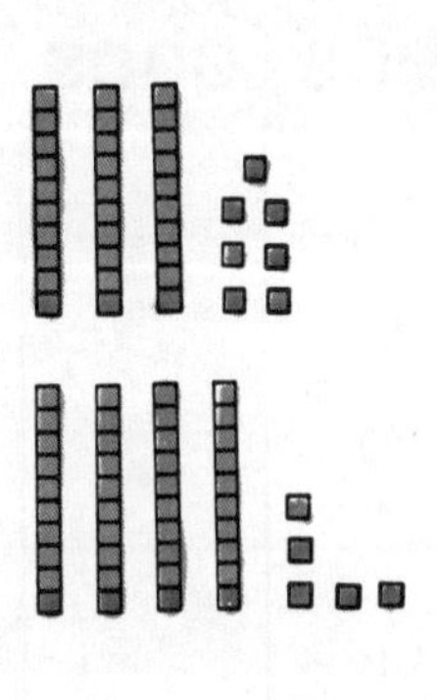

	tens	ones
	3	7
+	4	5

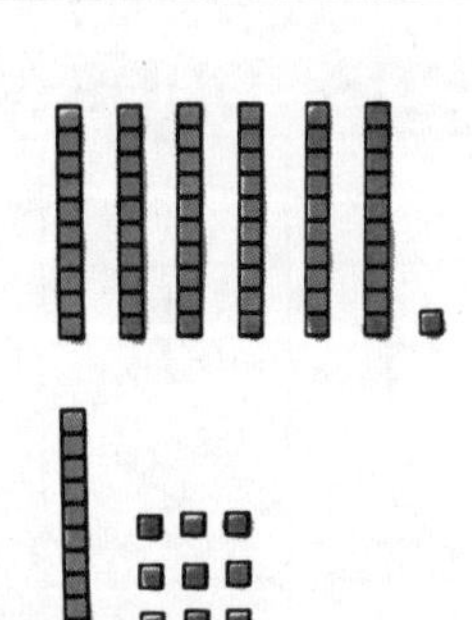

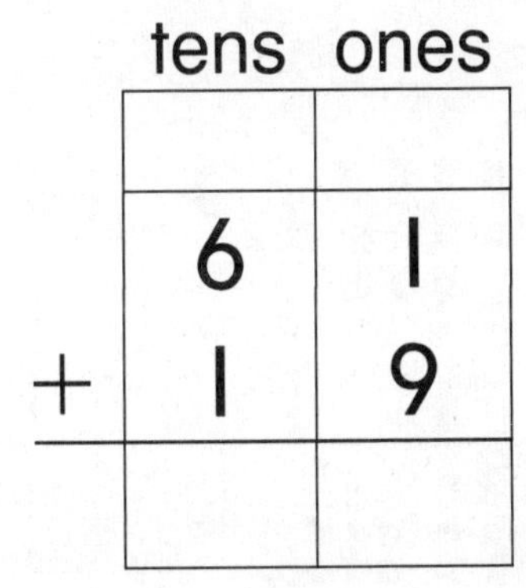

	tens	ones
	6	1
+	1	9

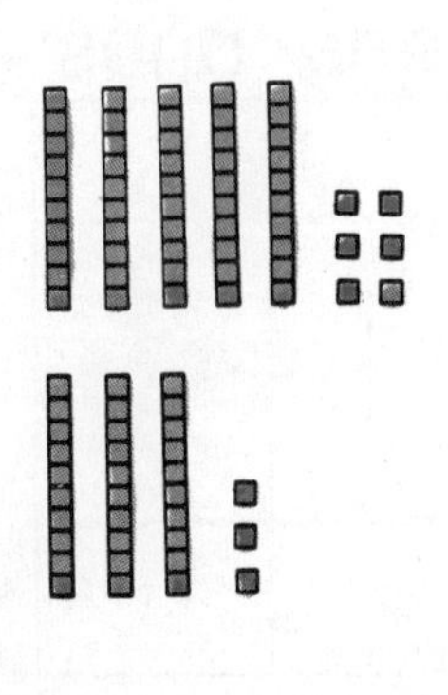

	tens	ones
	5	6
+	3	3

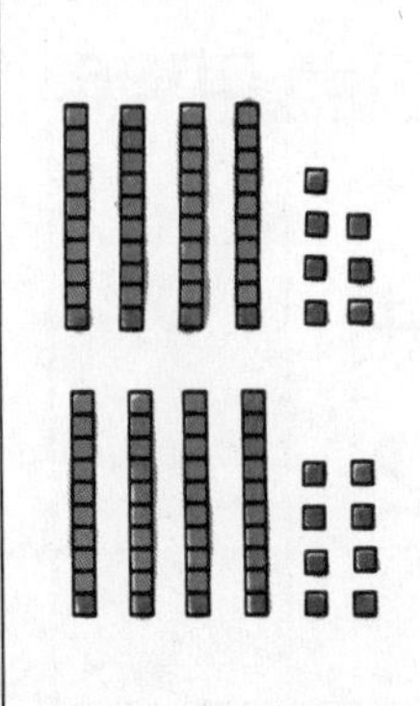

	tens	ones
	4	7
+	4	8

Add. Trade if needed.

	tens	ones
	3	4
+	4	3

	tens	ones
	1	3
+	2	9

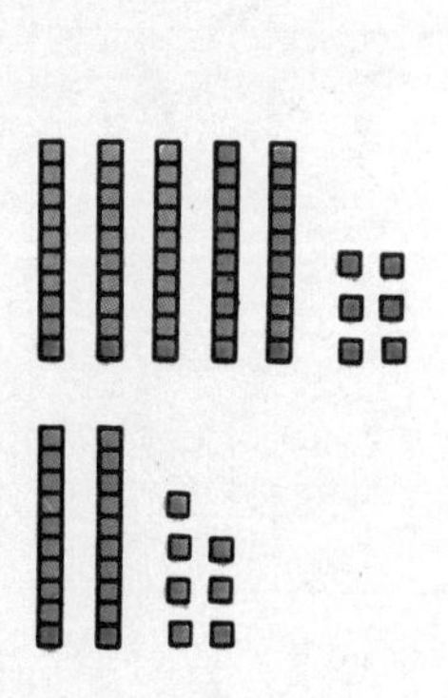

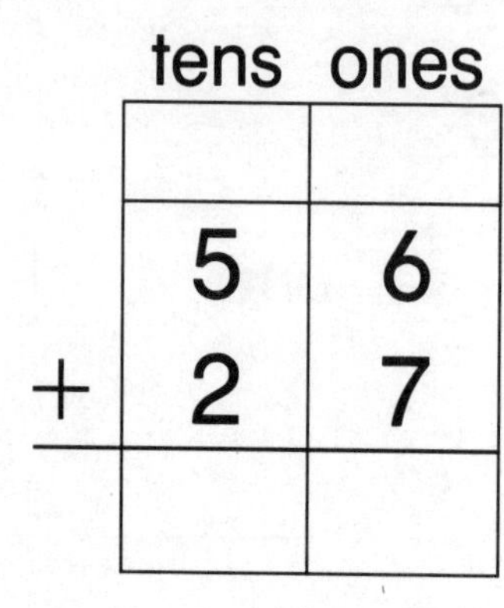

	tens	ones
	5	6
+	2	7

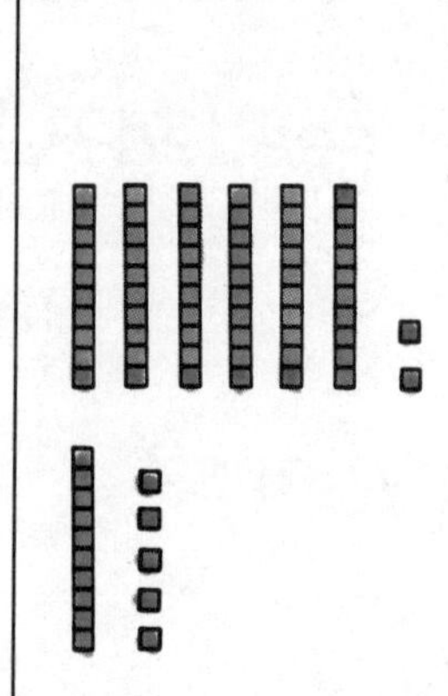

	tens	ones
	6	2
+	1	5

	tens	ones
	4	7
+	2	9

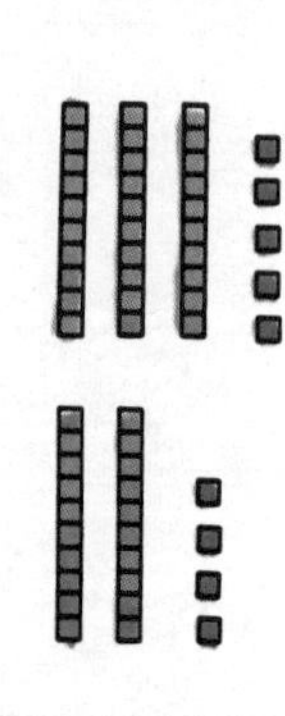

	tens	ones
	3	5
+	2	4

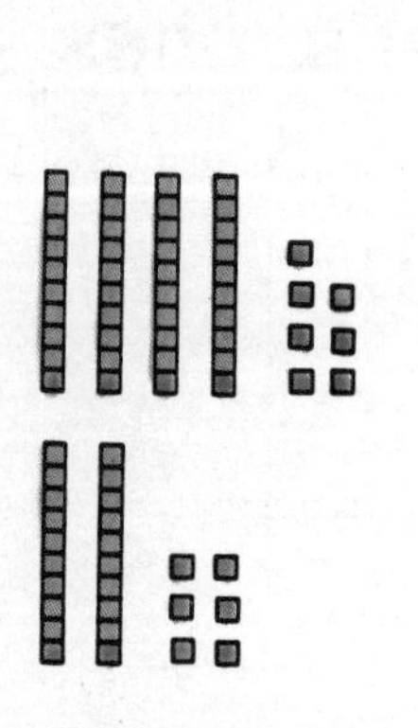

	tens	ones
	4	7
+	2	6

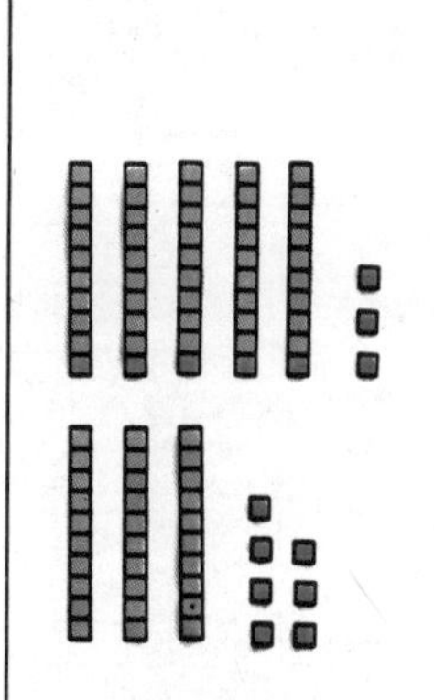

	tens	ones
	5	3
+	3	7

Name ______________________________

Add the ones first. Trade if needed.

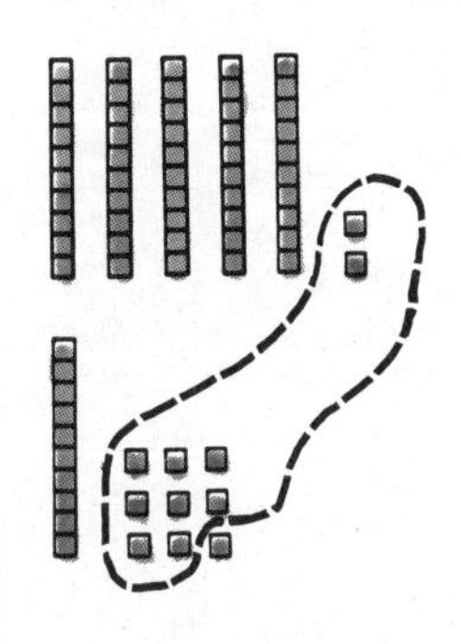

	tens	ones
	1	
	5	2
+	1	9
	7	1

	tens	ones
	8	7
+	1	2

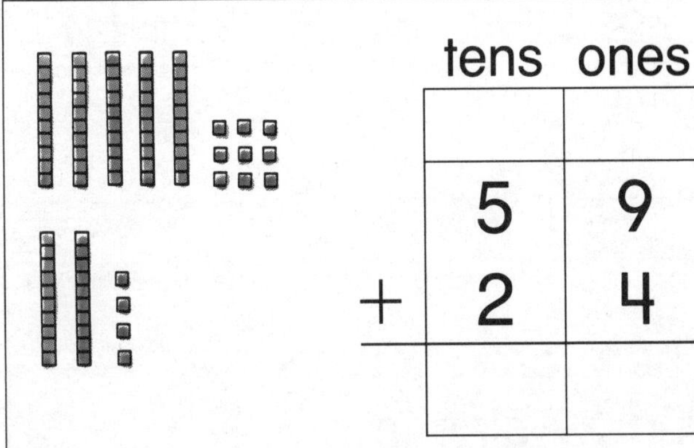

	tens	ones
	5	9
+	2	4

	tens	ones
	3	8
+	4	9

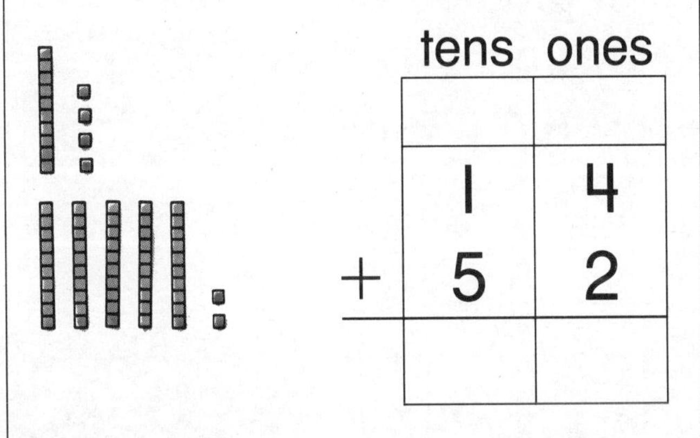

	tens	ones
	1	4
+	5	2

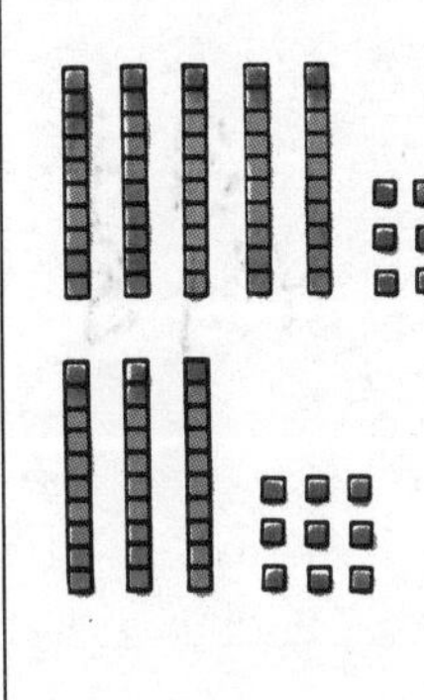

	tens	ones
	5	6
+	3	9

$$\begin{array}{r} 23 \\ +62 \\ \hline \end{array} \quad \begin{array}{r} 44 \\ +37 \\ \hline \end{array} \quad \begin{array}{r} 34 \\ +48 \\ \hline \end{array} \quad \begin{array}{r} 61 \\ +28 \\ \hline \end{array} \quad \begin{array}{r} 55 \\ +25 \\ \hline \end{array} \quad \begin{array}{r} 76 \\ +16 \\ \hline \end{array}$$

Add the ones first. Trade if needed.

81	24	45	79	56	29
+17	+29	+52	+15	+24	+42

27	48	36	59	69	42
+31	+37	+33	+21	+26	+17

Solve.

The top shelf holds 34 books. The next shelf holds 48. How many books are there in all?

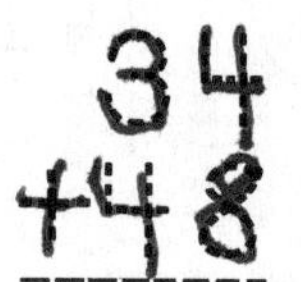

____ books

There are 25 boys and 29 girls in first grade. How many children are there in all?

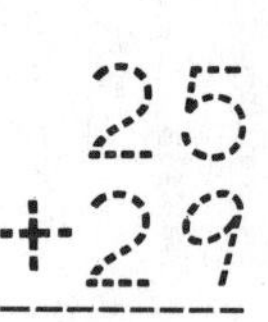

____ children

Ruth has 38 brown marbles and 37 red ones. How many does she have in all?

____ marbles

Gary had 47 baseball cards. He bought 24 more. How many does he have in all?

____ cards

Name ____

	tens	ones
	7	0
+	4	0
	11	0

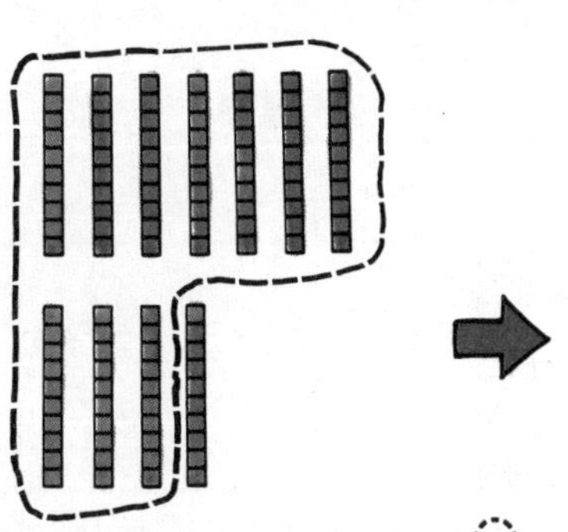

	hundreds	tens	ones
	1		
		7	0
+		4	0
	1	1	0

How many ones? $0 + 0 =$ 0

How many tens? $7 + 4 =$ 11 Is a trade needed? Yes

11 tens = 1 hundred 1 ten

1 hundred 1 ten 0 ones = 110

Add. Trade 10 tens for 1 hundred.

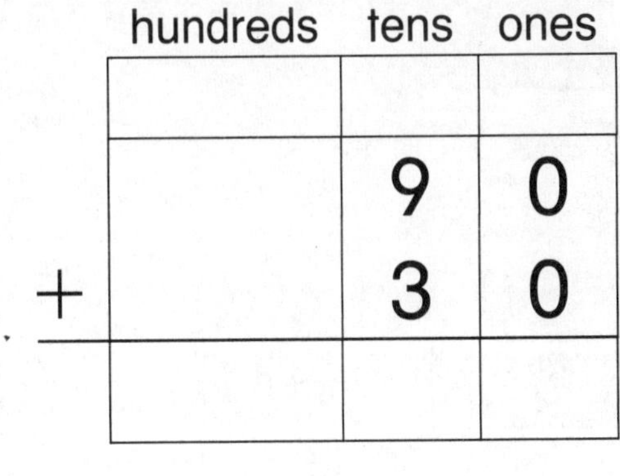

	hundreds	tens	ones
		9	0
+		3	0

____ hundreds ____ tens ____ ones = ______

	hundreds	tens	ones
		8	0
+		7	0

____ hundreds ____ tens ____ ones = ______

Add. Trade 10 tens for 1 hundred.

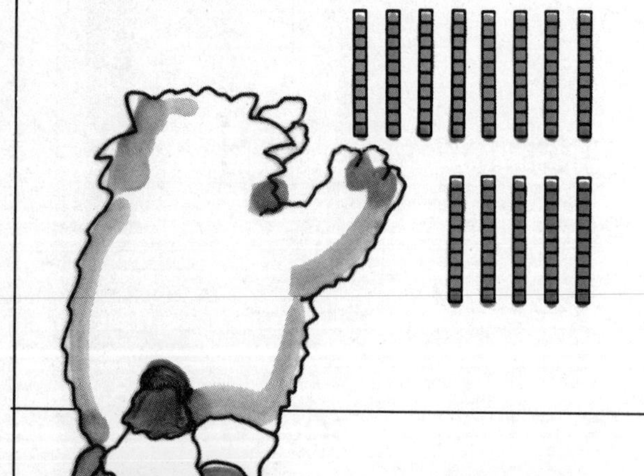

	hundreds	tens	ones
		8	0
+		5	0

______

	hundreds	tens	ones
		5	0
+		9	0

______

50	90	60	20	90	40
+80	+70	+50	+90	+90	+80
130	160				

70	80	10	30	50	60
+80	+50	+90	+80	+70	+90

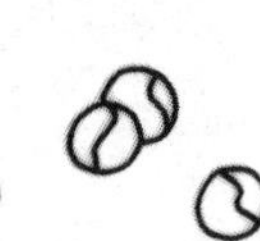

Name ____________________

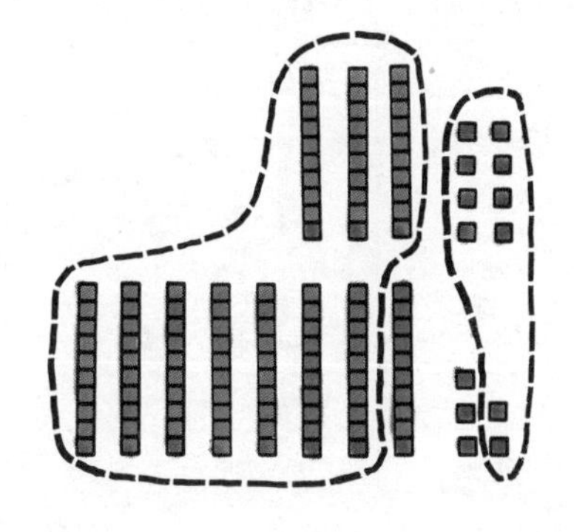

	hundreds	tens	ones
	1	1	
		3	8
+		8	5
	1	2	3

123

How many ones? 8 + 5 = 13

13 ones = 1 ten 3 ones

How many tens? 1 + 3 + 8 = 12

12 tens = 1 hundred 2 tens

Add. Trade where needed.

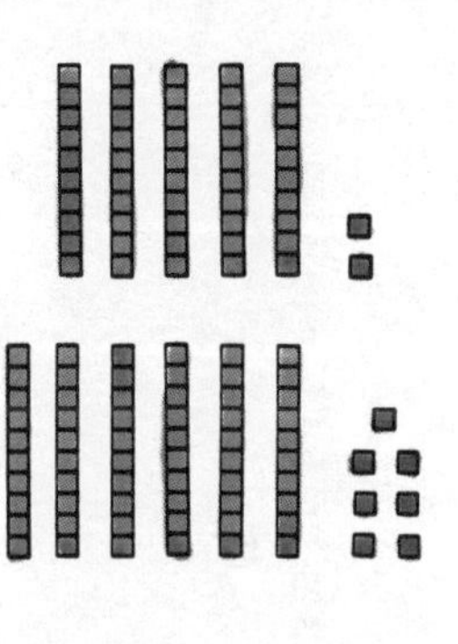

	hundreds	tens	ones
		5	2
+		6	7

____

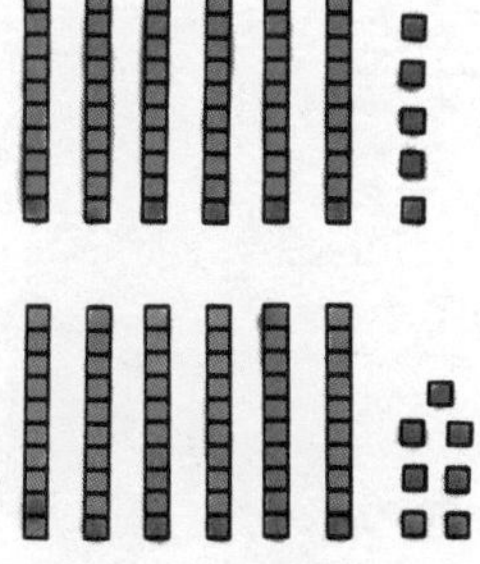

	hundreds	tens	ones
		6	5
+		6	7

____

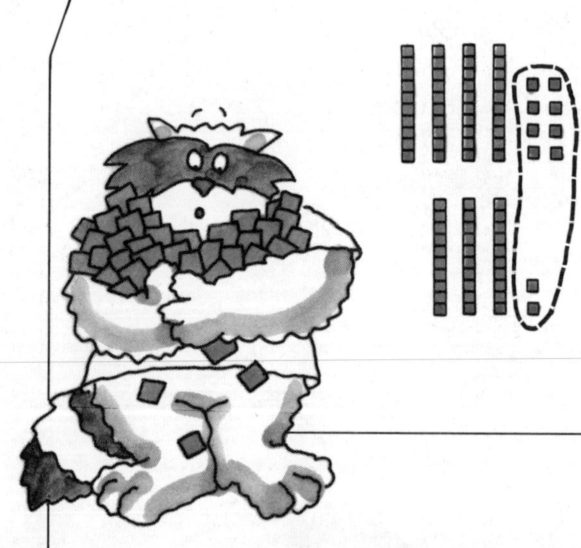

hundreds	tens	ones
	1	
	4	8
+	3	2
	8	0

80

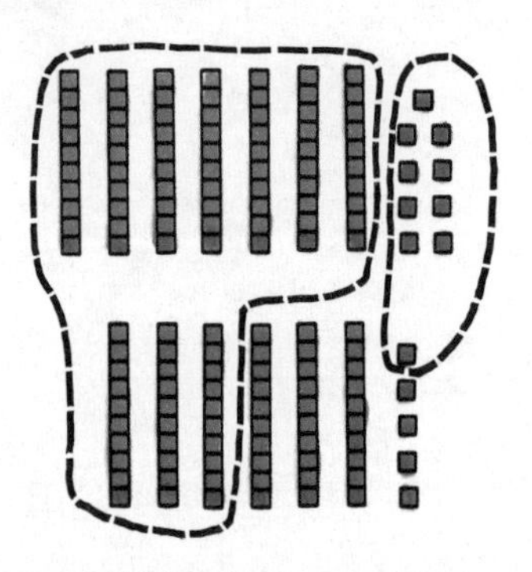

hundreds	tens	ones
1	1	
	7	9
+	6	5
1	4	4

144

Add. Trade where needed.

75	48	49	91	65	49
+62	+76	+72	+35	+65	+66
137	124				

99	57	93	35	83	99
+91	+57	+ 9	+85	+44	+99

Name ______________________

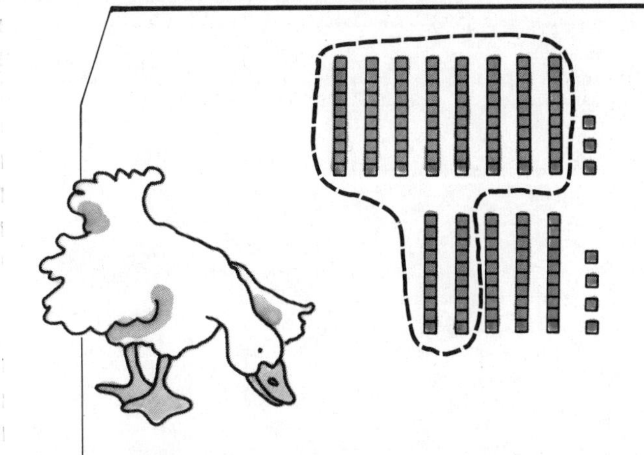

	hundreds	tens	ones
	1		
		8	3
+		5	4
	1	3	7

137

Add. Trade where needed.

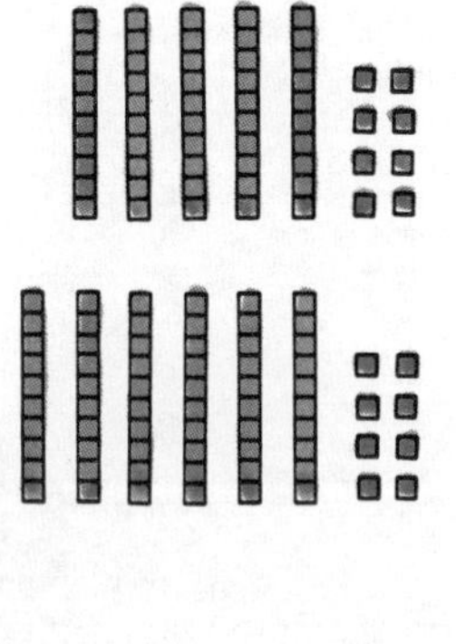

	hundreds	tens	ones
		5	8
+		6	8

______

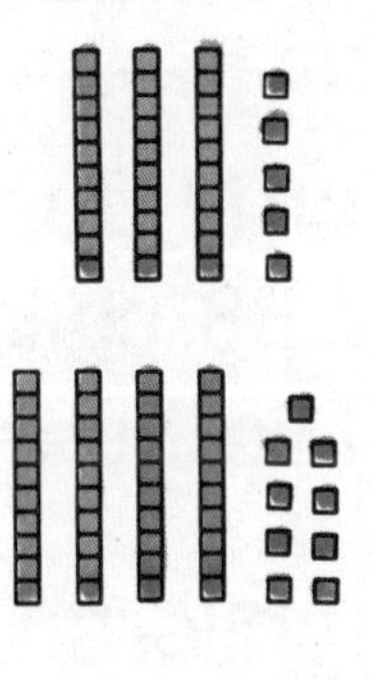

	hundreds	tens	ones
		3	5
+		4	9

______

1 46 +34 80	1 97 +64 161	83 +26	74 +56	66 +86	88 +88

	hundreds	tens	ones
	1	1	
		6	2
+		4	8
	1	1	0

110

Add. Trade where needed.

$$\begin{array}{r} 75 \\ +75 \\ \hline \end{array} \quad \begin{array}{r} 86 \\ +47 \\ \hline \end{array} \quad \begin{array}{r} 93 \\ +84 \\ \hline \end{array} \quad \begin{array}{r} 66 \\ +75 \\ \hline \end{array} \quad \begin{array}{r} 91 \\ +93 \\ \hline \end{array} \quad \begin{array}{r} 88 \\ +88 \\ \hline \end{array}$$

Solve.

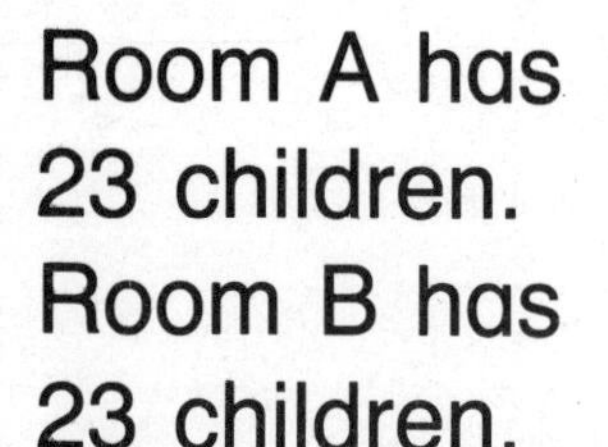

Room A has
23 children.
Room B has
23 children.
There are ____
children in all.

$$\begin{array}{r} 23 \\ +23 \\ \hline \end{array}$$

The red bus holds
45 children.
The gray bus
holds 38 children.
The two buses hold

____ children.

Angie hopped
29 times.
Lu hopped
28 times.
The two girls

hopped ____ times.

The first recess
is 38 minutes long.
The second recess
is 46 minutes long.
The two recesses

are ____ minutes long.

Name ______________________________

$1.00	10¢	1¢	
1	1		
	5	6	¢
+	6	5	¢
1	2	1	¢

How many pennies? 6 + 5 = 11

11 pennies = 1 dime 1 penny

How many dimes? 1 + 5 + 6 = 12

12 dimes = 1 dollar 2 dimes

121 ¢ = $ 1.21

Add. Trade where needed.

$1.00	10¢	1¢	
	7	2	¢
+	5	3	¢
			¢

_____ ¢ = $ ___.___

$1.00	10¢	1¢	
	8	5	¢
+	2	5	¢
			¢

_____ ¢ = $ ___.___

$1.00	10¢	1¢	
	4	5	¢
+	6	7	¢
			¢

_____ ¢ = $ ___.___

$1.00	10¢	1¢	
	8	8	¢
+	3	4	¢
			¢

_____ ¢ = $ ___.___

Add. Trade where needed.

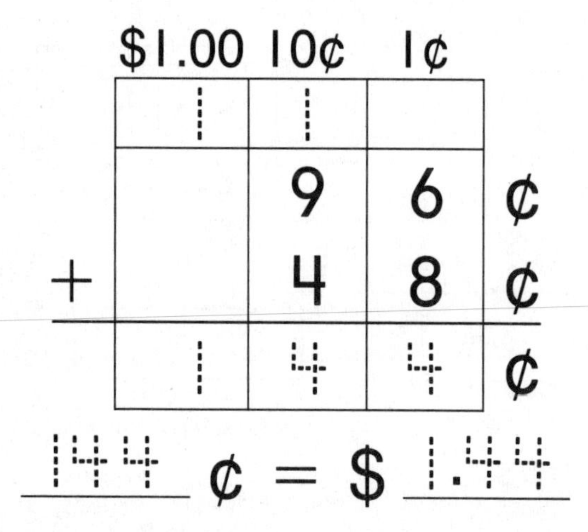

	$1.00	10¢	1¢	
		8	5	¢
+		7	6	¢
				¢

_____ ¢ = $ ___.___

91 ¢	65 ¢	87 ¢	59 ¢	77 ¢
+83 ¢	+75 ¢	+38 ¢	+64 ¢	+25 ¢
¢	¢	¢	¢	¢
$ ___.___	$ ___.___	$ ___.___	$ ___.___	$ ___.___

Solve.

Sal spent 85¢ for his movie ticket and 45¢ for a fruit roll.

85 ¢
+45 ¢
¢

Sal spent $ ___.___.

Wayne bought a 

and a 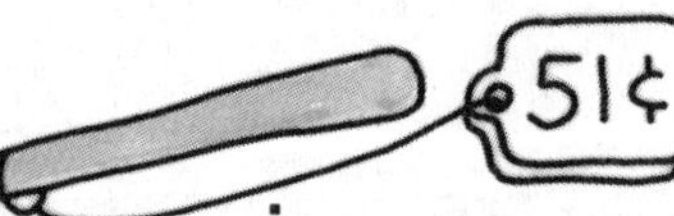

.

48 ¢
+51 ¢
¢

_____ ¢ = $ ___.___

Wayne spent $ ___.___.

Name ____________________

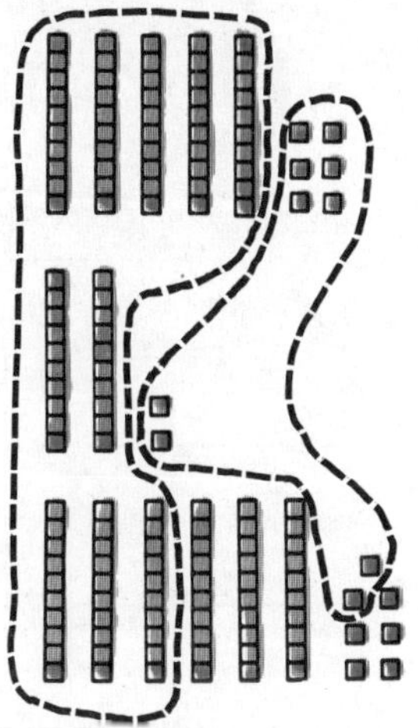

	hundreds	tens	ones
	1	1	
		5	6
		2	2
+		6	7
	1	4	5

145

How many ones? 6 + 2 + 7 = 15

15 ones = 1 ten 5 ones

How many tens? 1 + 5 + 2 + 6 = 14

14 tens = 1 hundred 4 tens

Add. Trade where needed.

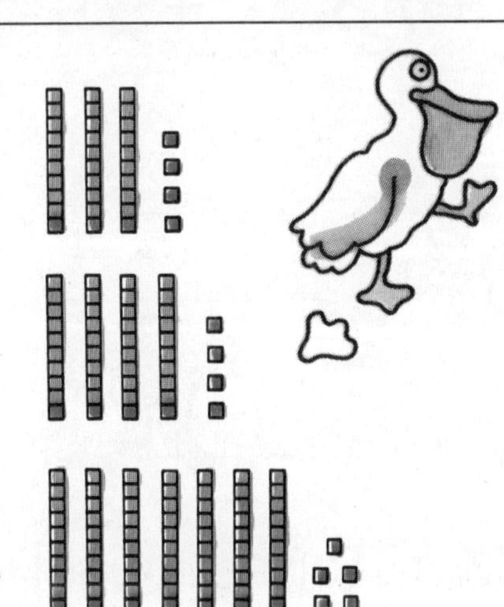

	hundreds	tens	ones
		3	4
		4	4
+		7	5

______

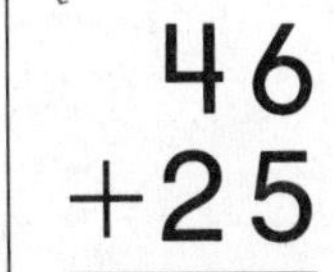

$\begin{array}{r} 46 \\ +25 \\ \hline \end{array}$ $\begin{array}{r} 72 \\ +84 \\ \hline \end{array}$ $\begin{array}{r} 68 \\ +32 \\ \hline \end{array}$ $\begin{array}{r} 54 \\ +63 \\ \hline \end{array}$ $\begin{array}{r} 85 \\ +69 \\ \hline \end{array}$ $\begin{array}{r} 36 \\ +78 \\ \hline \end{array}$

Add. Trade where needed.

	hundreds	tens	ones
		3	5
		4	5
+		7	9

	hundreds	tens	ones
		8	2
		6	7
+		2	9

$$\begin{array}{r} 41 \\ 33 \\ +25 \\ \hline \end{array} \quad \begin{array}{r} 43 \\ 31 \\ +32 \\ \hline \end{array} \quad \begin{array}{r} 45 \\ 54 \\ +36 \\ \hline \end{array} \quad \begin{array}{r} 55 \\ 21 \\ +73 \\ \hline \end{array} \quad \begin{array}{r} 34 \\ 44 \\ +54 \\ \hline \end{array} \quad \begin{array}{r} 82 \\ 64 \\ +24 \\ \hline \end{array}$$

Solve.

Li swam these races:
60 yard race
45 yard race
50 yard race
Li raced ______ yards.

Mrs. Torres taught three classes:
42 children for music
27 children for math
64 children for gym
Mrs. Torres taught ______ children.

Name ____________________

Add. Trade if needed.

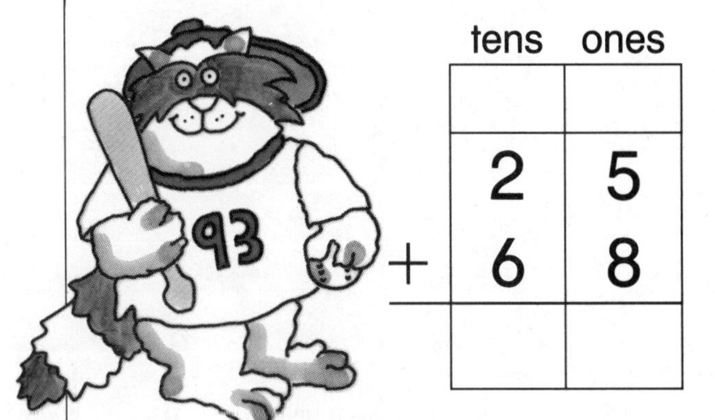

	tens	ones
	2	5
+	6	8

	hundreds	tens	ones
		7	8
+		5	7

$40 + 30$	$56 + 27$	$37 + 46$
$49 + 94$	$60 + 70$	$62 + 55$

$96 + 96$	$53 + 85$	$67 + 35$	$58 + 42$	$45 + 82$	$94 + 46$
$44 + 78$	$97 + 91$	$55 + 55$	$93 + 66$	$88 + 88$	$69 + 75$
$38 + 9$	$34 + 63$	$78 + 19$	$66 + 88$	$37 + 91$	$55 + 77$

Solve.

Ellen bought 53¢ and 75¢.

Ellen spent 128 ¢ or $ 1.28.

	53¢
+	75¢
	128¢

Rita has 48 marbles. Wanda has 67 marbles. How many in all?

They have ______ marbles in all.

Craig bought a 59¢ and a 85¢.
How much did Craig spend?

Craig spent ______ ¢ or $ ___.___.

Lon hopped 37 times
on his left foot.
He hopped 63 times
on his right foot.
How many times
did Lon hop?

Lon hopped ______ times.

Adam jumped
a rope 57 times.
Then he jumped
65 more times.
Adam jumped rope

______ times.

Royce likes to read.

Monday–43 minutes
Tuesday–45 minutes
Wednesday–37 minutes

Royce read for ______ minutes.

Name ____________________

CHAPTER CHECKUP

Add.

	tens	ones
	4	5
+		9

$\begin{array}{r} 52 \\ +\ \ 8 \\ \hline \end{array}$ $\begin{array}{r} 47 \\ +\ \ 6 \\ \hline \end{array}$ $\begin{array}{r} 60¢ \\ +30¢ \\ \hline ¢ \end{array}$ $\begin{array}{r} 50 \\ +20 \\ \hline \end{array}$

	tens	ones
	3	7
+	4	6

$\begin{array}{r} 28 \\ +45 \\ \hline \end{array}$ $\begin{array}{r} 37 \\ +57 \\ \hline \end{array}$ $\begin{array}{r} 12 \\ +29 \\ \hline \end{array}$ $\begin{array}{r} 71¢ \\ +28¢ \\ \hline ¢ \end{array}$

$\begin{array}{r} 85 \\ +36 \\ \hline \end{array}$ $\begin{array}{r} 94 \\ +17 \\ \hline \end{array}$ $\begin{array}{r} 68¢ \\ +54¢ \\ \hline ¢ \end{array}$ $\begin{array}{r} 37 \\ +97 \\ \hline \end{array}$ $\begin{array}{r} 38 \\ 41 \\ +67 \\ \hline \end{array}$ $\begin{array}{r} 53 \\ 36 \\ +48 \\ \hline \end{array}$

Solve.

Janis counted the pets in her neighborhood:
24 cats, 32 dogs and 15 hamsters.
How many in all?

____ pets

ROUNDUP REVIEW

Add or subtract.

$\begin{array}{r} 5 \\ +6 \\ \hline \end{array}$ $\begin{array}{r} 3 \\ +8 \\ \hline \end{array}$ $\begin{array}{r} 9 \\ -4 \\ \hline \end{array}$ $\begin{array}{r} 12 \\ -\ 5 \\ \hline \end{array}$ $\begin{array}{r} 13 \\ -\ 7 \\ \hline \end{array}$ $\begin{array}{r} 7 \\ +8 \\ \hline \end{array}$ $\begin{array}{r} 14 \\ -\ 6 \\ \hline \end{array}$

$\begin{array}{r} 15 \\ -\ 6 \\ \hline \end{array}$ $\begin{array}{r} 8 \\ +8 \\ \hline \end{array}$ $\begin{array}{r} 9 \\ +8 \\ \hline \end{array}$ $\begin{array}{r} 13 \\ -\ 4 \\ \hline \end{array}$ $\begin{array}{r} 8 \\ -3 \\ \hline \end{array}$ $\begin{array}{r} 7 \\ +7 \\ \hline \end{array}$ $\begin{array}{r} 4 \\ +9 \\ \hline \end{array}$

Write the missing number.

105, 106, ____, ____, ____, ____, ____, ____

Subtract.

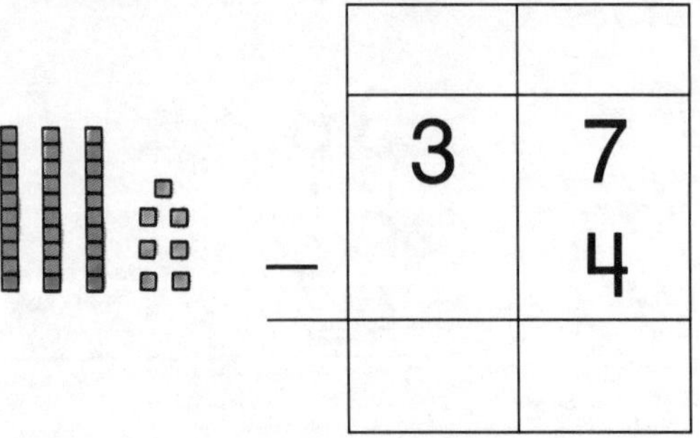

	tens	ones
	3	7
−		4

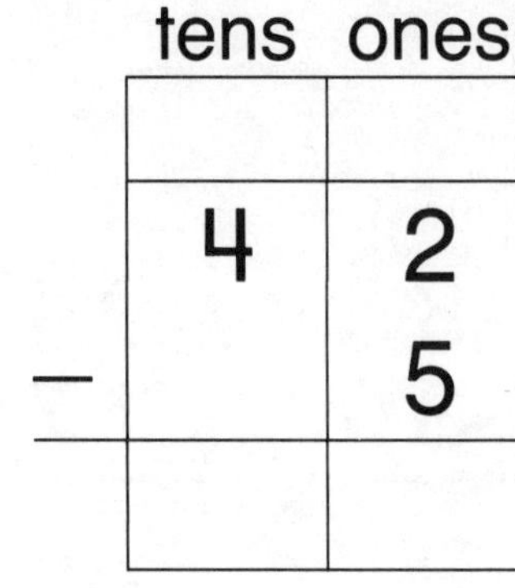

	tens	ones
	4	2
−		5

Add.

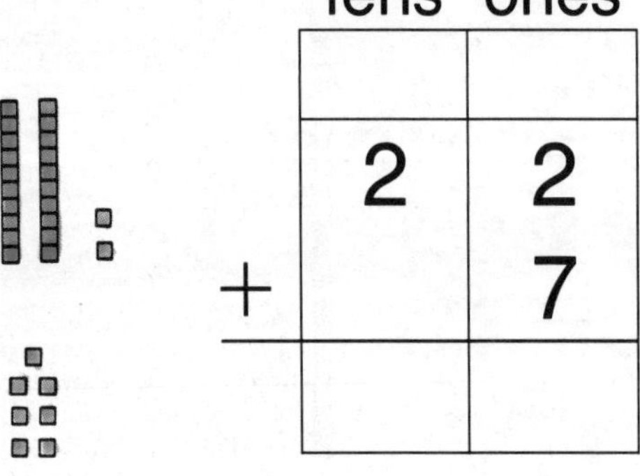

	tens	ones
	2	2
+		7

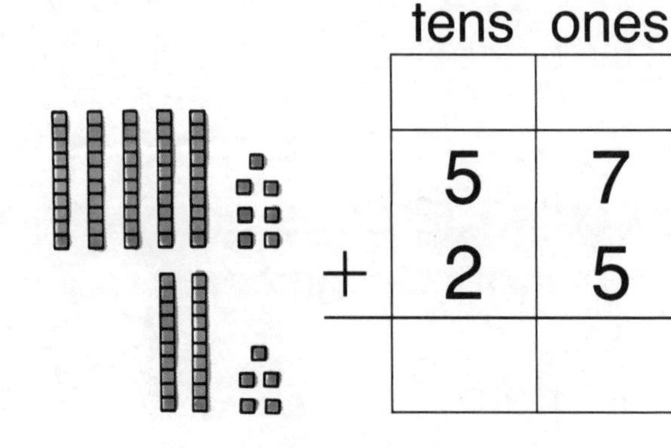

	tens	ones
	5	7
+	2	5

Name ______________________________

14 GEOMETRY AND MEASUREMENT

X the squares. Circle the triangles.

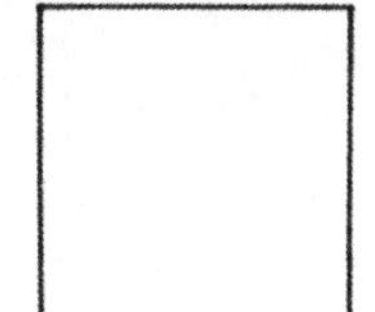

Square

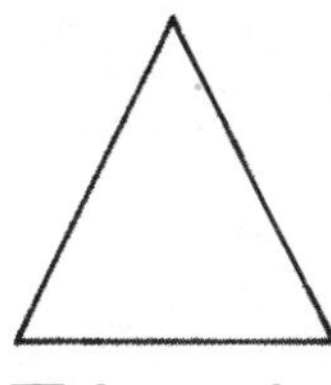

Triangle

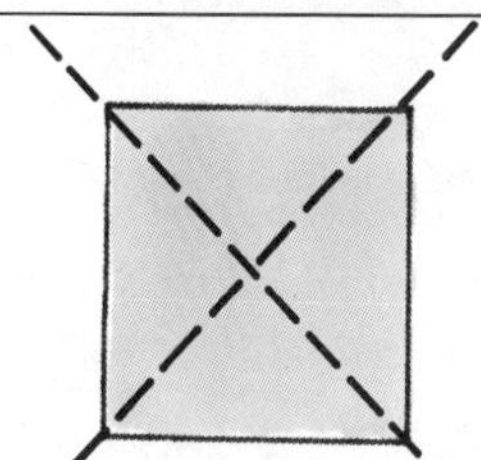

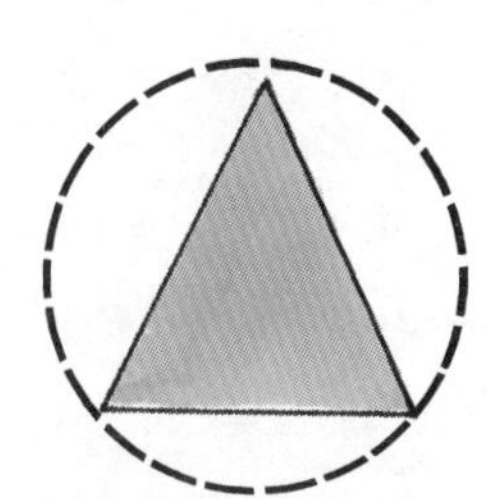

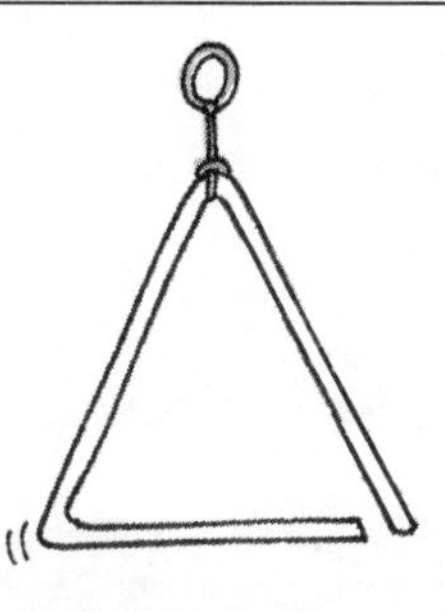

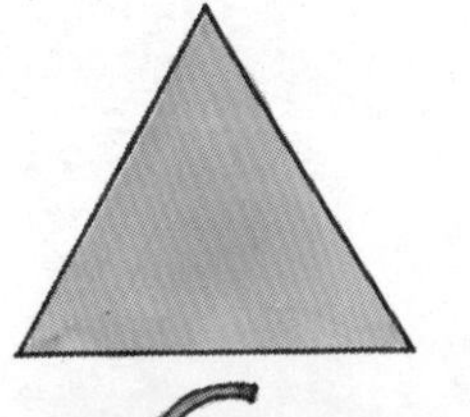

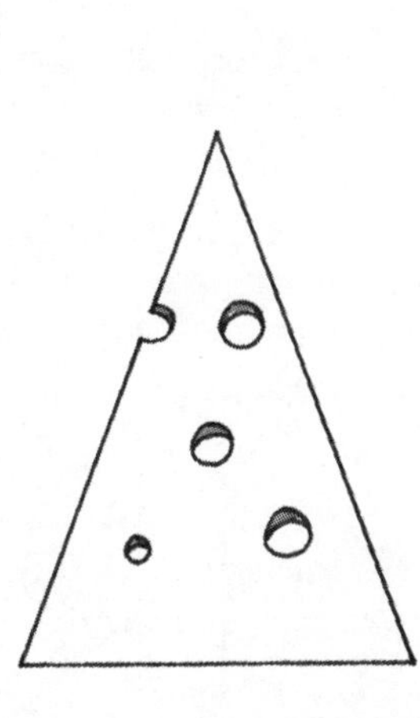

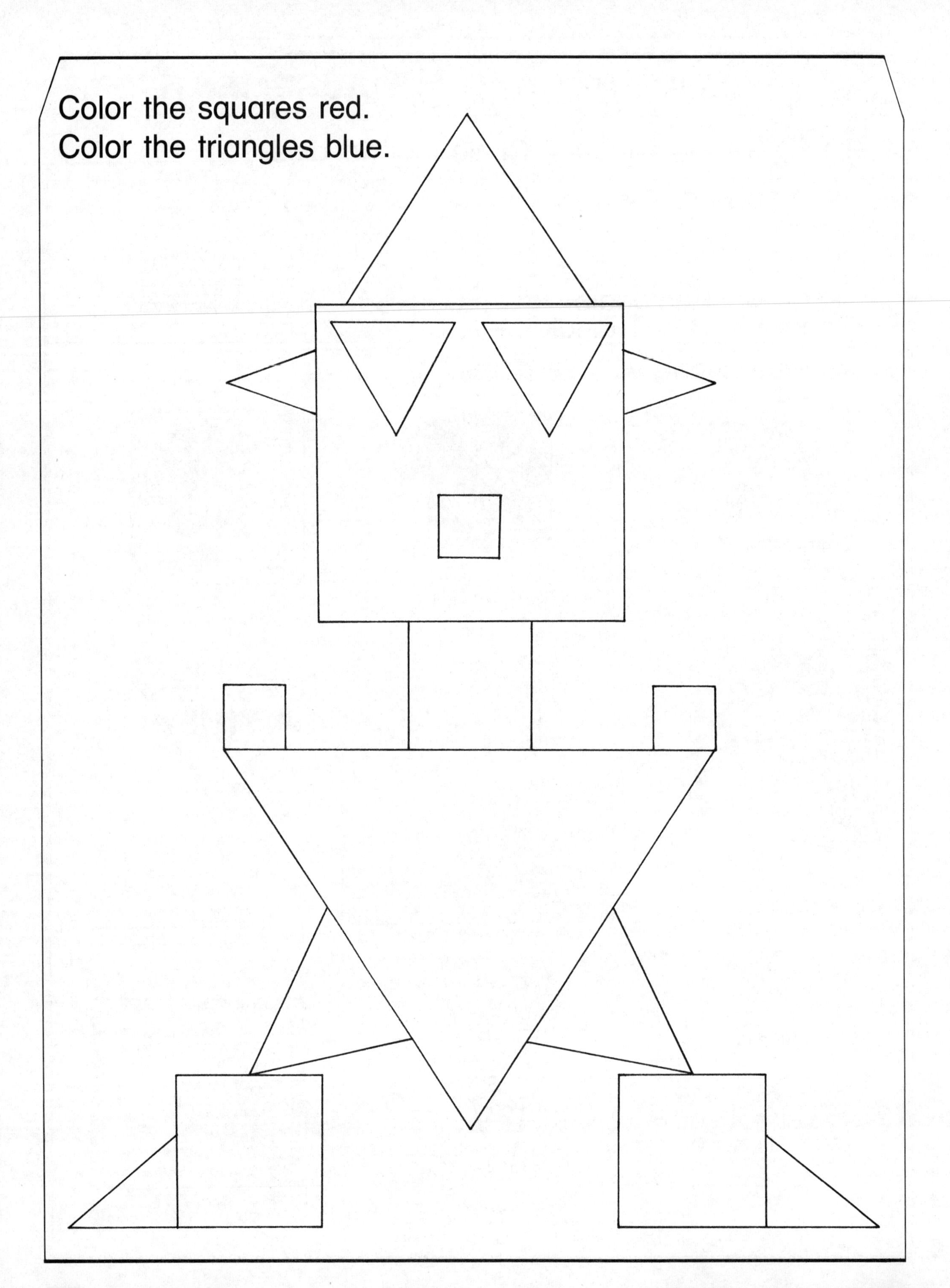
Color the squares red.
Color the triangles blue.

Name ____

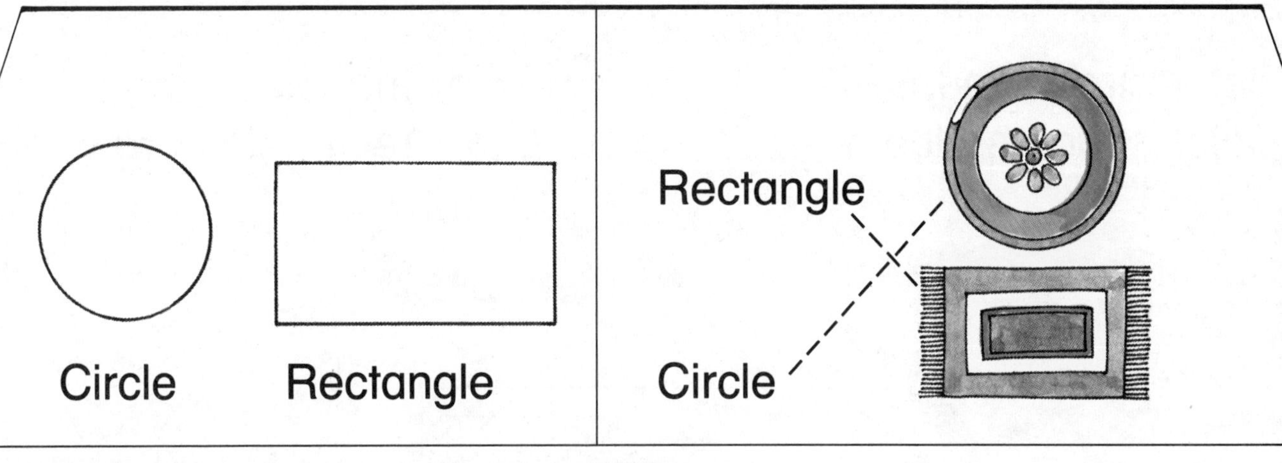

Match the shape with its name.

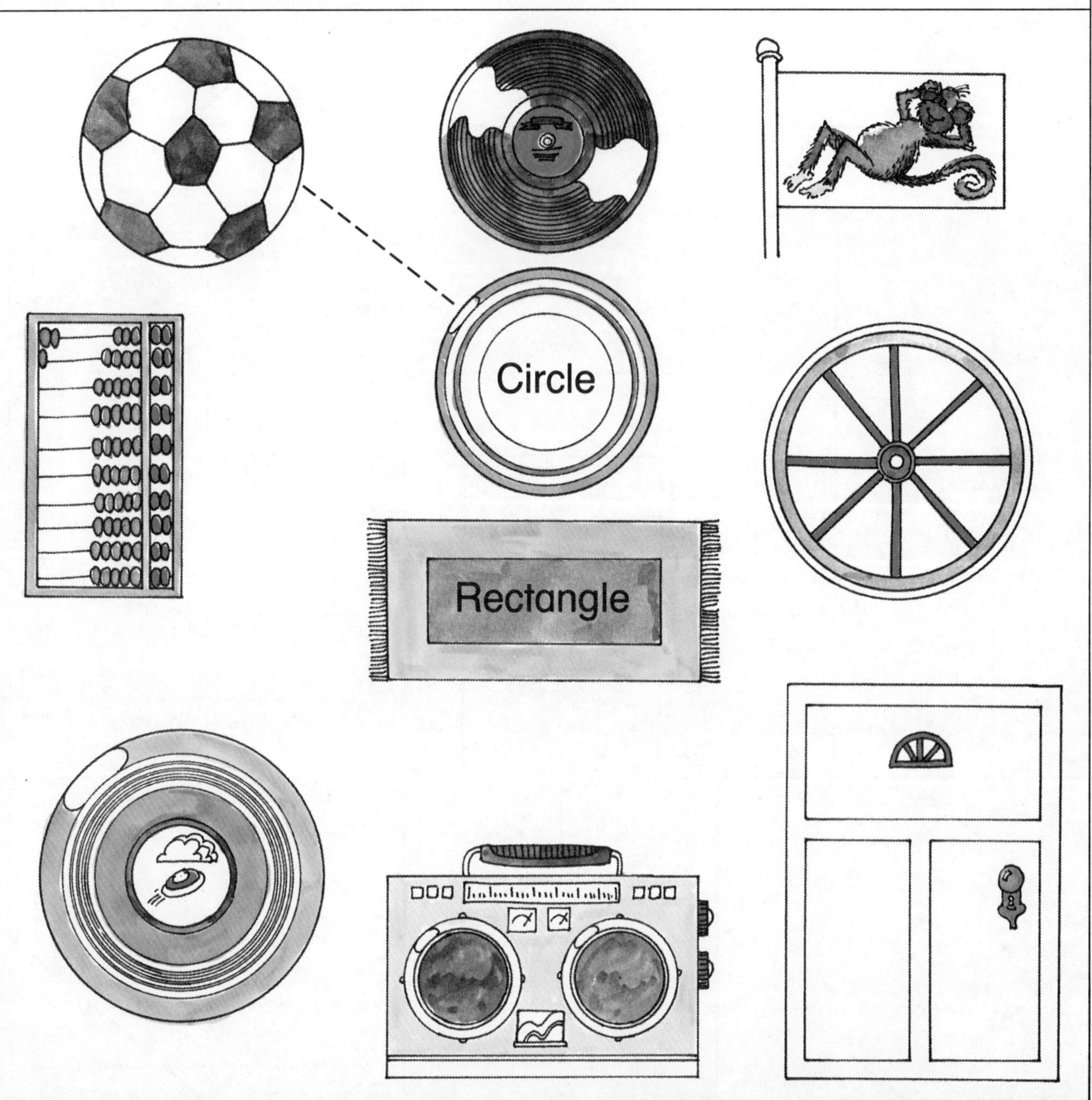

Color circles red.
Color squares blue.
Color triangles green.
Color rectangles brown.

Name ___________________________

____ hands

____ feet

Use your hands to measure these lengths.

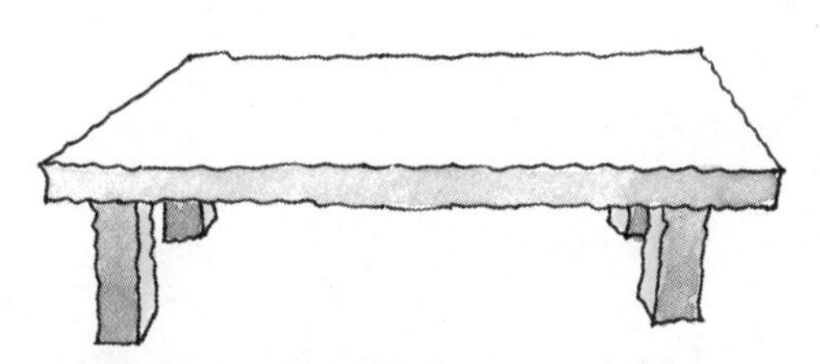

Length of table

____ hands

Length of desk

____ hands

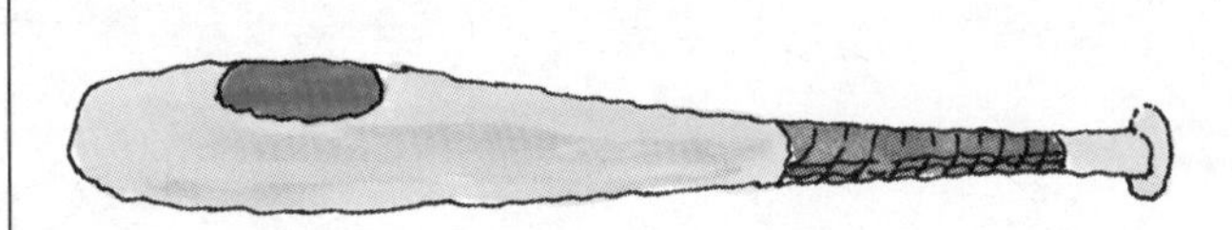

Length of bat

____ hands

Use your feet to measure these lengths.

Length of classroom

____ feet

Length of rope

____ feet

Length of shelf

____ feet

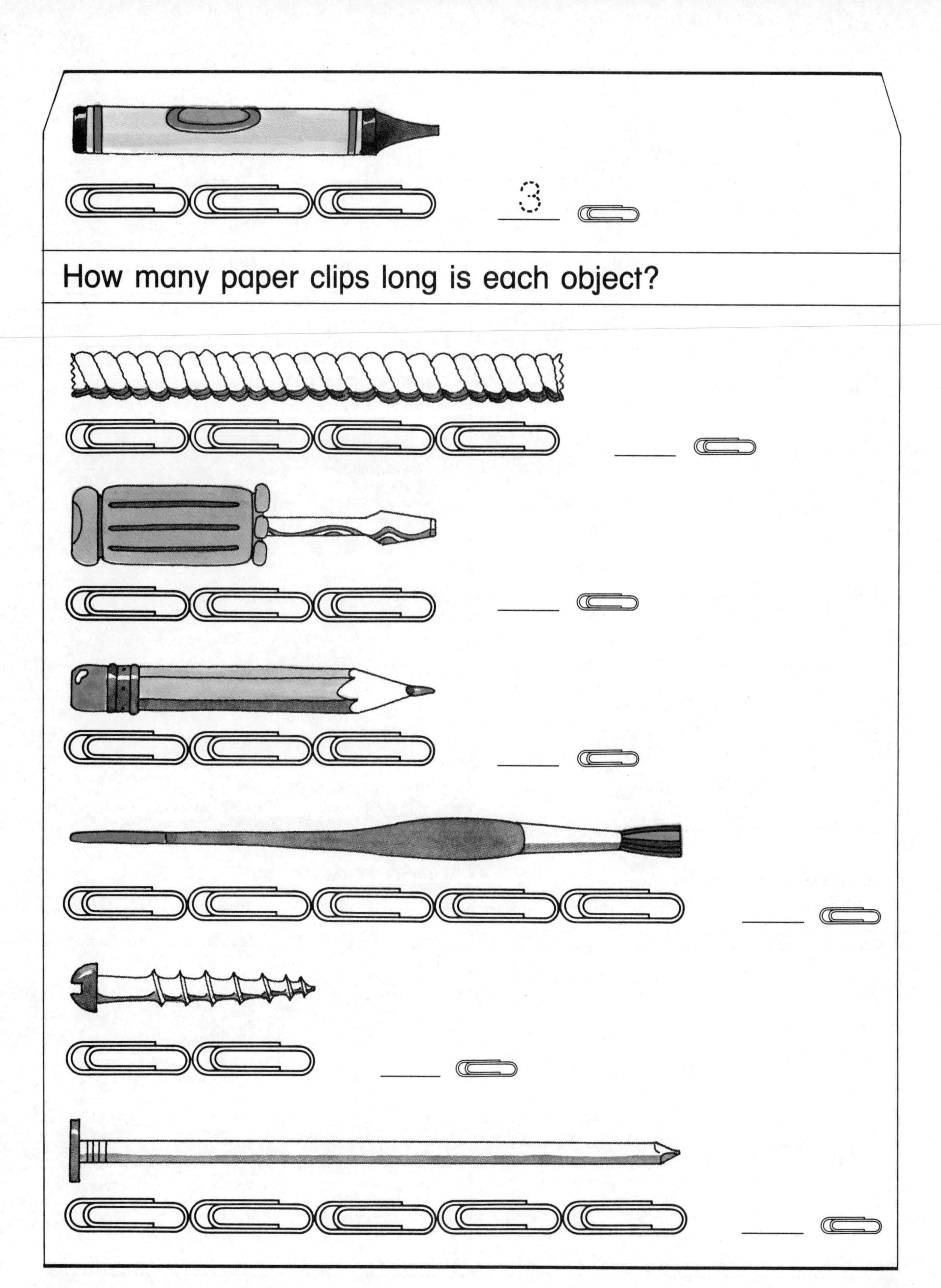
3
How many paper clips long is each object?

Name ___

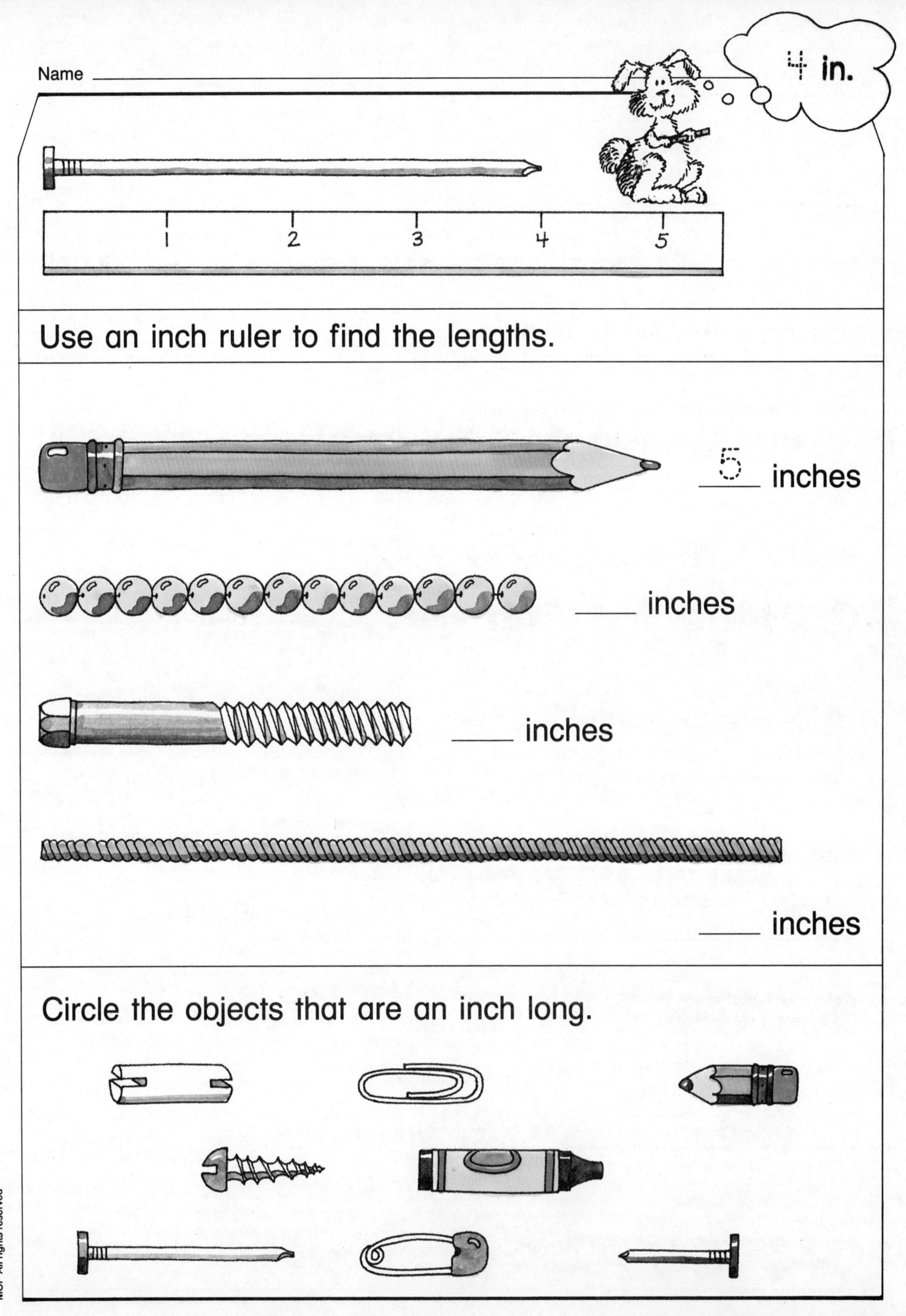

Use an inch ruler to find the lengths.

5 inches

___ inches

___ inches

___ inches

Circle the objects that are an inch long.

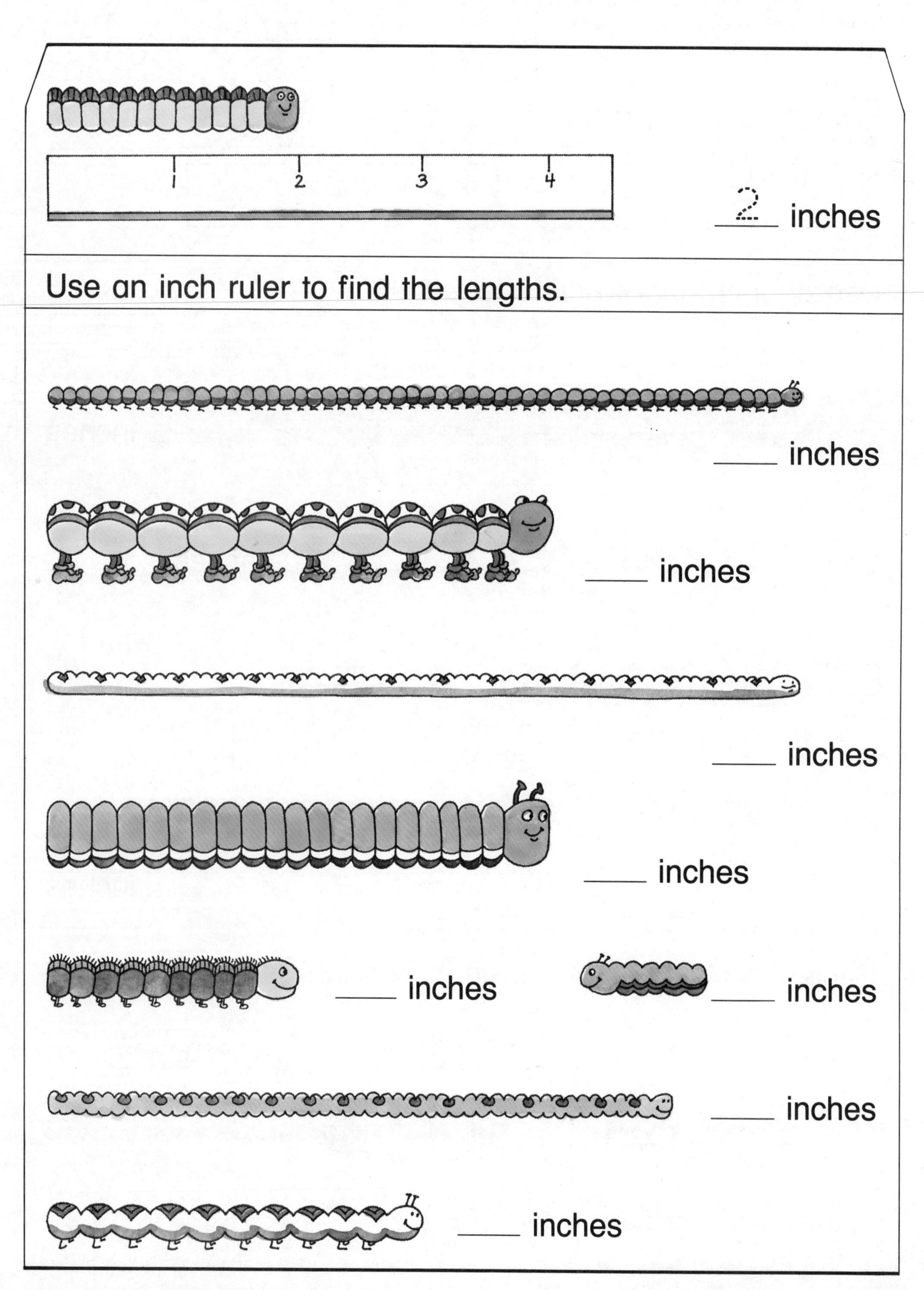
1
2
3
4
2 inches
Use an inch ruler to find the lengths.
___ inches
___ inches
___ inches
___ inches
___ inches
___ inches
___ inches
___ inches

Name ______________________________

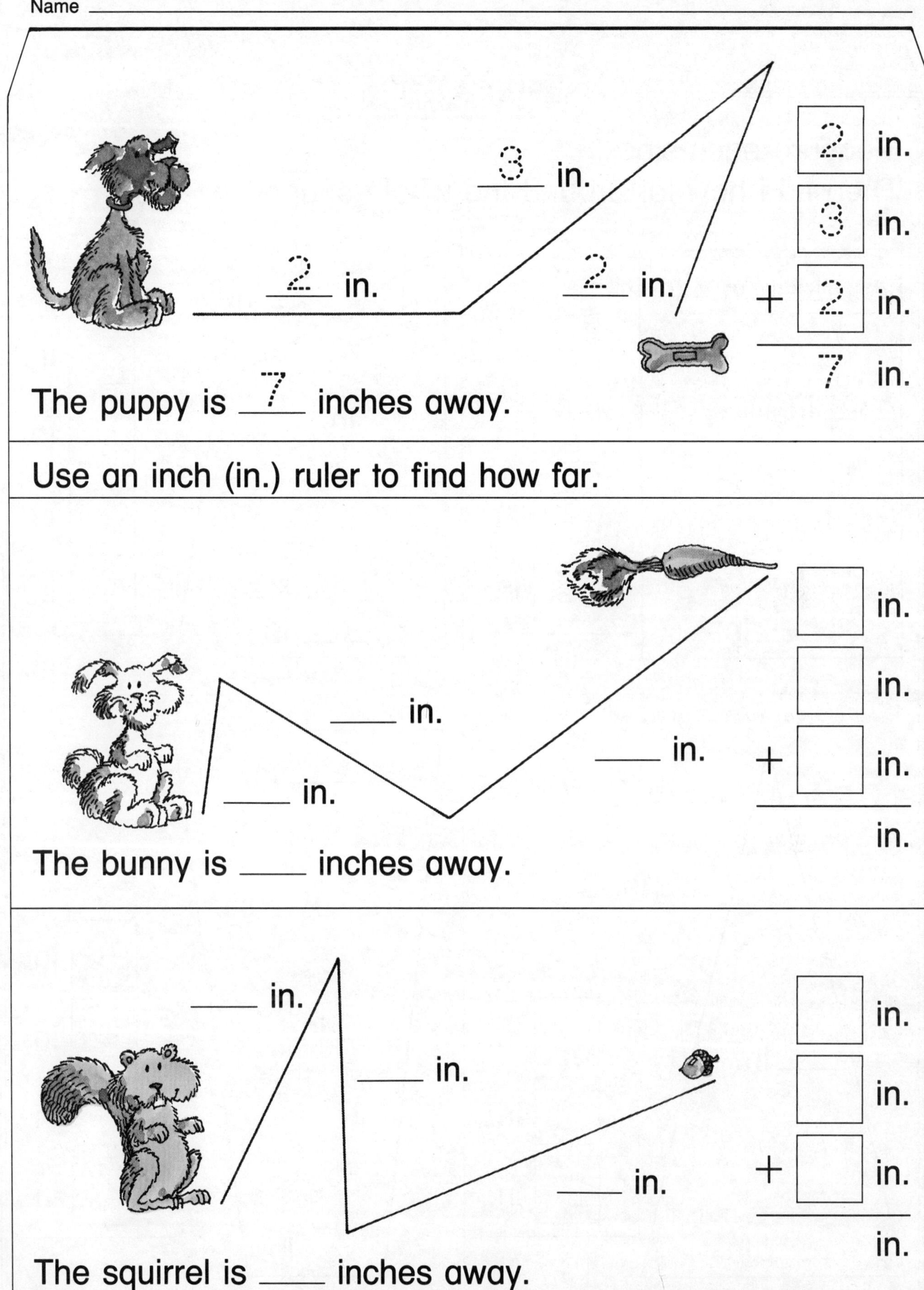

The puppy is 7 inches away.

Use an inch (in.) ruler to find how far.

The bunny is ___ inches away.

The squirrel is ___ inches away.

FIELD TRIP

Measure each side.
Then find how far around the whole shape.

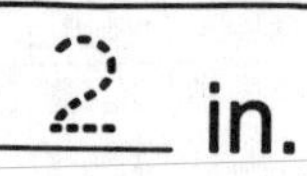

2 in.

3 in.

3 in.

2 in.

	2	in.
	3	in.
	2	in.
+	3	in.
	10	in.

___ in.

___ in.

___ in.

___ in.

	☐	in.
	☐	in.
	☐	in.
+	☐	in.
		in.

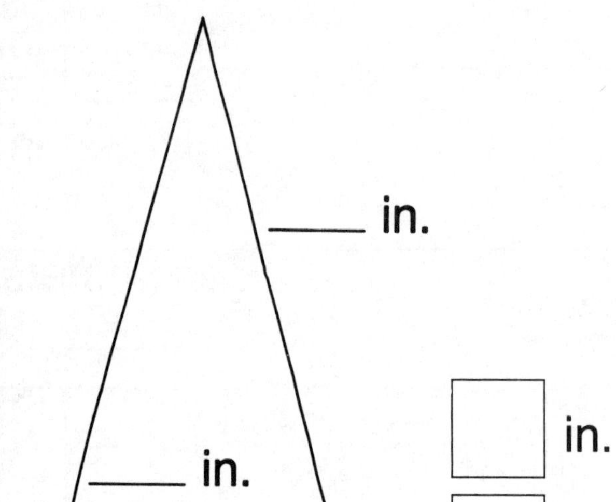

___ in.

___ in.

___ in.

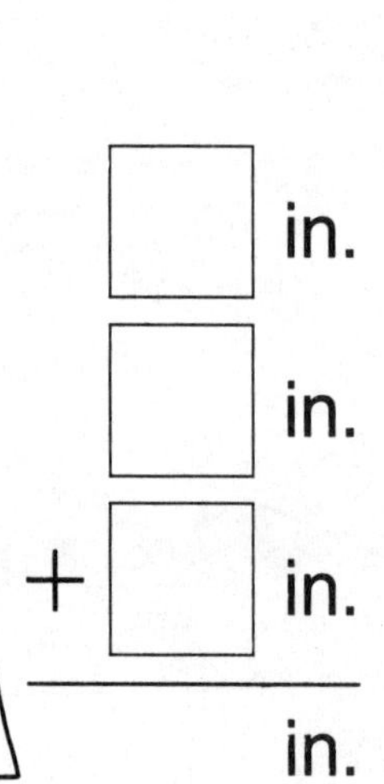

	☐	in.
	☐	in.
+	☐	in.
		in.

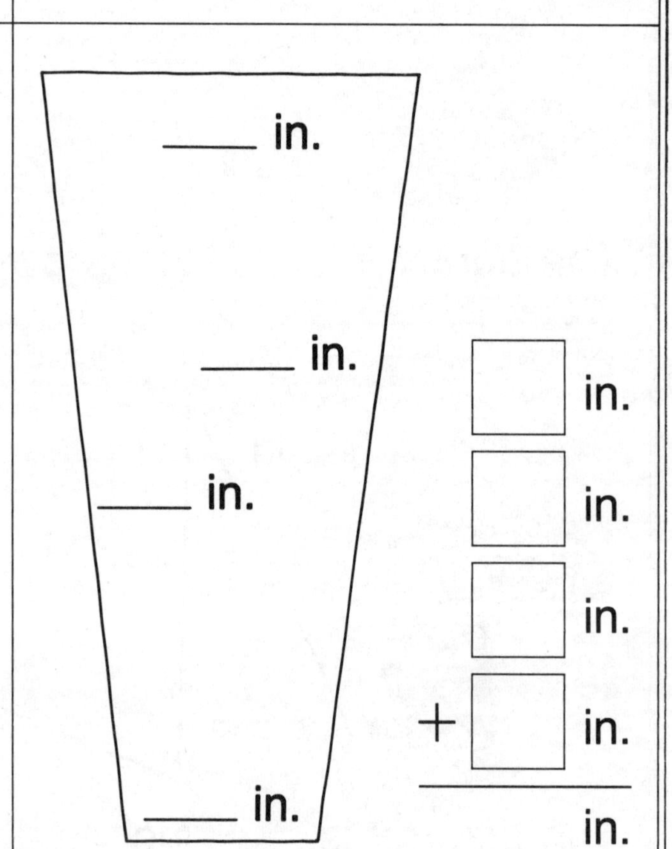

___ in.

___ in.

___ in.

___ in.

	☐	in.
	☐	in.
	☐	in.
+	☐	in.
		in.

Name ____________________

10cm

1 2 3 4 5 6 7 8 9 10 11

10 centimeters

Use a centimeter ruler to find the lengths.

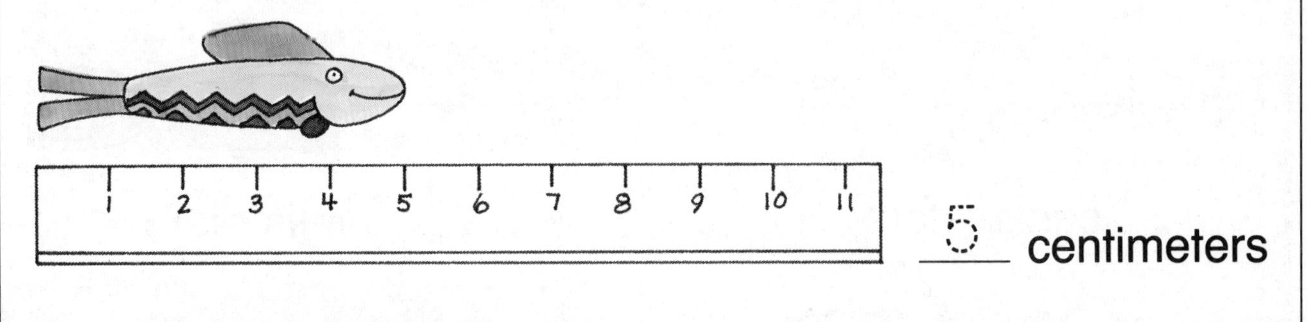

5 centimeters

____ centimeters

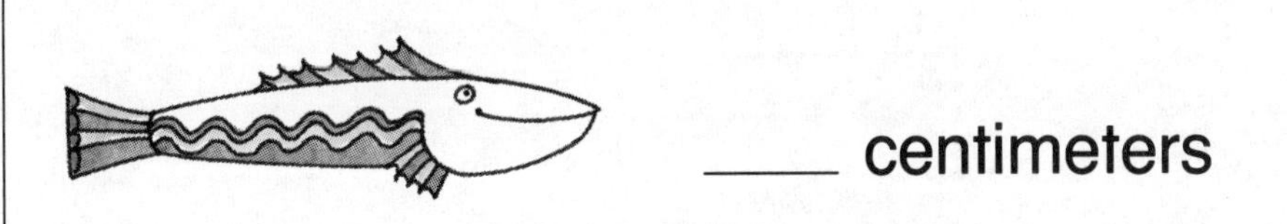

____ centimeters

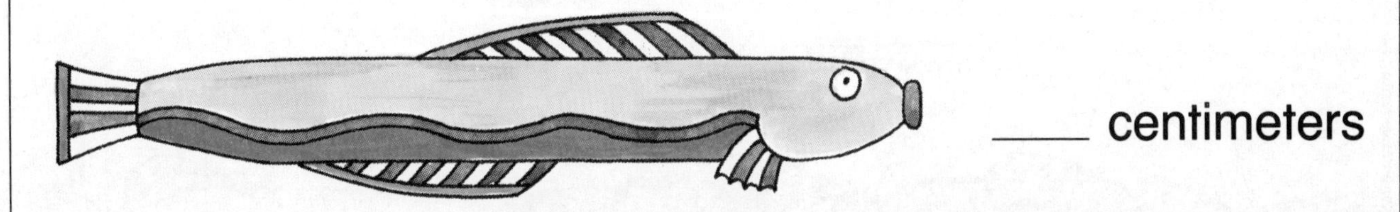

____ centimeters

Circle the objects that are 1 centimeter long.

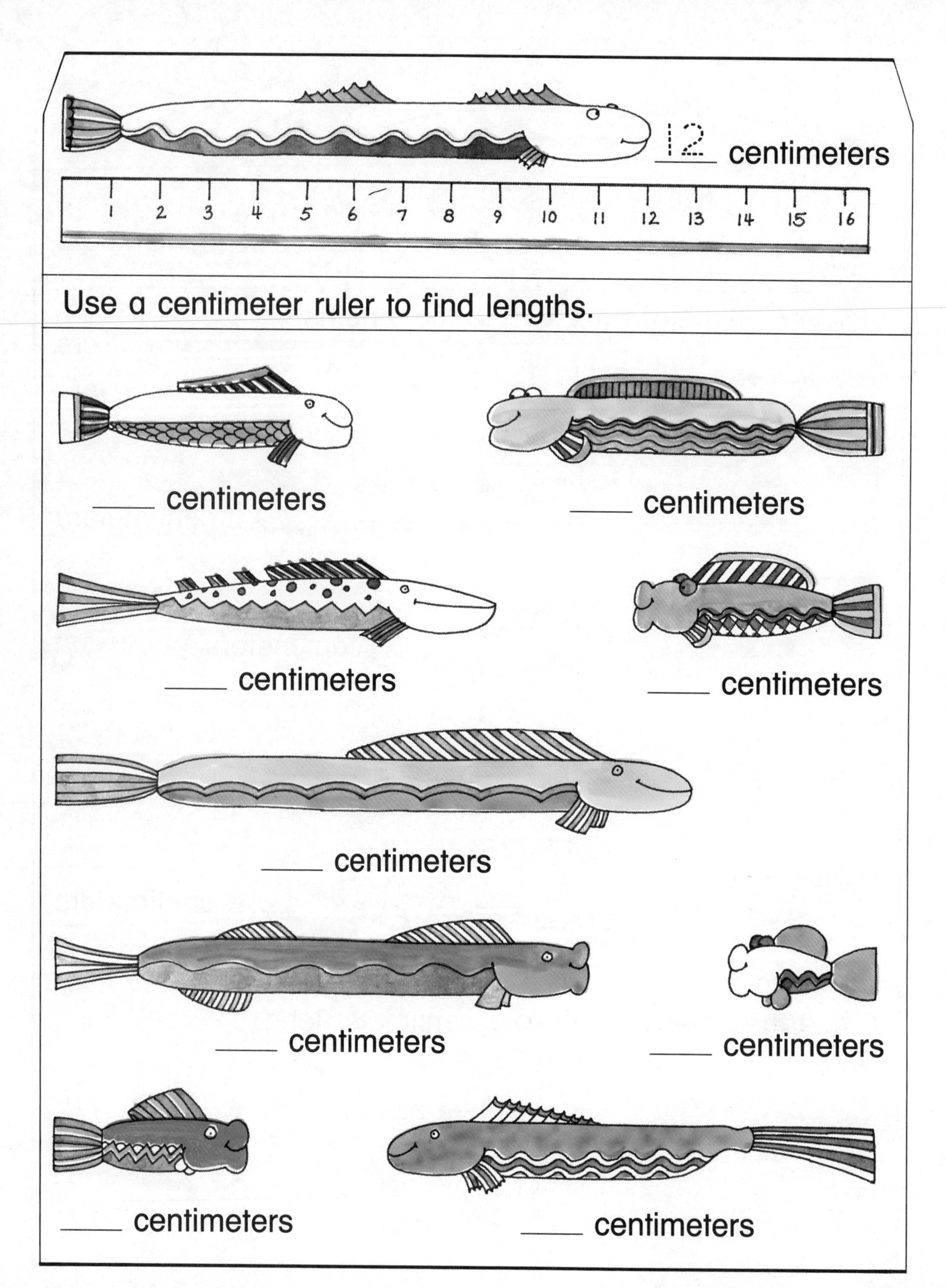

12 centimeters
1
2
3
4
5
6
7
8
9
10
11
12
13
14
15
16
Use a centimeter ruler to find lengths.
____ centimeters
____ centimeters
____ centimeters
____ centimeters
____ centimeters
____ centimeters
____ centimeters
____ centimeters
____ centimeters

Name ______________________

5 cm

4 cm

6 cm

	5	cm
	4	cm
+	6	cm
	15	cm

The frog is 15 centimeters away.

Use a centimeter (cm) ruler to find how far.

____ cm

____ cm

____ cm

		cm
		cm
+		cm
		cm

The bird is ____ centimeters away.

____ cm

____ cm

____ cm

		cm
		cm
+		cm
		cm

The dog is ____ centimeters away.

FIELD TRIP

Measure each side.
Then find how far around the whole shape.

4 cm

4 cm

4 cm

4 cm

4 cm
4 cm
4 cm
+ 4 cm
16 cm

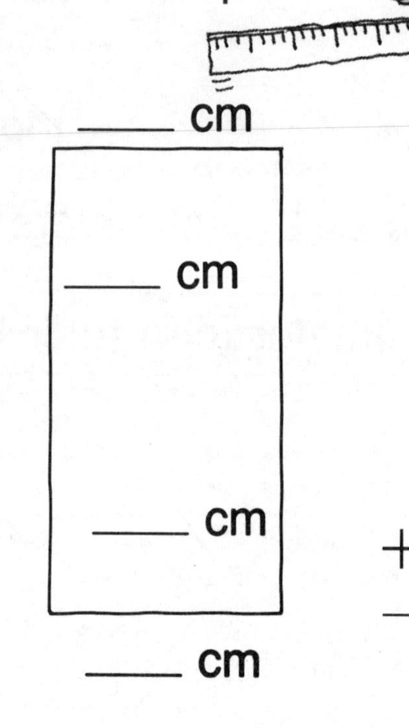

___ cm

___ cm

___ cm

___ cm

☐ cm
☐ cm
☐ cm
+ ☐ cm
cm

___ cm

___ cm

___ cm

___ cm

☐ cm
☐ cm
☐ cm
+ ☐ cm
cm

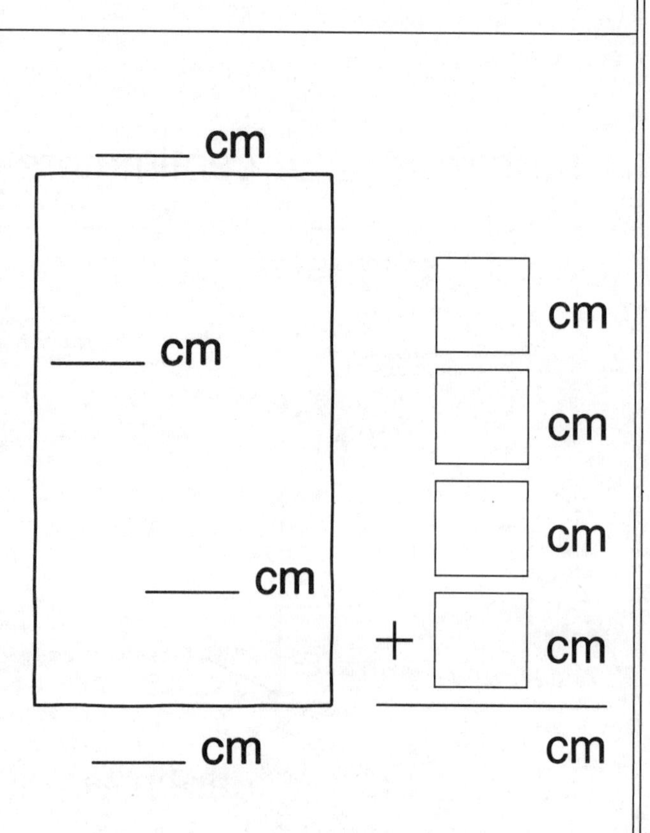

___ cm

___ cm

___ cm

___ cm

☐ cm
☐ cm
☐ cm
+ ☐ cm
cm

Name ___________________________________

CHAPTER CHECKUP

Match the shape to its name.

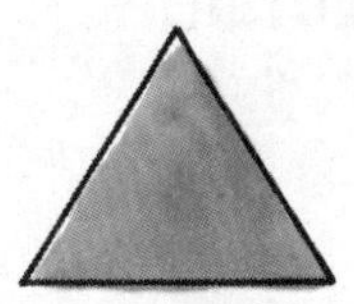

square

circle

triangle

rectangle

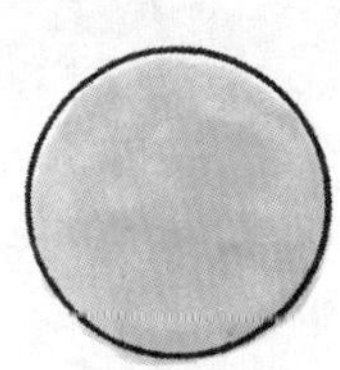

Use an inch ruler to find the length.

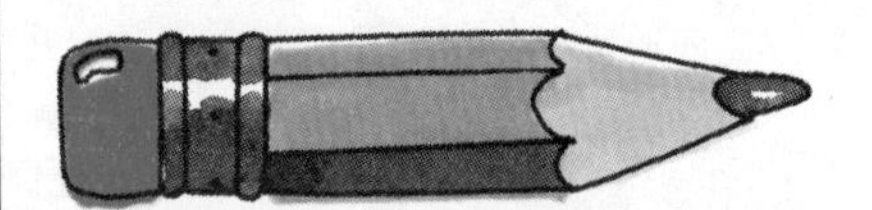

____ inches

____ inches

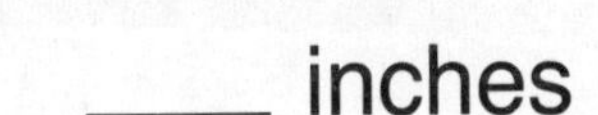

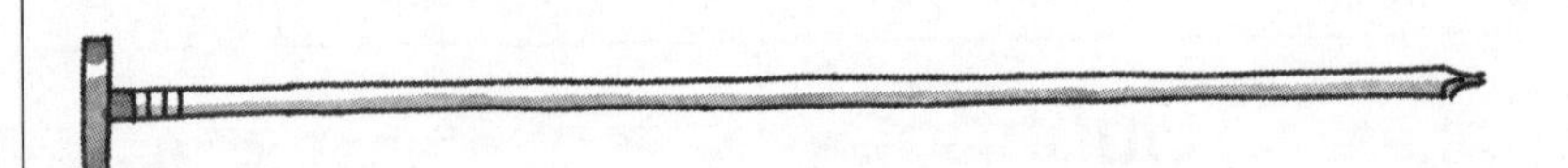

____ inches

____ inches

Use a centimeter ruler to find the length.

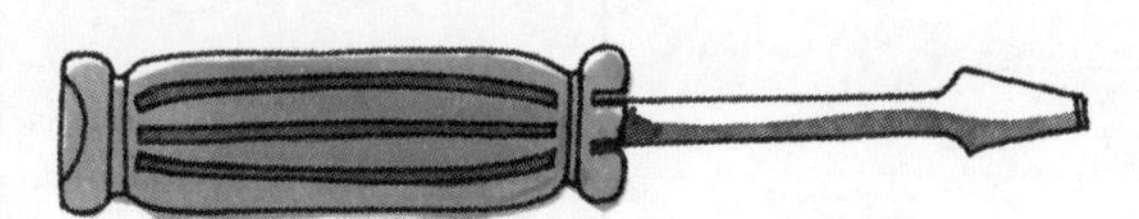

____ centimeters

____ centimeters

____ centimeters

____ centimeters

ROUNDUP REVIEW

Add or subtract.

$$\begin{array}{r} 3 \\ +9 \\ \hline \end{array} \quad \begin{array}{r} 12 \\ -\ 9 \\ \hline \end{array} \quad \begin{array}{r} 4 \\ +5 \\ \hline \end{array} \quad \begin{array}{r} 14 \\ -\ 9 \\ \hline \end{array} \quad \begin{array}{r} 4 \\ +9 \\ \hline \end{array} \quad \begin{array}{r} 8 \\ +7 \\ \hline \end{array} \quad \begin{array}{r} 11 \\ -\ 7 \\ \hline \end{array}$$

$$\begin{array}{r} 10 \\ -\ 4 \\ \hline \end{array} \quad \begin{array}{r} 16 \\ -\ 7 \\ \hline \end{array} \quad \begin{array}{r} 6 \\ +5 \\ \hline \end{array} \quad \begin{array}{r} 7 \\ +9 \\ \hline \end{array} \quad \begin{array}{r} 11 \\ -\ 6 \\ \hline \end{array} \quad \begin{array}{r} 13 \\ -\ 8 \\ \hline \end{array} \quad \begin{array}{r} 8 \\ +6 \\ \hline \end{array}$$

Write the missing numbers.

102, 103, ____, ____, ____, ____, ____, ____

Add.

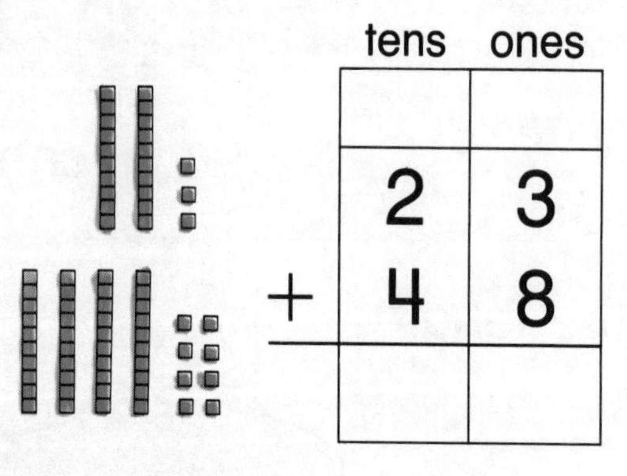

	tens	ones
	2	3
+	4	8

Subtract.

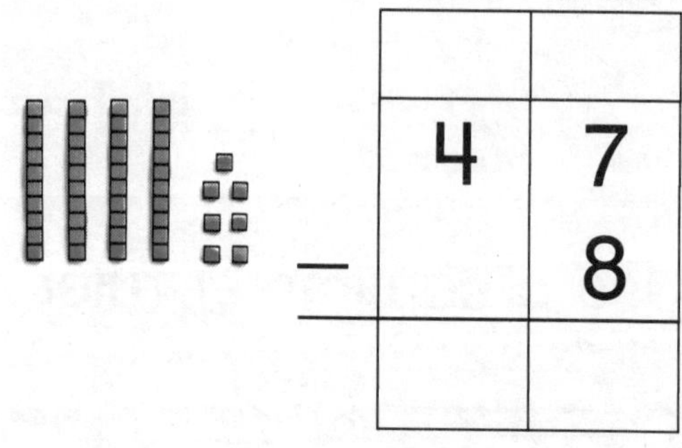

	tens	ones
	4	7
−		8

Add.

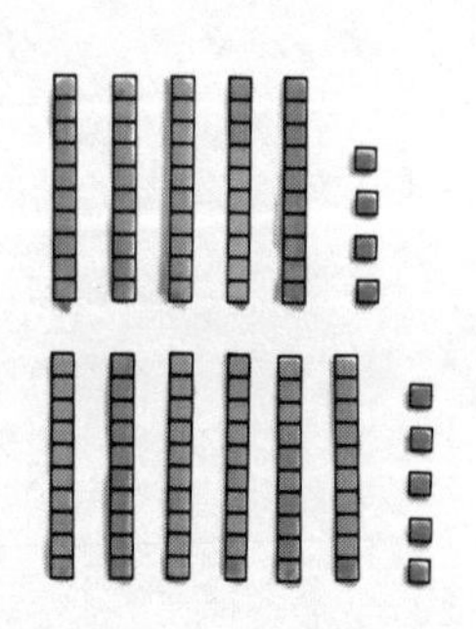

	hundreds	tens	ones
		5	4
+		6	5

Name ______________________________

15 FRACTIONS AND GRAPHING

Circle the shapes with equal parts.

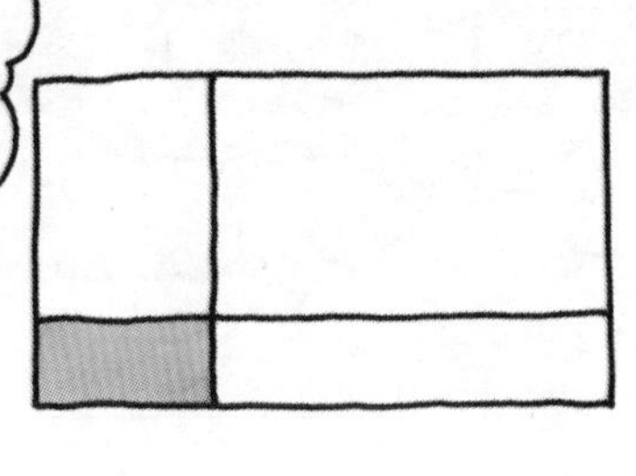

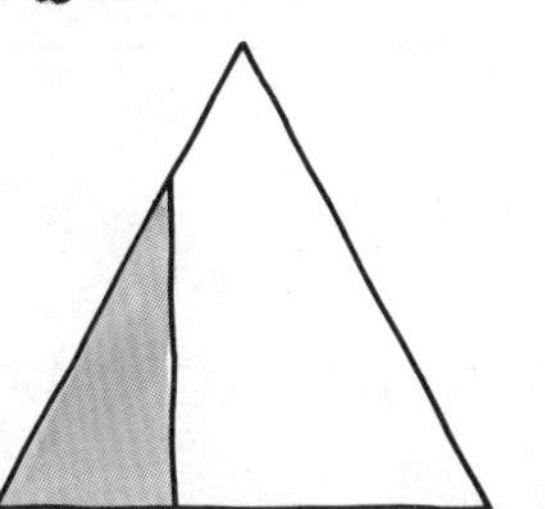

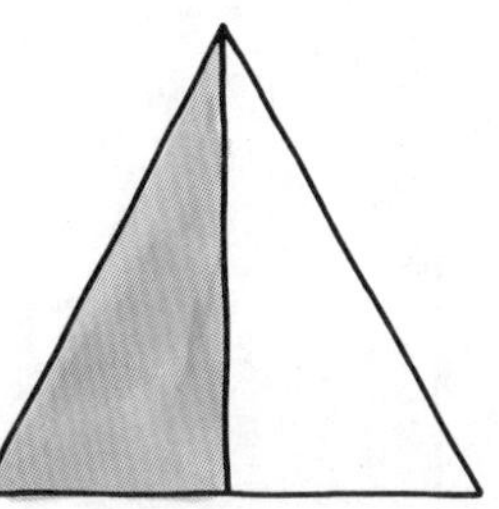

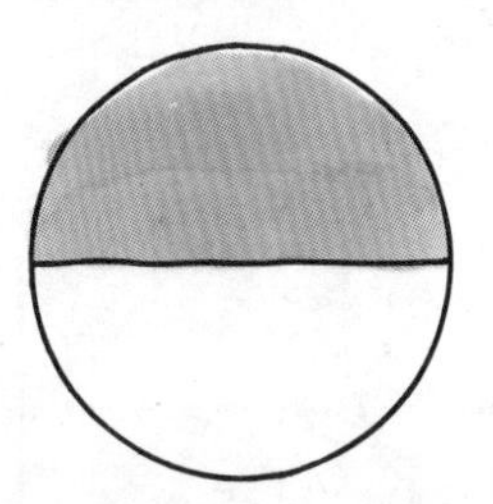

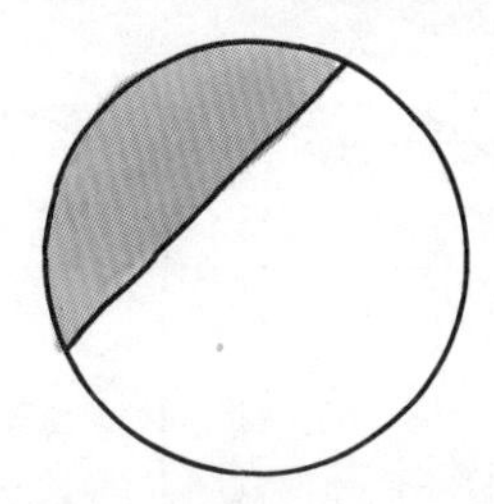

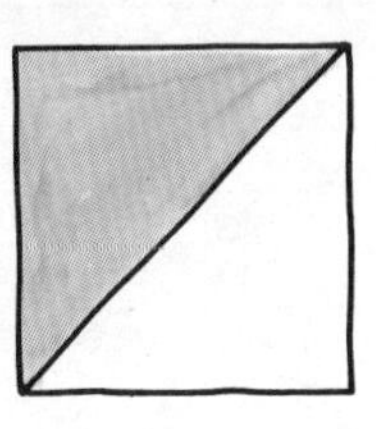

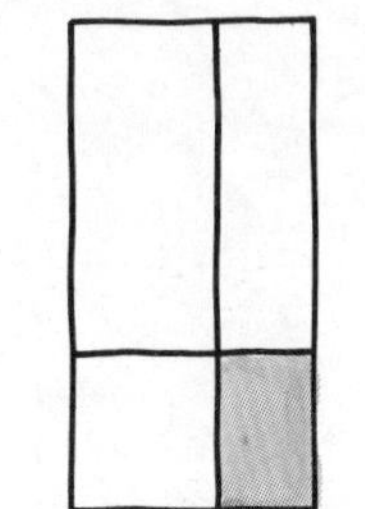

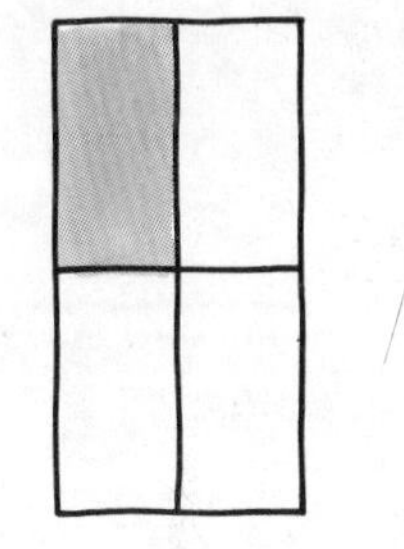

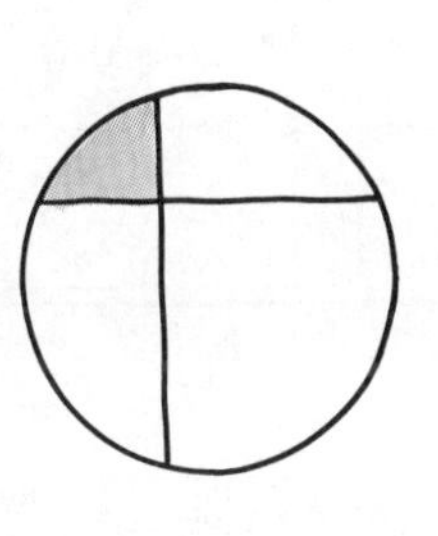

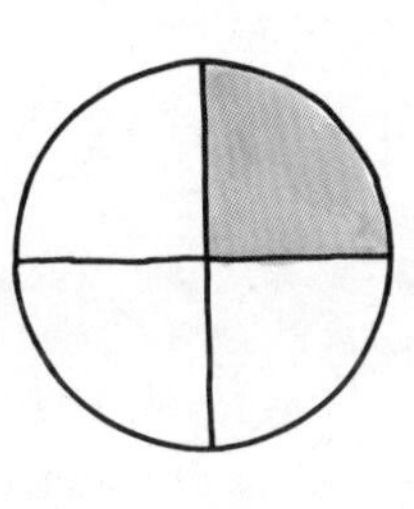

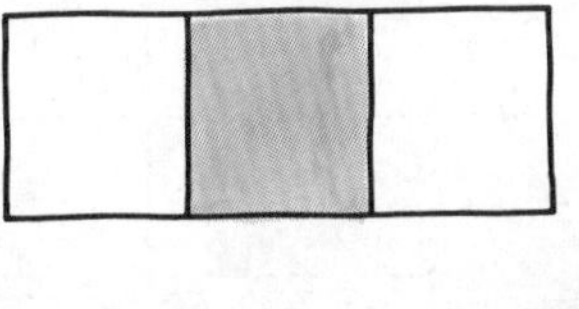

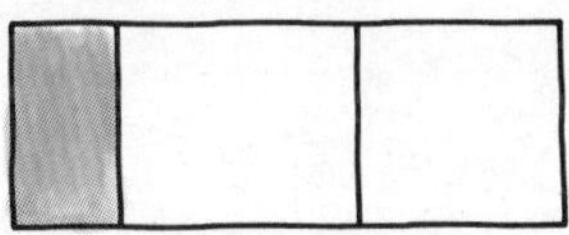

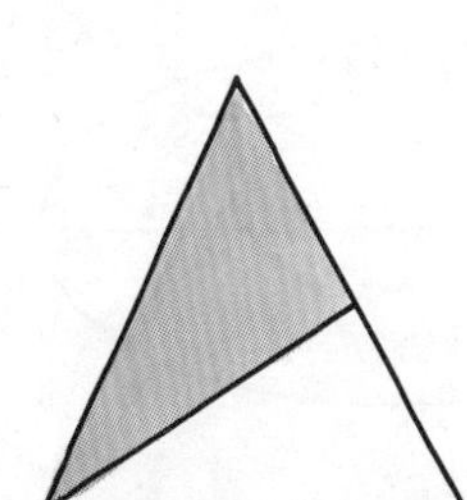

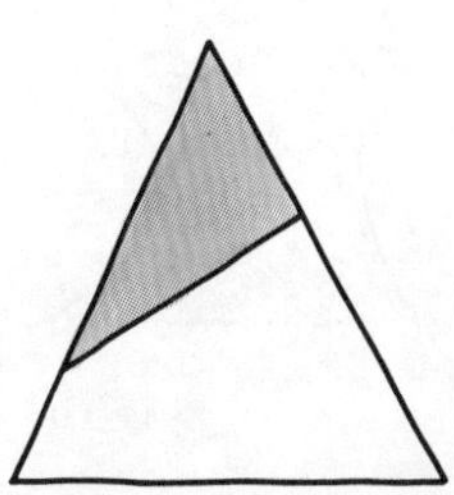

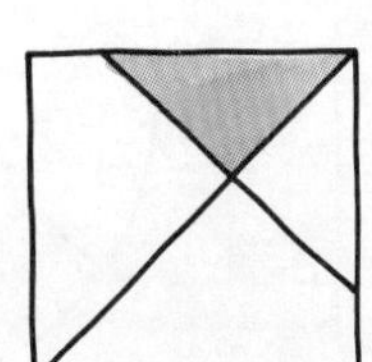

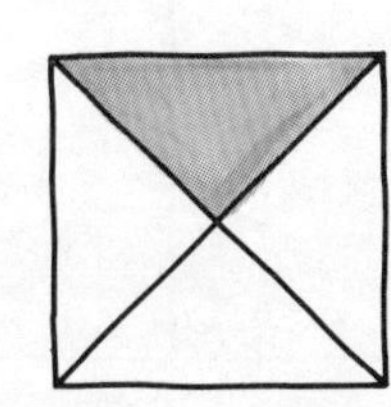

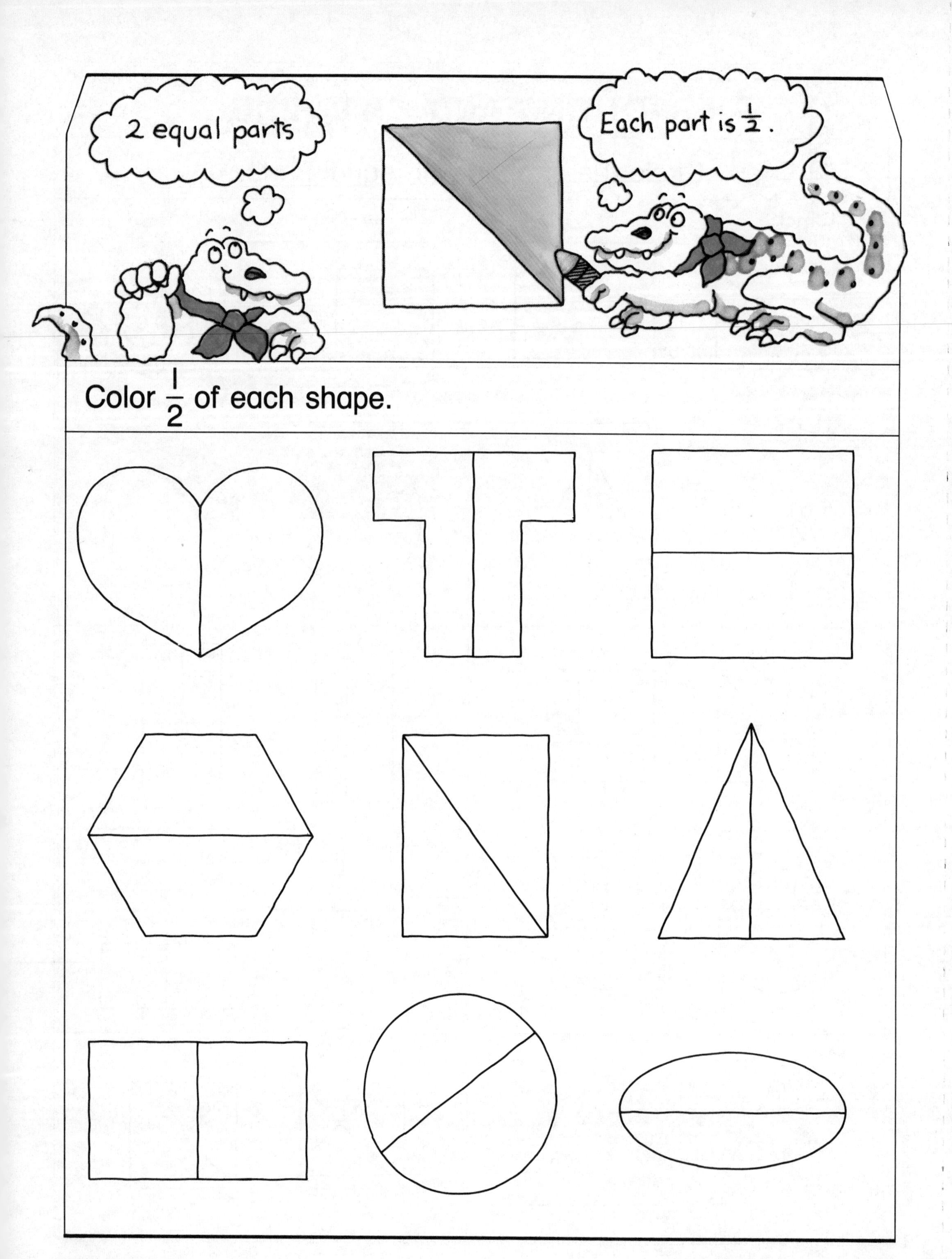
2 equal parts
Each part is $\frac{1}{2}$.
Color $\frac{1}{2}$ of each shape.

Name ______________________________

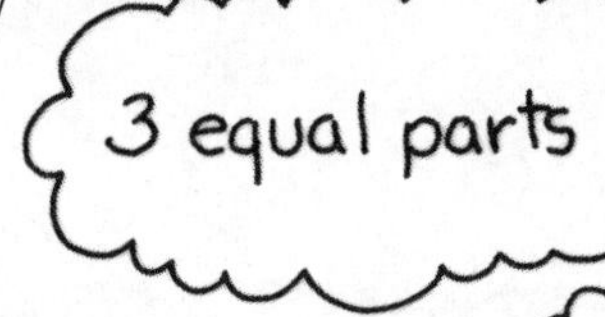

Color $\frac{1}{3}$ of each shape.

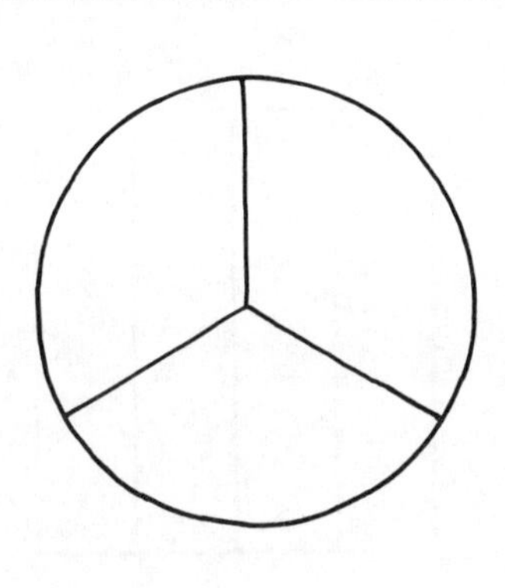

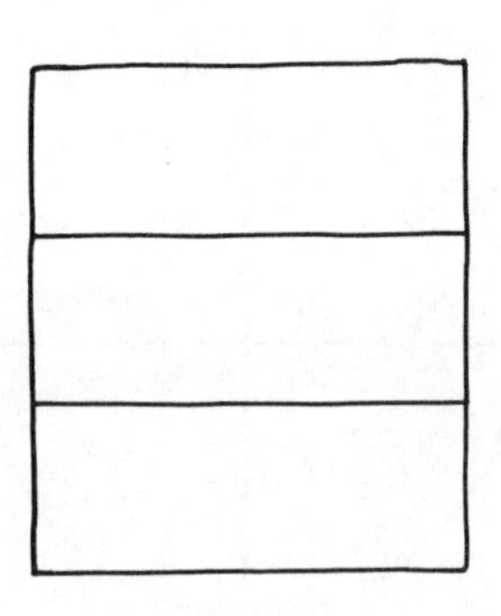

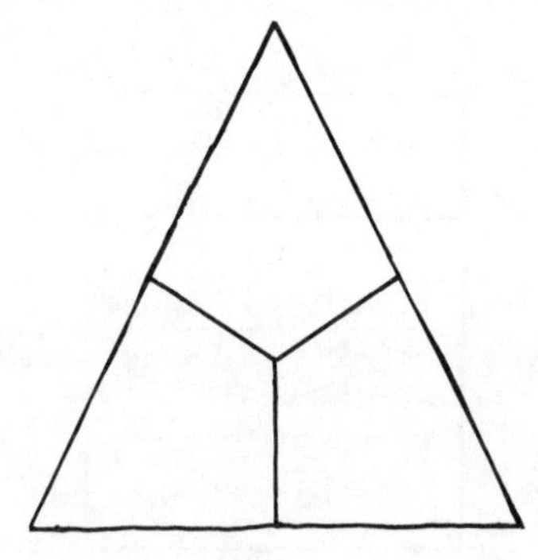

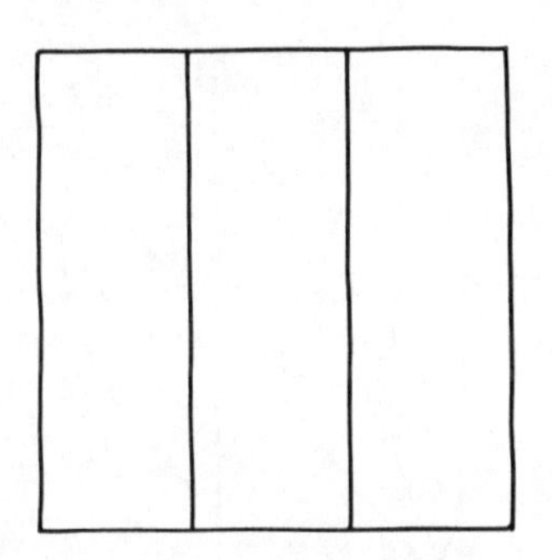

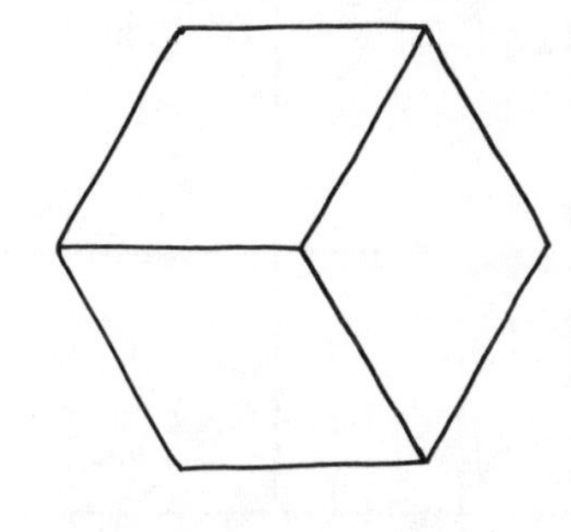

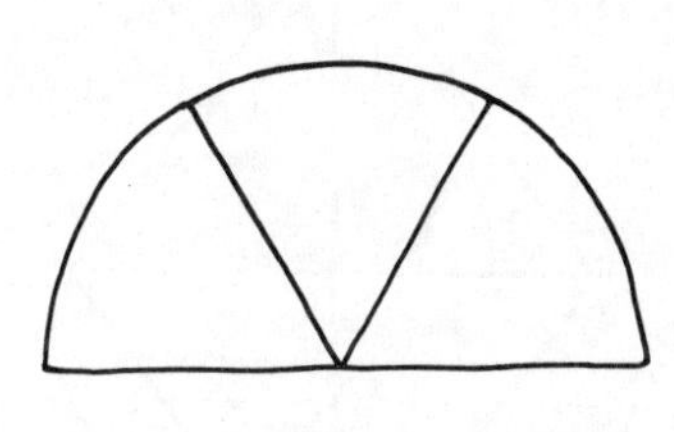

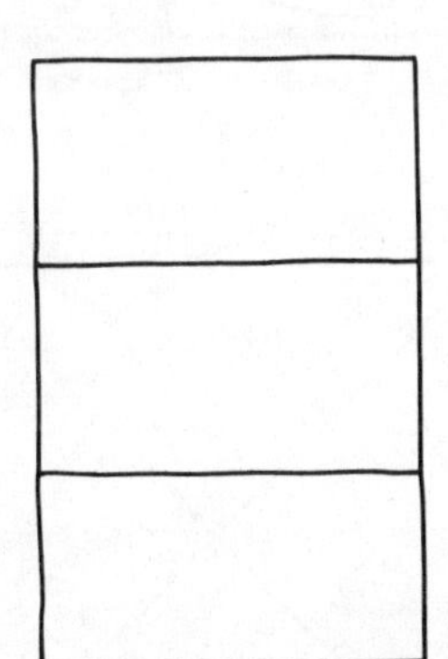

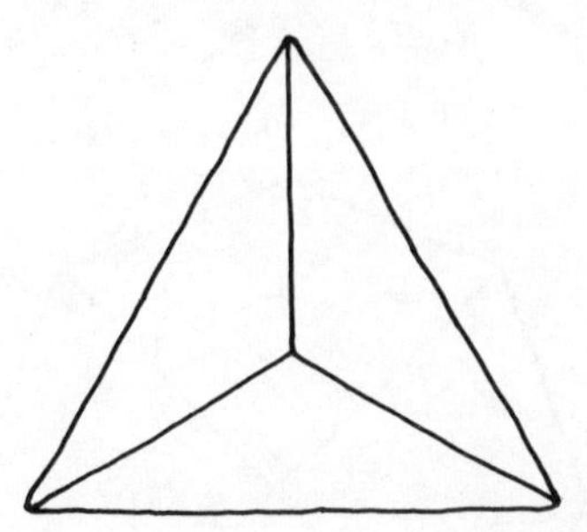

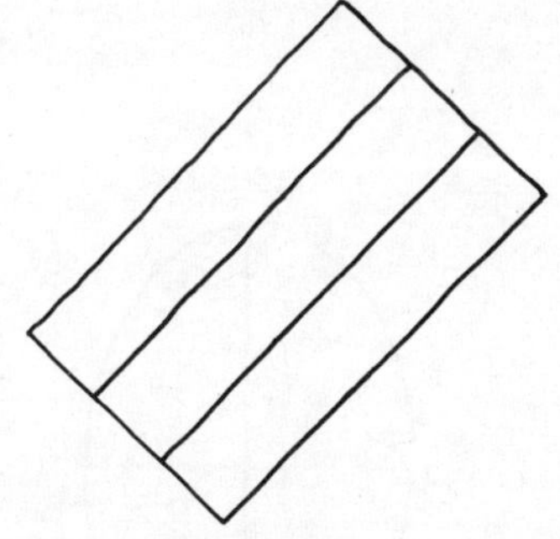

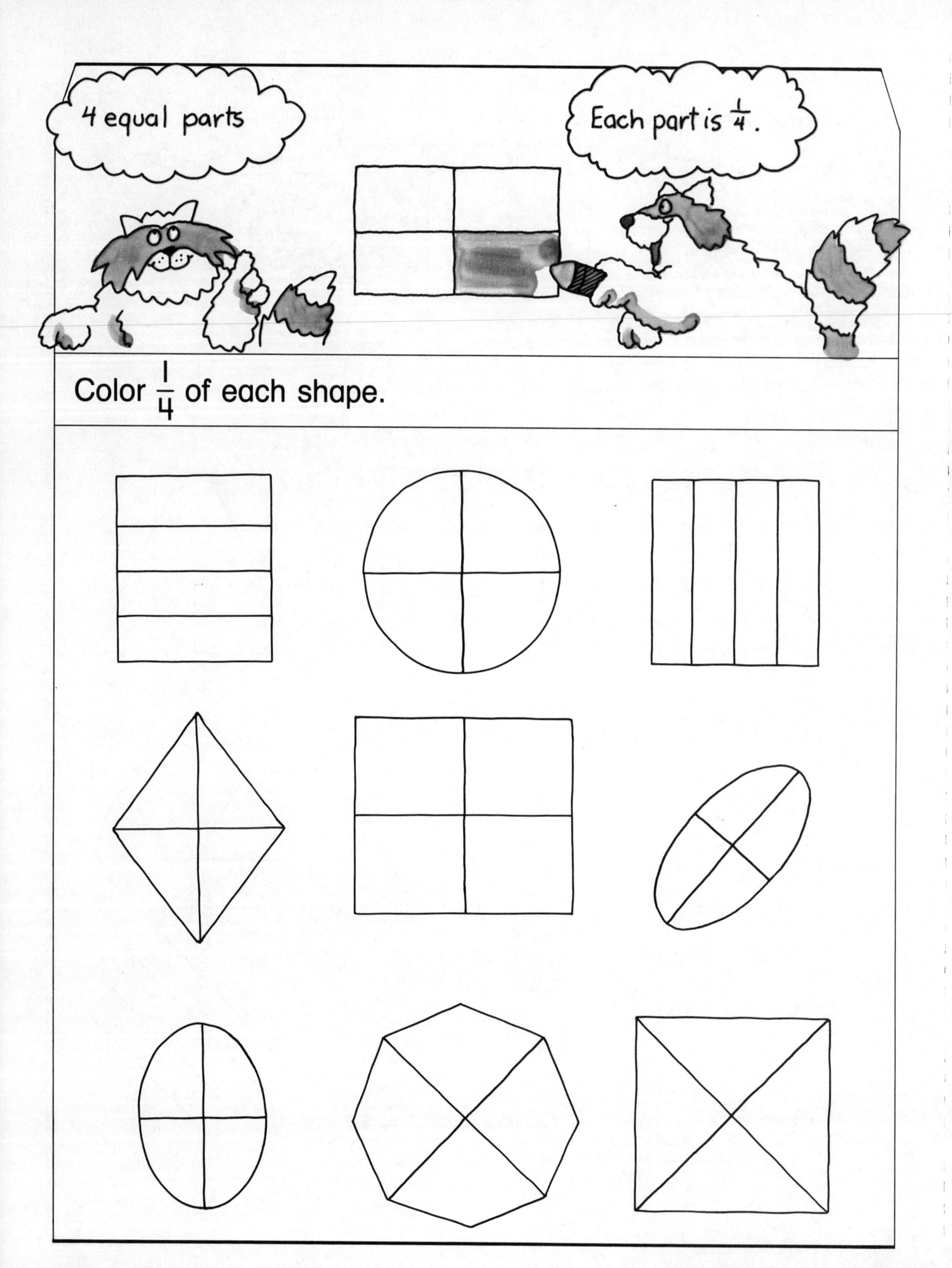
4 equal parts
Each part is $\frac{1}{4}$.
Color $\frac{1}{4}$ of each shape.

Name ______________________________

$\frac{1}{2}$

 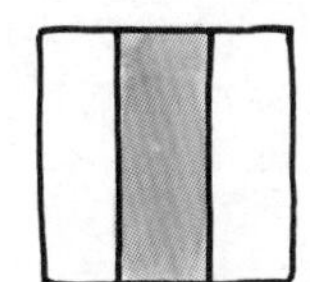 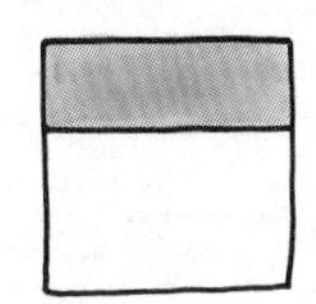 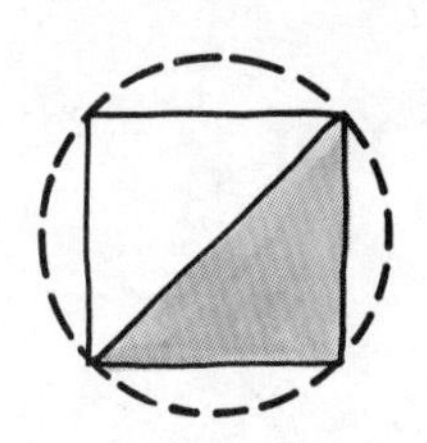

Circle the shape that matches the fraction.

$\frac{1}{3}$

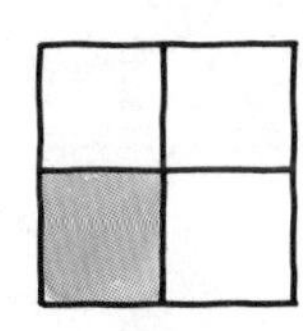 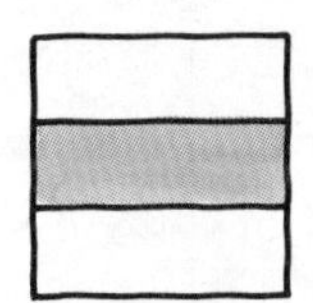 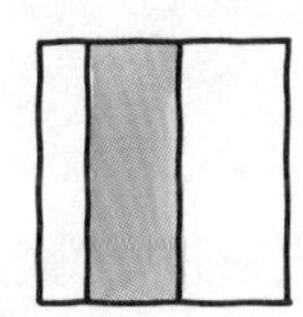 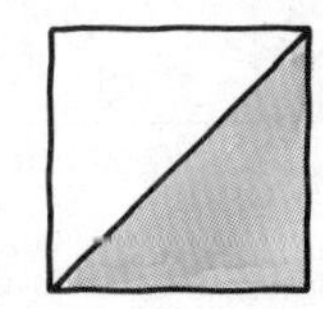

$\frac{1}{2}$

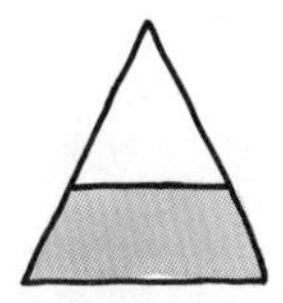   

$\frac{1}{4}$

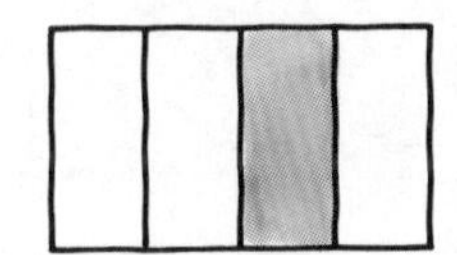 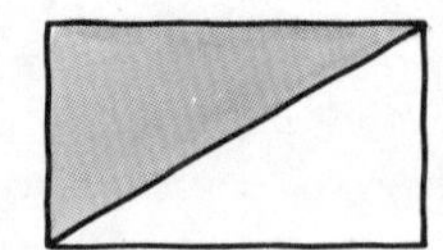 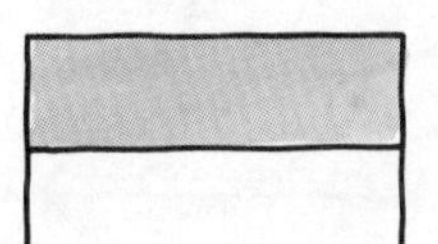 

$\frac{1}{3}$

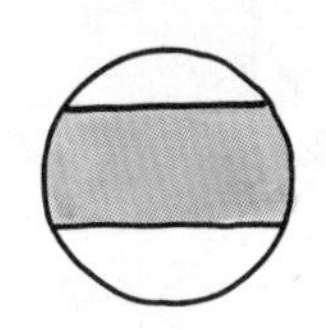 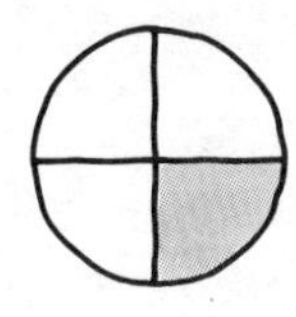

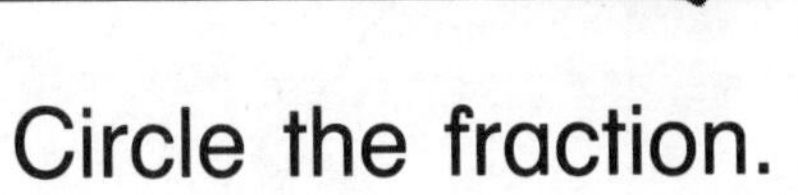

FIELD TRIP

Circle the fraction.

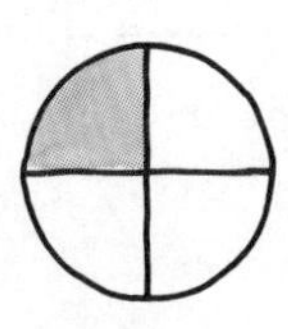

$\frac{1}{2}$ $\frac{1}{3}$ $\frac{1}{4}$

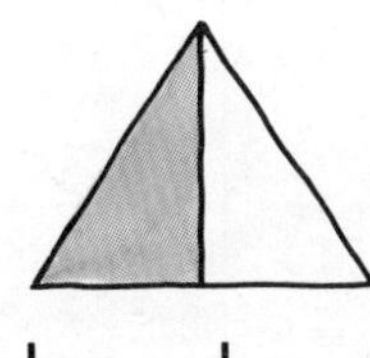

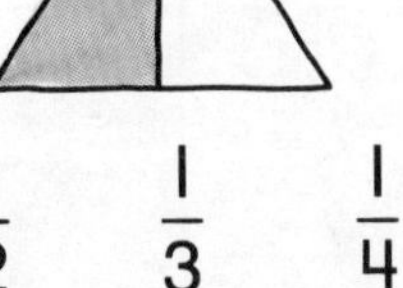

$\frac{1}{2}$ $\frac{1}{3}$ $\frac{1}{4}$

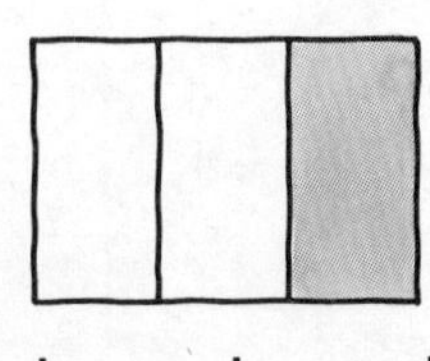

$\frac{1}{2}$ $\frac{1}{3}$ $\frac{1}{4}$

Color $\frac{1}{3}$.

Color $\frac{1}{2}$.

Color $\frac{1}{4}$.

Color $\frac{1}{3}$.

Color $\frac{1}{2}$.

Color $\frac{1}{4}$.

Name ______________________

Count the shapes.

How many △ ? 2

How many □ ? ___

How many ○ ? ___

How many ▭ ? ___

Color a ▭ for each shape.

Number of Shapes

Count the coins.

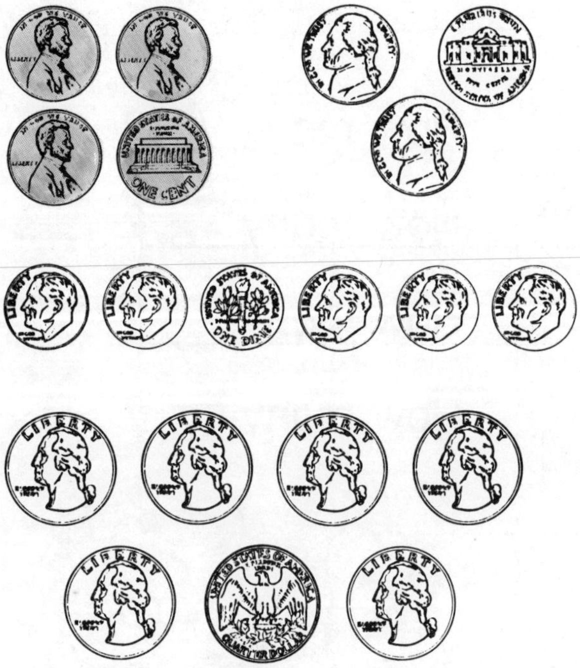

How many pennies? 4

How many nickels? ____

How many dimes? ____

How many quarters? ____

Color a ▭ for each coin.

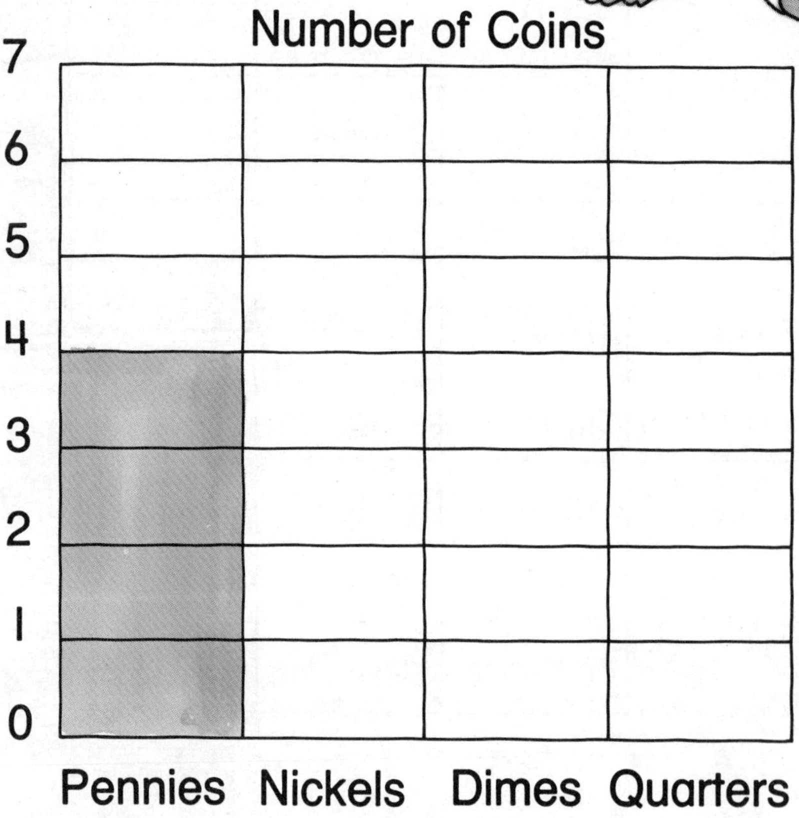

Number of Coins

7
6
5
4
3
2
1
0

Pennies Nickels Dimes Quarters

Name ______________________________

Use the graph to answer the questions.

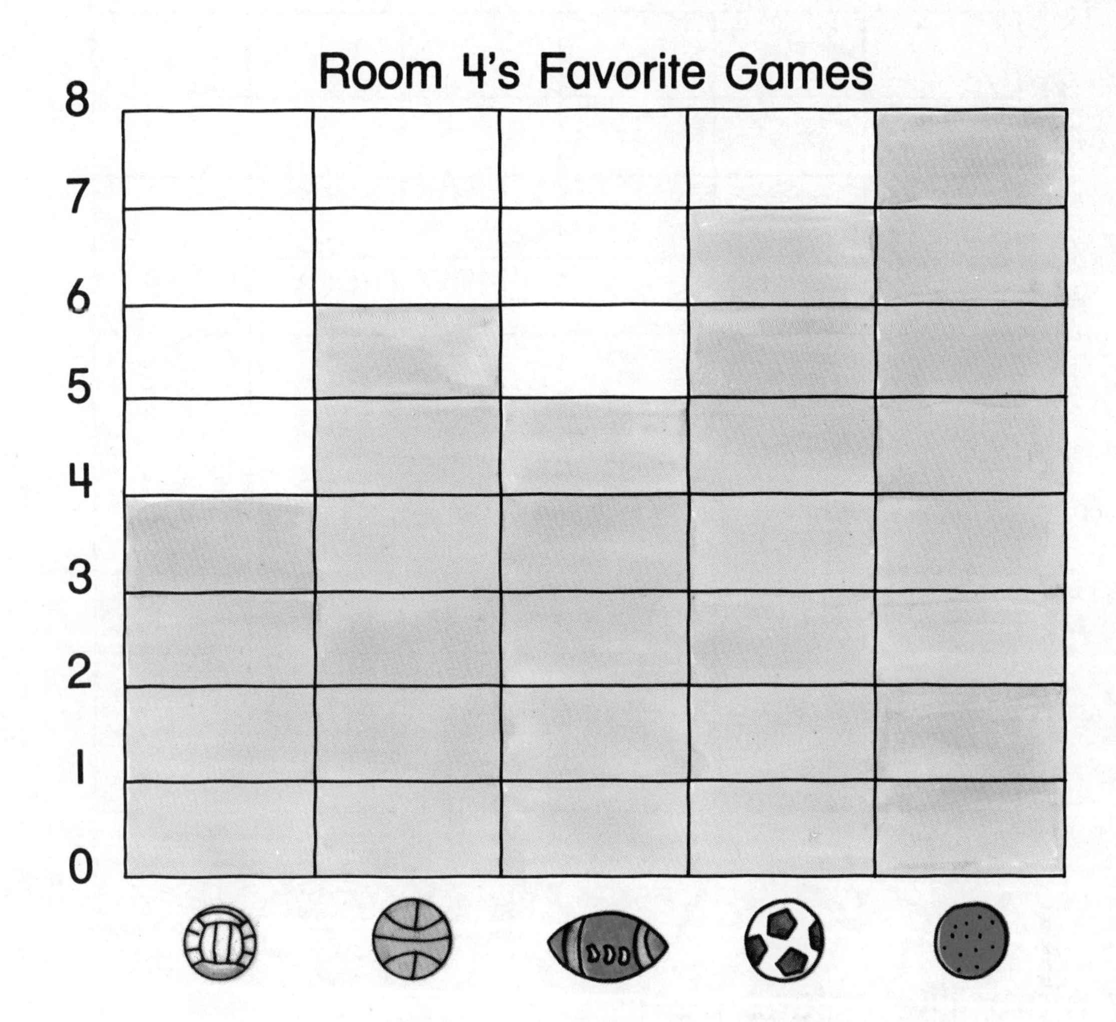

How many children like volleyball? 4

How many children like basketball? ____

How many children like football? ____

How many children like soccer? ____

How many children like kickball? ____

How many children are in Room 4? ____

Use the graph to answer the questions.

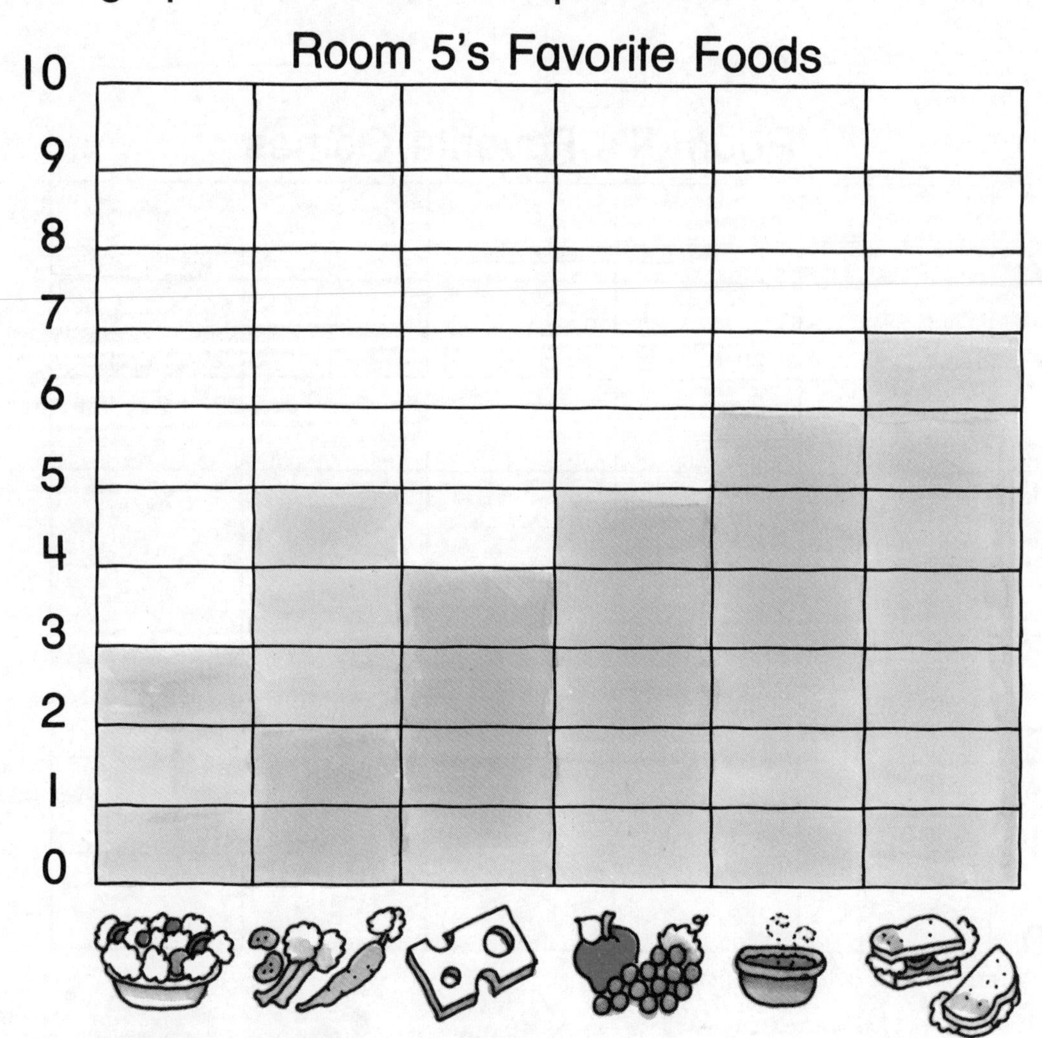

How many like salads best? ____

How many like vegetables best? ____

How many like cheese best? ____

How many like fruit best? ____

How many like soup best? ____

How many like sandwiches best? ____

How many children are in room 5? ____

Name ____________________

CHAPTER CHECKUP

Circle the correct fraction.

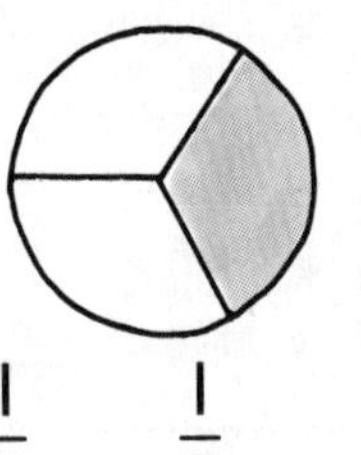

$\frac{1}{2}$ $\frac{1}{3}$ $\frac{1}{4}$

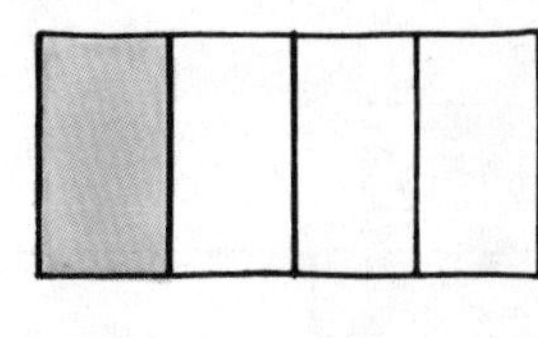

$\frac{1}{2}$ $\frac{1}{3}$ $\frac{1}{4}$

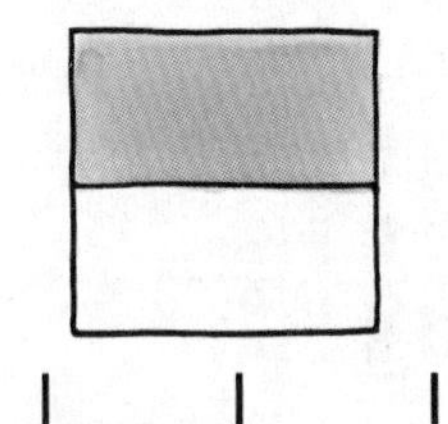

$\frac{1}{2}$ $\frac{1}{3}$ $\frac{1}{4}$

Color $\frac{1}{4}$.

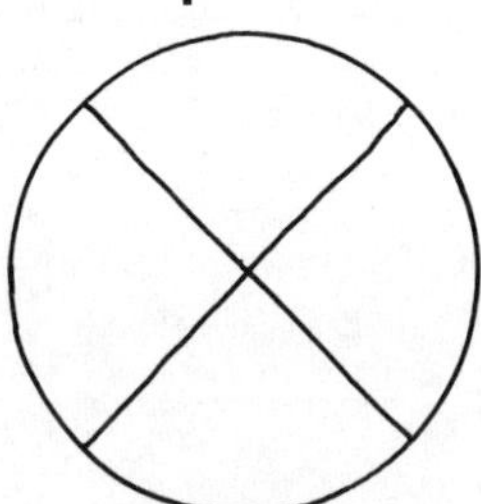

Color $\frac{1}{2}$.

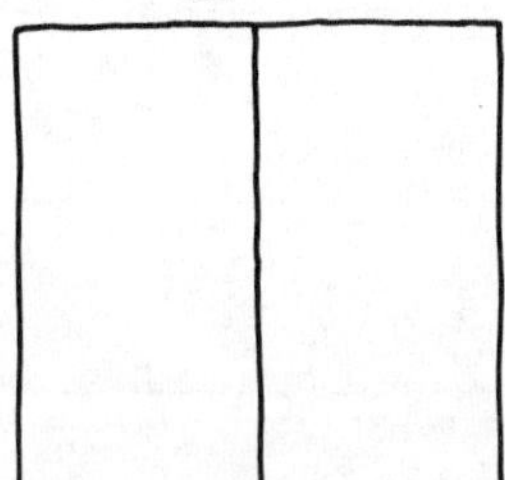

Color $\frac{1}{3}$.

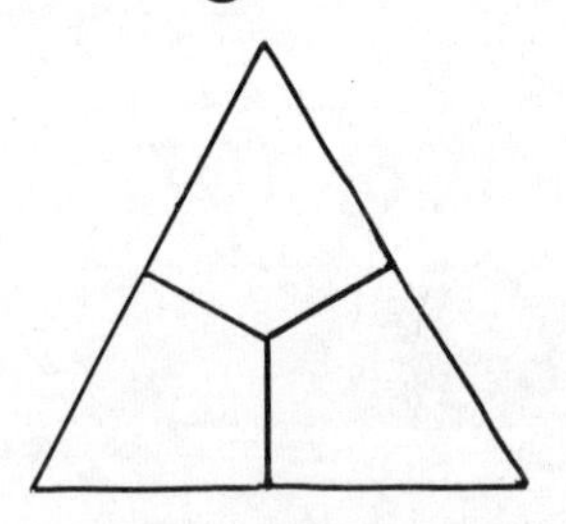

Use the graph to answer the questions.

Our Pets

7
6
5
4
3
2
1
0

How many children have a bird? ____

How many children have a dog? ____

How many children have a rabbit? ____

How many children have a cat? ____

How many children have pets? ____

ROUNDUP REVIEW

How many?

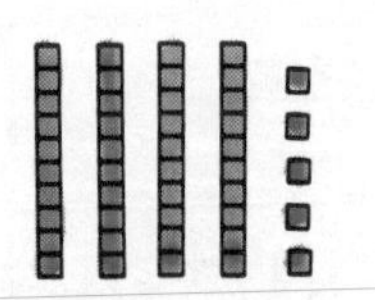 ____

 ____

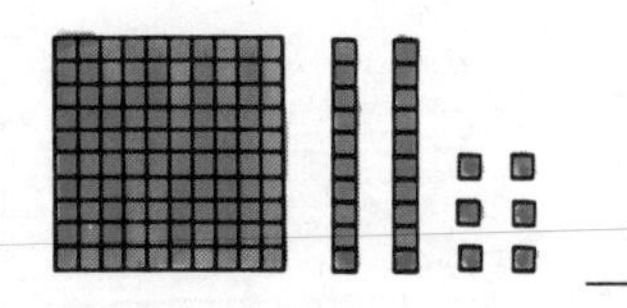 ____

Write the missing numbers.

74, 75, 76, ____, ____, ____, ____, ____, ____

105, 106, 107, ____, ____, ____, ____, ____

70, 80, ____, ____, ____, ____, ____, ____

80, 85, 90, ____, ____, ____, ____, ____, ____

Subtract.

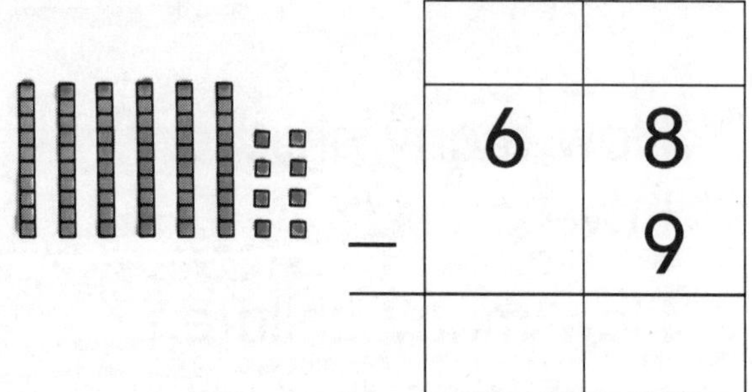

	tens	ones
	6	8
−		9

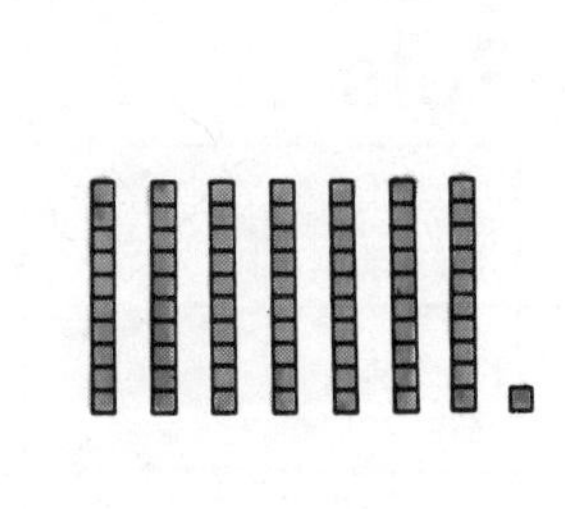

	tens	ones
	7	1
−		5

Add.

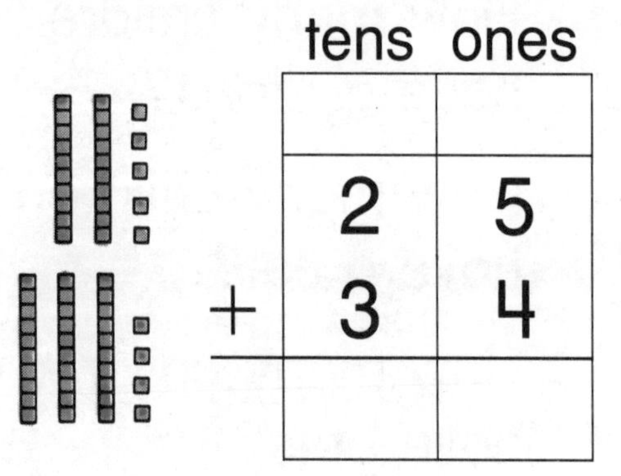

	tens	ones
	2	5
+	3	4

	tens	ones
	4	8
+	2	7

Name ______________________

Add.

2	6	1	5	3	1	7	4	7	0
+8	+0	+2	+1	+2	+9	+2	+1	+3	+7
1	3	4	0	3	5	0	9	1	0
+4	+3	+3	+9	+5	+5	+1	+1	+6	+5
6	4	3	1	9	2	6	3	0	5
+4	+5	+4	+3	+0	+0	+2	+6	+0	+0
4	2	0	5	2	0	2	0	6	0
+0	+3	+2	+3	+5	+4	+1	+3	+1	+6
7	4	7	3	3	5	8	2	1	5
+0	+2	+1	+0	+7	+2	+1	+6	+0	+4
1	4	2	2	0	1	8	4	6	1
+8	+4	+2	+7	+8	+1	+0	+6	+3	+7
3	6	2	7	8	1	8	3	8	3
+1	+5	+4	+7	+2	+5	+4	+8	+6	+9
8	9	5	8	9	7	4	7	9	4
+3	+4	+6	+8	+5	+4	+8	+6	+3	+7
9	5	9	7	6	8	2	6	7	4
+7	+8	+2	+5	+9	+5	+9	+6	+8	+9
6	5	9	7	9	8	5	9	8	6
+8	+7	+8	+9	+9	+7	+9	+6	+9	+7

Subtract.

$4 - 0$ $9 - 3$ $10 - 2$ $4 - 1$ $5 - 5$ $10 - 1$ $8 - 5$ $10 - 6$ $3 - 3$ $10 - 7$

$4 - 3$ $9 - 1$ $6 - 5$ $7 - 7$ $9 - 5$ $9 - 4$ $0 - 0$ $9 - 6$ $7 - 0$ $7 - 5$

$2 - 0$ $5 - 4$ $8 - 8$ $9 - 2$ $5 - 3$ $6 - 0$ $7 - 6$ $3 - 1$ $1 - 1$ $7 - 3$

$10 - 9$ $9 - 0$ $10 - 4$ $4 - 2$ $5 - 1$ $10 - 8$ $3 - 0$ $6 - 3$ $9 - 7$ $10 - 3$

$8 - 7$ $5 - 0$ $3 - 2$ $7 - 1$ $8 - 4$ $9 - 8$ $7 - 4$ $8 - 1$ $1 - 0$ $7 - 2$

$6 - 1$ $8 - 0$ $5 - 2$ $6 - 4$ $8 - 2$ $4 - 4$ $8 - 6$ $6 - 2$ $2 - 1$ $6 - 6$

$8 - 3$ $2 - 2$ $10 - 5$ $9 - 9$ $15 - 6$ $11 - 5$ $12 - 3$ $13 - 7$ $11 - 2$ $12 - 6$

$11 - 4$ $13 - 5$ $11 - 6$ $14 - 7$ $15 - 9$ $13 - 6$ $12 - 8$ $16 - 9$ $11 - 8$ $12 - 7$

$13 - 9$ $12 - 5$ $13 - 4$ $11 - 9$ $12 - 4$ $14 - 5$ $11 - 7$ $16 - 8$ $15 - 8$ $14 - 8$

$16 - 7$ $17 - 9$ $13 - 8$ $18 - 9$ $14 - 6$ $17 - 8$ $12 - 9$ $11 - 3$ $14 - 9$ $15 - 7$

Name ______________________________

ALTERNATE CHAPTER 1 CHECKUP

Match the stars to their numbers.

7

4

5

2

6

10

8

9

Name ______________________________

ALTERNATE CHAPTER 2 CHECKUP

Add.

$5 + 5 =$ ___ $1 + 3 =$ ___ $6 + 3 =$ ___

$2 + 4 =$ ___ $3 + 3 =$ ___ $7 + 2 =$ ___

$1 + 6 =$ ___ $4 + 4 =$ ___ $3 + 7 =$ ___

6	2	4	3	1	2
+4	+8	+1	+5	+7	+3

Solve.

Have 6¢. Add 2¢ more.

6 ¢ + 2 ¢ = ___ ¢

5 ¢
+4 ¢
¢

Add.

5	1	7	4
3	2	1	2
+2	+4	+2	+3

Name ____________________

ALTERNATE CHAPTER 3 CHECKUP

Subtract.

$6 - 4 =$ ___	$8 - 2 =$ ___	$4 - 1 =$ ___	$5 - 3 =$ ___	$7 - 1 =$ ___	$3 - 2 =$ ___
$8 - 5 =$ ___	$10 - 5 =$ ___	$9 - 3 =$ ___	$5 - 2 =$ ___	$10 - 9 =$ ___	$8 - 4 =$ ___
$7 - 4 =$ ___	$9 - 8 =$ ___	$4 - 4 =$ ___	$7 - 3 =$ ___	$10 - 1 =$ ___	$9 - 2 =$ ___
$9 - 5 =$ ___	$10 - 7 =$ ___	$7 - 5 =$ ___	$5 - 0 =$ ___	$9 - 4 =$ ___	$8 - 6 =$ ___

Solve.

7¢
−3¢
___¢

Spent 3¢.

8¢
−5¢
___¢

Spent 5¢.

Name ____________________

ALTERNATE CHAPTER 4 CHECKUP

Add or subtract.

$\begin{array}{r} 3 \\ +6 \\ \hline \end{array}$ $\begin{array}{r} 8 \\ -2 \\ \hline \end{array}$ $\begin{array}{r} 4 \\ +1 \\ \hline \end{array}$ $\begin{array}{r} 5 \\ +3 \\ \hline \end{array}$ $\begin{array}{r} 7 \\ -1 \\ \hline \end{array}$ $\begin{array}{r} 4 \\ +4 \\ \hline \end{array}$

$\begin{array}{r} 9 \\ -3 \\ \hline \end{array}$ $\begin{array}{r} 6 \\ +2 \\ \hline \end{array}$ $\begin{array}{r} 10 \\ -\ 5 \\ \hline \end{array}$ $\begin{array}{r} 10 \\ -\ 8 \\ \hline \end{array}$ $\begin{array}{r} 1 \\ +9 \\ \hline \end{array}$ $\begin{array}{r} 8 \\ +1 \\ \hline \end{array}$

$\begin{array}{r} 5 \\ +4 \\ \hline \end{array}$ $\begin{array}{r} 9 \\ -8 \\ \hline \end{array}$ $\begin{array}{r} 3 \\ +7 \\ \hline \end{array}$ $\begin{array}{r} 7 \\ -3 \\ \hline \end{array}$ $\begin{array}{r} 2 \\ +8 \\ \hline \end{array}$ $\begin{array}{r} 9 \\ -2 \\ \hline \end{array}$

Solve.

How much did both cost?

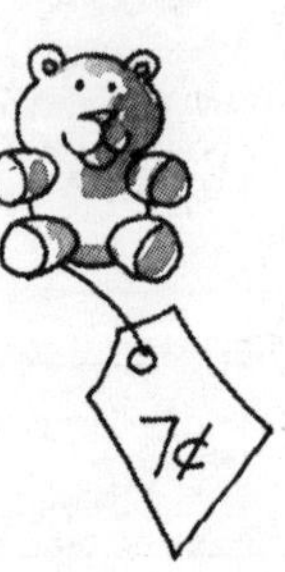
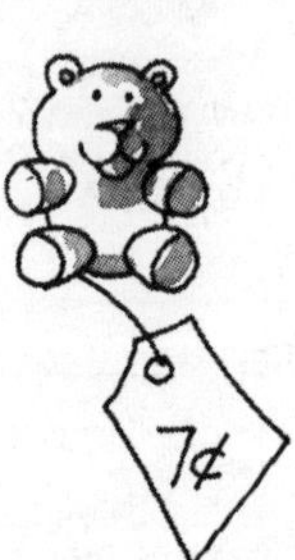

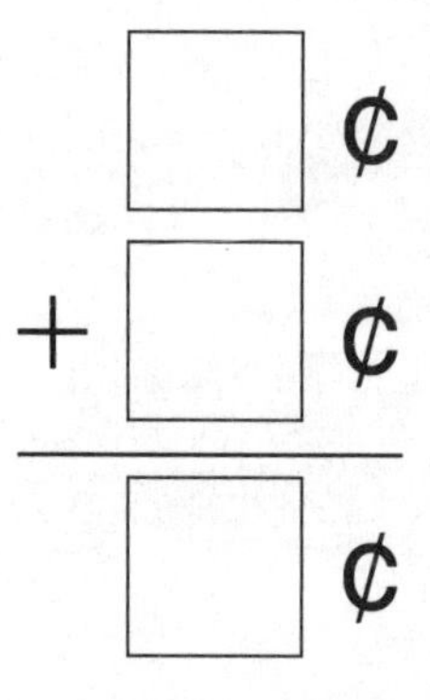

____¢

How much money was left?

Bought

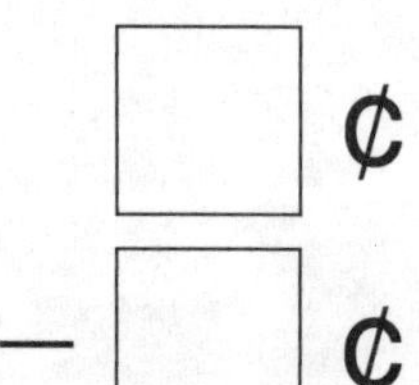
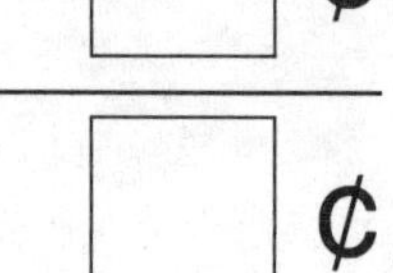

____¢

Name ____________________

ALTERNATE CHAPTER 5 CHECKUP

How many?

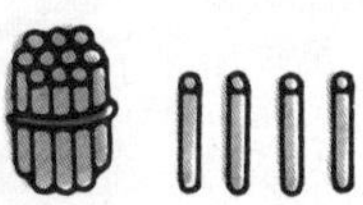

___ tens ___ ones

___

Match.

16	nineteen
11	sixteen
19	fourteen
14	eleven

How many?

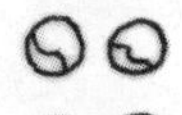

___ tens

___

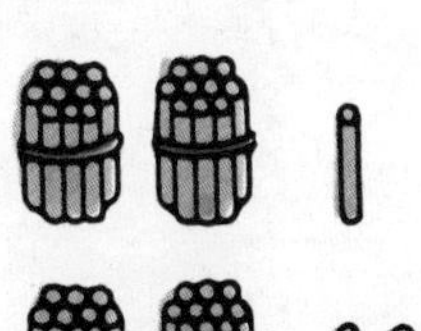

___ tens ___ ones

___

Write the missing numbers.

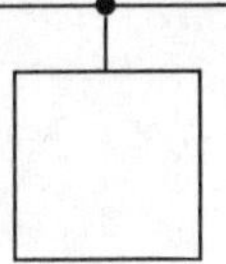
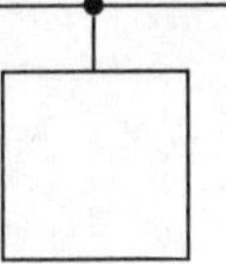
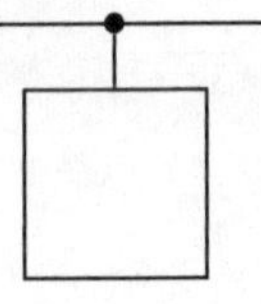
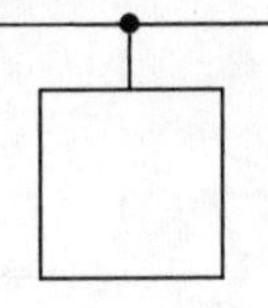
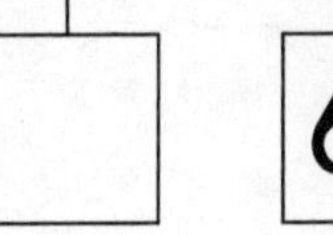

54	55					60	

How much money?

___ dimes

___¢

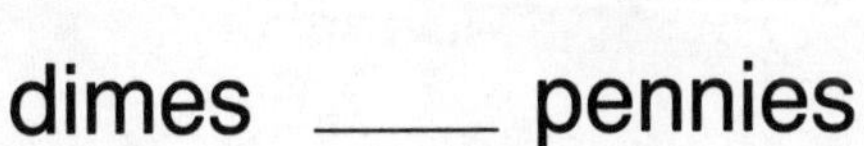

___ dimes ___ pennies

___¢

Circle the greater.

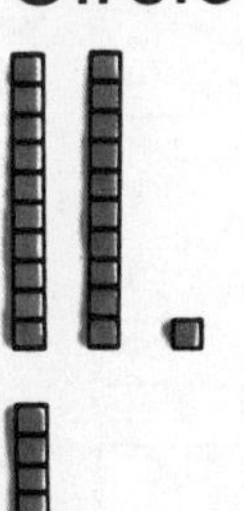

21

12

Circle the third dog.

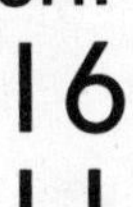

Name ____________________

ALTERNATE CHAPTER 6 CHECKUP

Add.

$\begin{array}{r} 9 \\ +9 \\ \hline \end{array}$ $\begin{array}{r} 8 \\ +6 \\ \hline \end{array}$ $\begin{array}{r} 6 \\ +7 \\ \hline \end{array}$ $\begin{array}{r} 9 \\ +4 \\ \hline \end{array}$ $\begin{array}{r} 7 \\ +8 \\ \hline \end{array}$ $\begin{array}{r} 6 \\ +6 \\ \hline \end{array}$ $\begin{array}{r} 9 \\ +3 \\ \hline \end{array}$

$\begin{array}{r} 5 \\ +8 \\ \hline \end{array}$ $\begin{array}{r} 9 \\ +6 \\ \hline \end{array}$ $\begin{array}{r} 7 \\ +7 \\ \hline \end{array}$ $\begin{array}{r} 5 \\ +9 \\ \hline \end{array}$ $\begin{array}{r} 8 \\ +4 \\ \hline \end{array}$ $\begin{array}{r} 9 \\ +2 \\ \hline \end{array}$ $\begin{array}{r} 8 \\ +8 \\ \hline \end{array}$

$4 + 9 =$ ___ $6 + 8 =$ ___ $9 + 5 =$ ___

$8 + 3 =$ ___ $2 + 9 =$ ___ $7 + 6 =$ ___

$9 + 7 =$ ___ $7 + 5 =$ ___ $8 + 7 =$ ___

$5 + 6 =$ ___ $9 + 8 =$ ___ $5 + 7 =$ ___

$6 + 9 =$ ___ $3 + 9 =$ ___ $4 + 8 =$ ___

$8 + 5 =$ ___ $4 + 7 =$ ___ $6 + 5 =$ ___

How much?

☐ ¢
+ ☐ ¢
___ ¢

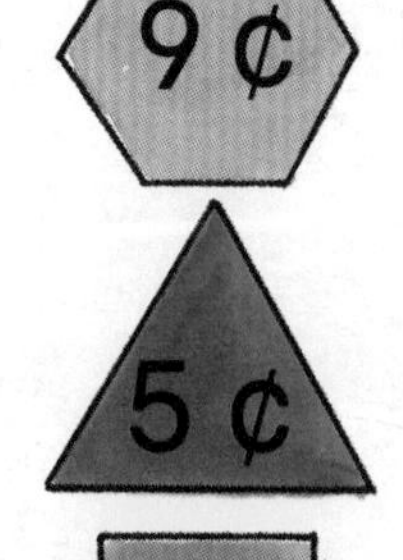

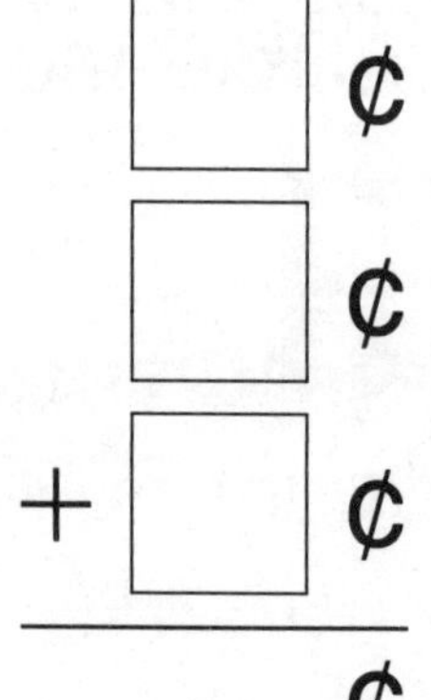

Name ____________________

ALTERNATE CHAPTER 7 CHECKUP

Subtract.

$18 - 9 =$ ____	$13 - 8 =$ ____	$14 - 6 =$ ____
$15 - 3 =$ ____	$18 - 4 =$ ____	$15 - 7 =$ ____
$14 - 5 =$ ____	$17 - 8 =$ ____	$18 - 5 =$ ____
$17 - 6 =$ ____	$12 - 7 =$ ____	$13 - 9 =$ ____
$16 - 7 =$ ____	$16 - 2 =$ ____	$12 - 4 =$ ____

$\begin{array}{r} 16 \\ -\ 9 \\ \hline \end{array}$ $\begin{array}{r} 14 \\ -\ 8 \\ \hline \end{array}$ $\begin{array}{r} 12 \\ -\ 3 \\ \hline \end{array}$ $\begin{array}{r} 18 \\ -\ 7 \\ \hline \end{array}$ $\begin{array}{r} 13 \\ -\ 6 \\ \hline \end{array}$ $\begin{array}{r} 15 \\ -\ 8 \\ \hline \end{array}$

$\begin{array}{r} 17 \\ -\ 5 \\ \hline \end{array}$ $\begin{array}{r} 13 \\ -\ 4 \\ \hline \end{array}$ $\begin{array}{r} 15 \\ -\ 6 \\ \hline \end{array}$ $\begin{array}{r} 12 \\ -\ 8 \\ \hline \end{array}$ $\begin{array}{r} 14 \\ -\ 9 \\ \hline \end{array}$ $\begin{array}{r} 16 \\ -\ 4 \\ \hline \end{array}$

Solve.

Mary had 17¢.
She bought a toy car for 9¢.
How much does Mary have left?

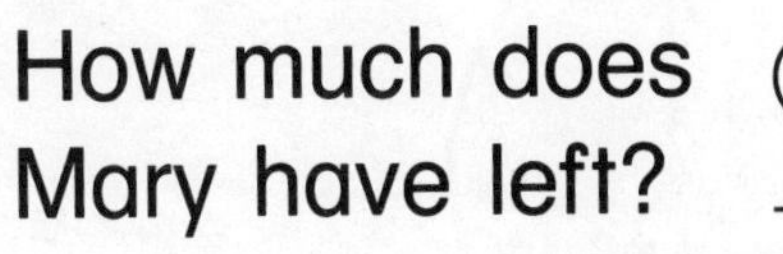

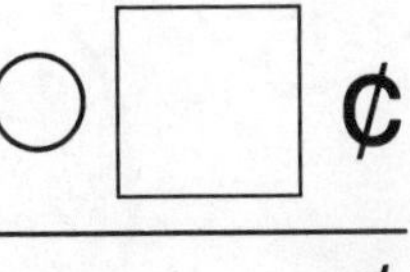

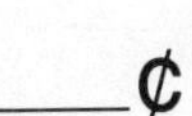

____¢

Jason had 15 fish.
He gave Juan 4 fish. How many fish does Jason have now?

____ fish

Name ______________________________

ALTERNATE CHAPTER 8 CHECKUP

Count the money.

____ ¢

____ ¢

____ ¢

____ ¢

Check the coins you need to buy the glove.

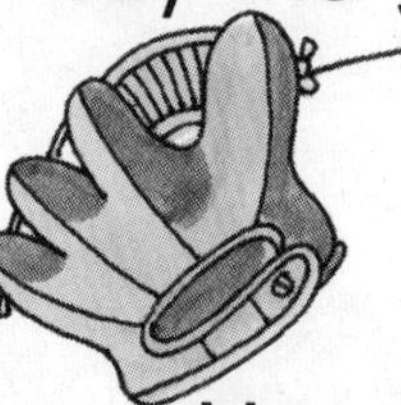

How much is left? ____ ¢

Check the coins you need to buy the toy boat.

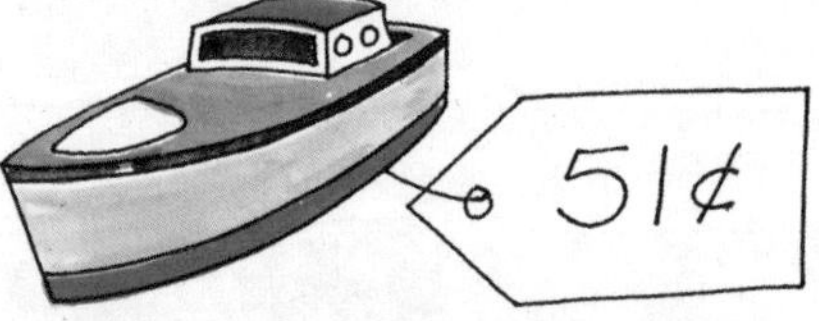

How much is left? ____ ¢

Write the times.

____

____

Name ______________________

ALTERNATE CHAPTER 9 CHECKUP

Add or subtract.

9 +9	14 − 5	6 +7	16 − 9	7 +8	6 +3	12 − 5
9 +6	17 − 8	13 − 7	5 +9	18 − 6	15 − 7	8 +8
8 +6	12 − 9	14 − 6	9 +4	7 +7	16 − 7	4 +5
3 +9	13 − 4	8 +5	8 −2	15 − 6	8 +4	11 − 3

Solve.

Julia had 18¢. She bought a 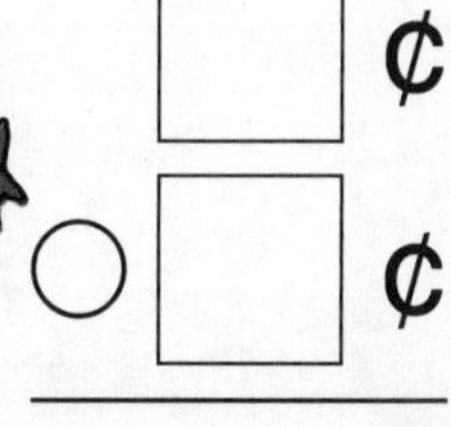 for 6¢. How much was left?

☐ ¢
○ ☐ ¢
____ ¢

____ ¢

Stan ran 9 blocks. Then he ran 4 more. How many blocks did he run in all?

☐
○ ☐
____

____ blocks

Name ______________________________

ALTERNATE CHAPTER 10 CHECKUP

How many?

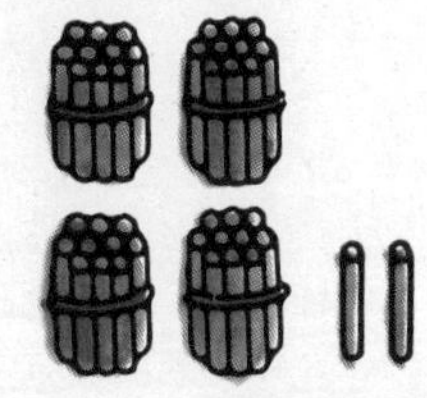

____ tens ____ ones

____

7 tens 3 ones ____

forty-four ____

58 is ____ tens ____ ones.

Write the missing numbers.

48, 49, ____, ____, ____, ____, ____, ____, ____, 57

65, 66, ____, ____, ____, ____, ____

Add.

$$\begin{array}{r} 7 \\ +9 \\ \hline \end{array} \quad \begin{array}{r} 4 \\ +6 \\ \hline \end{array} \quad \begin{array}{r} 5 \\ +7 \\ \hline \end{array} \quad \begin{array}{r} 9 \\ +4 \\ \hline \end{array} \quad \begin{array}{r} 7 \\ +8 \\ \hline \end{array} \quad \begin{array}{r} 5 \\ +6 \\ \hline \end{array} \quad \begin{array}{r} 3 \\ +9 \\ \hline \end{array}$$

Add.

	tens	ones
	4	5
+		4

	tens	ones
	5	7
+		7

	10¢	1¢	
	6	2	¢
+		9	¢
			¢

Name ____________________

ALTERNATE CHAPTER 11 CHECKUP

Trade if needed. Subtract.

	tens	ones
	3	7
−		6

	tens	ones
	2̸	1̸
−		8

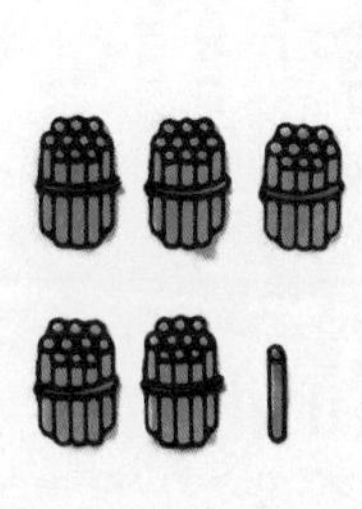

	tens	ones
	4̸	3̸
−		5

	tens	ones
	5̸	1̸
−		8

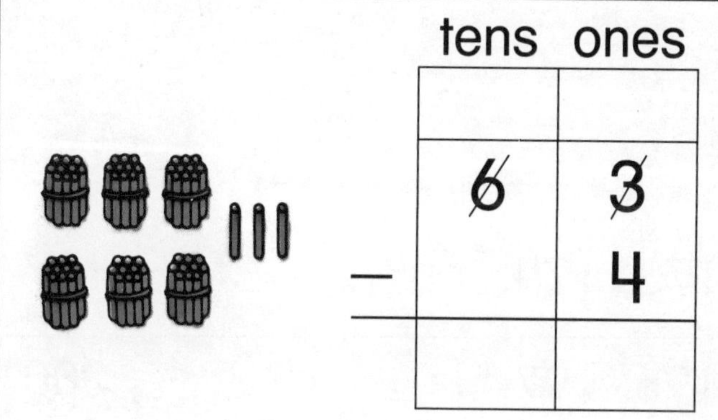

	tens	ones
	6̸	3̸
−		4

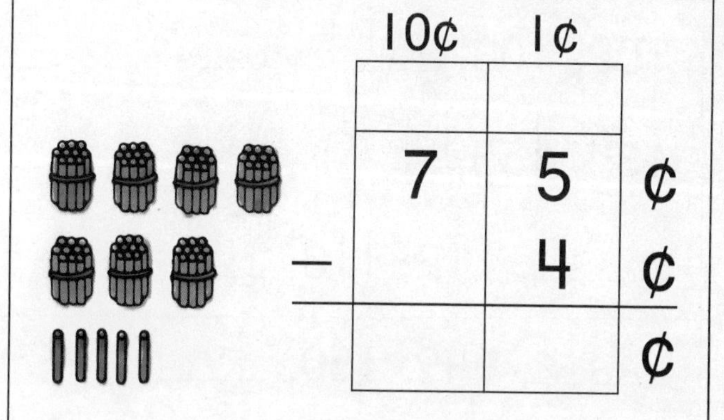

	10¢	1¢	
	7	5	¢
−		4	¢
			¢

Solve.

Flo had 74¢.
She bought a 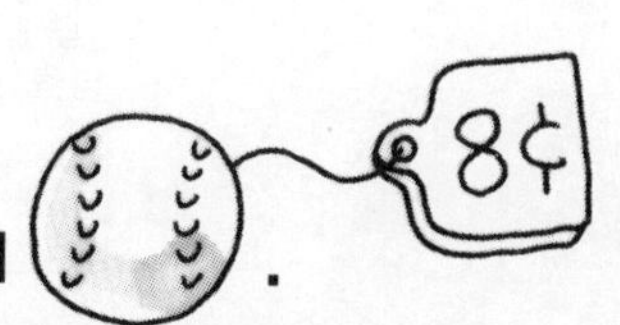.

How much does she have left? ____ ¢

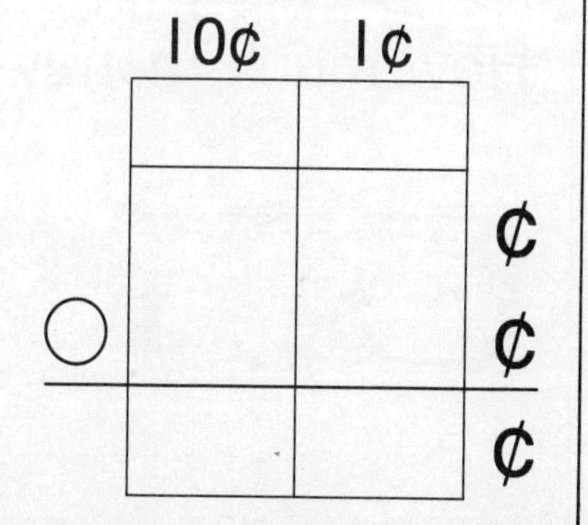

	10¢	1¢	
			¢
○			¢
			¢

Name ______________________________

ALTERNATE CHAPTER 12 CHECKUP

How many?

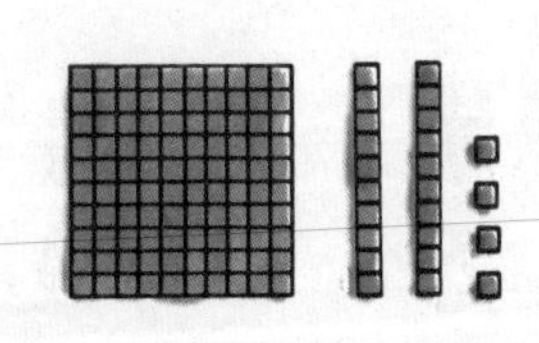

hundreds	tens	ones

_____

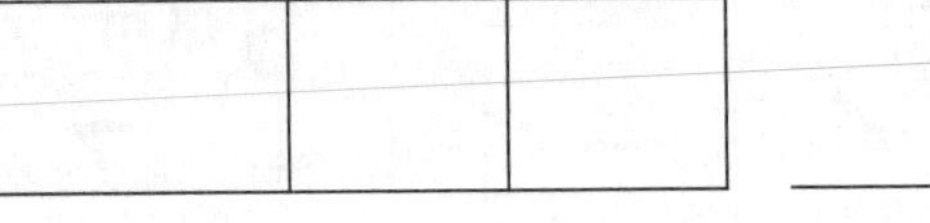

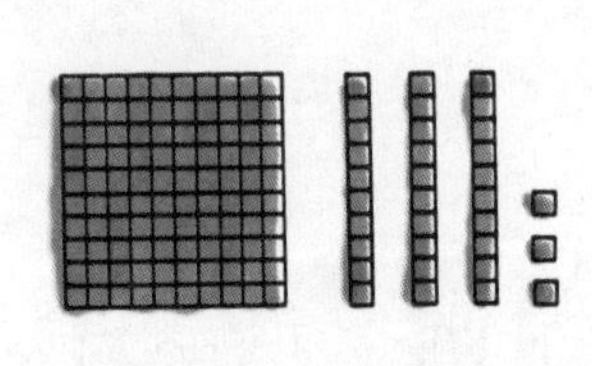

hundreds	tens	ones

_____

Write the missing numbers.

77, 78, 79, _____, _____, _____, _____, _____

102, 103, 104, _____, _____, _____, _____, _____

154, 155, 156, _____, _____, _____, _____, _____

_____, 112, 113, _____ 173, 174, _____, _____, 177

_____, 149, 150, _____ 196, 197, _____, _____, 200

How much money?

	$1.00	10¢	1¢
$			

$ ____.____

Name ____________________

ALTERNATE CHAPTER 13 CHECKUP

Add.

	tens	ones
	2	2
+		9

$$\begin{array}{r} 45 \\ +\ \ 7 \\ \hline \end{array} \qquad \begin{array}{r} 38 \\ +\ \ 6 \\ \hline \end{array} \qquad \begin{array}{r} 30¢ \\ +40¢ \\ \hline ¢ \end{array} \qquad \begin{array}{r} 60 \\ +20 \\ \hline \end{array}$$

	tens	ones
	4	8
+	2	9

$$\begin{array}{r} 31 \\ +39 \\ \hline \end{array} \qquad \begin{array}{r} 77 \\ +16 \\ \hline \end{array} \qquad \begin{array}{r} 26 \\ +48 \\ \hline \end{array} \qquad \begin{array}{r} 54¢ \\ +29¢ \\ \hline ¢ \end{array}$$

$$\begin{array}{r} 88 \\ +19 \\ \hline \end{array} \qquad \begin{array}{r} 92 \\ +16 \\ \hline \end{array} \qquad \begin{array}{r} 35¢ \\ +76¢ \\ \hline ¢ \end{array} \qquad \begin{array}{r} 47 \\ +46 \\ \hline \end{array} \qquad \begin{array}{r} 51 \\ 24 \\ +66 \\ \hline \end{array} \qquad \begin{array}{r} 27 \\ 73 \\ +42 \\ \hline \end{array}$$

Solve.

Justin counted the pets in his neighborhood:
33 cats, 41 dogs and 12 hamsters.
How many in all?

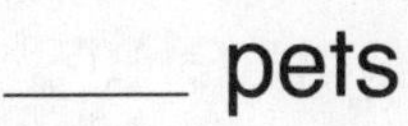

____ pets

Name ________________________________

ALTERNATE CHAPTER 14 CHECKUP

Match the shape to its name.

rectangle

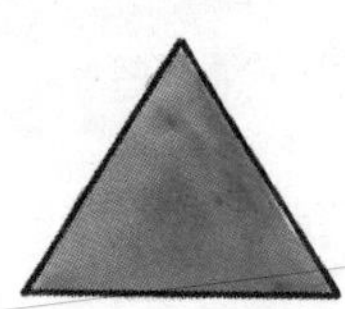

square

circle

triangle

Use an inch ruler to find the length.

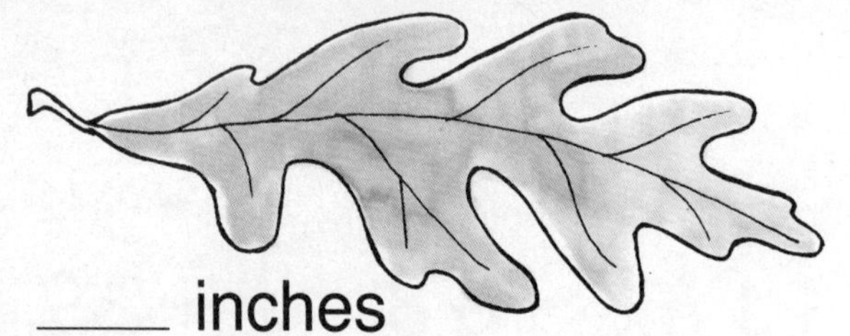

____ inches

____ inches

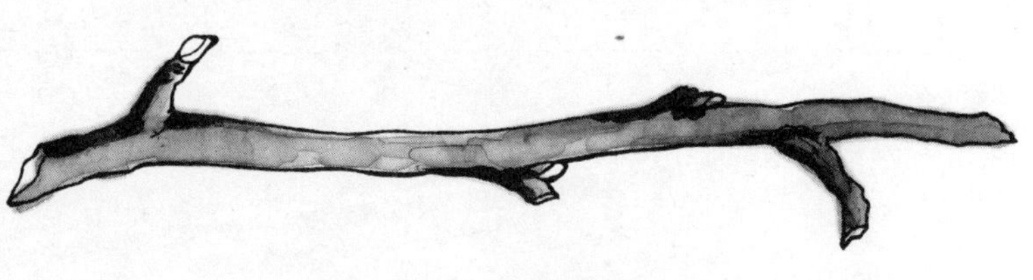

____ inches

____ inches

Use a centimeter ruler to find the length.

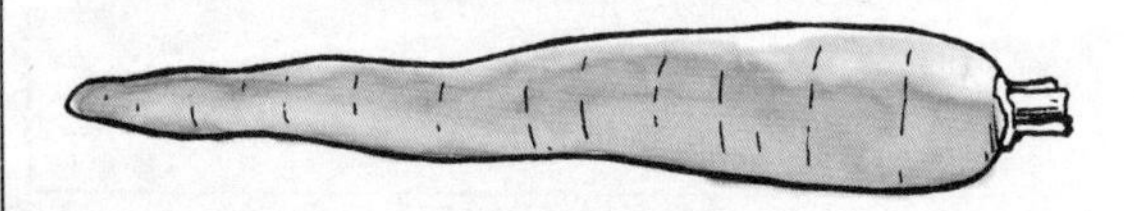

____ centimeters

____ centimeters

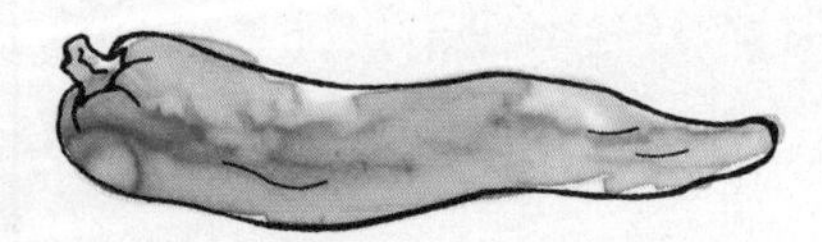

____ centimeters

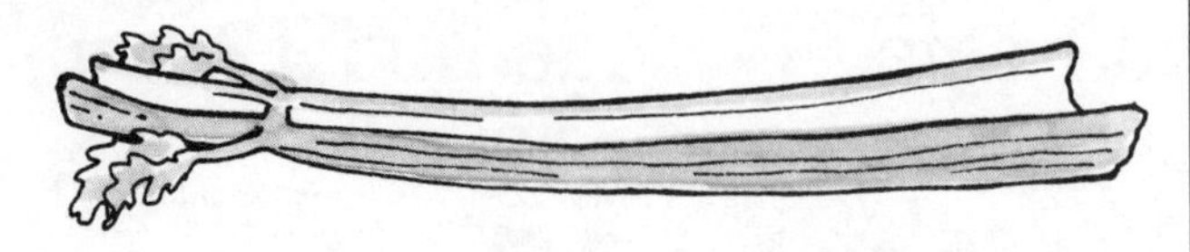

____ centimeters

Name

ALTERNATE CHAPTER 15 CHECKUP

Circle the correct fraction.

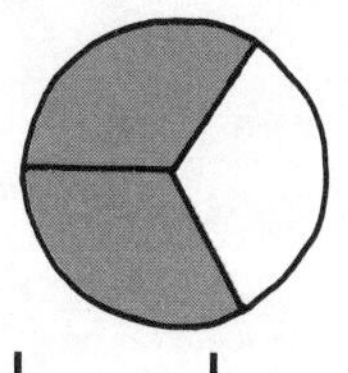

$\frac{1}{2}$ $\frac{1}{4}$ $\frac{2}{3}$

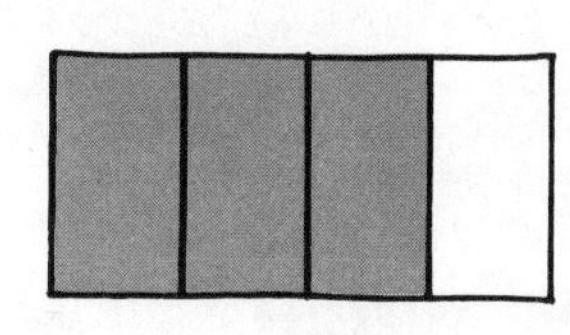

$\frac{1}{3}$ $\frac{3}{4}$ $\frac{3}{5}$

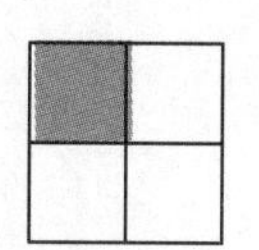

$\frac{1}{2}$ $\frac{1}{3}$ $\frac{1}{4}$

Color $\frac{3}{4}$.

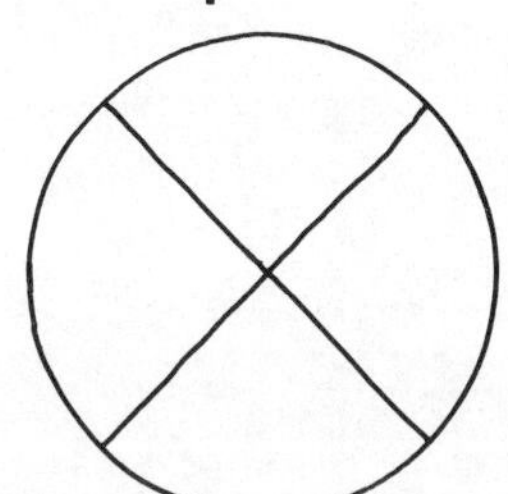

Color $\frac{1}{2}$.

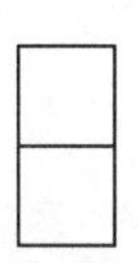

Color $\frac{2}{3}$.

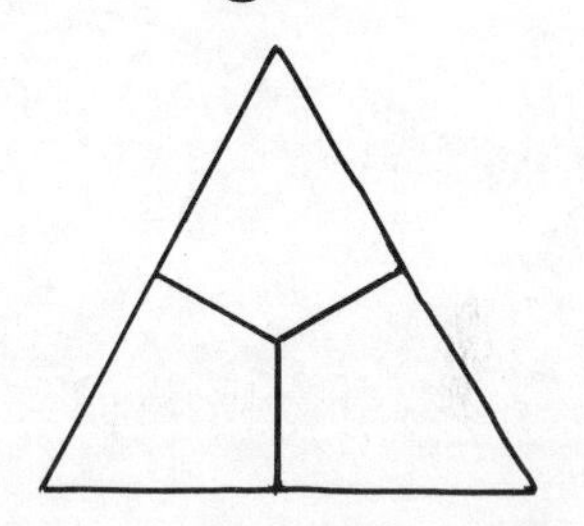

Use the graph to answer the questions.

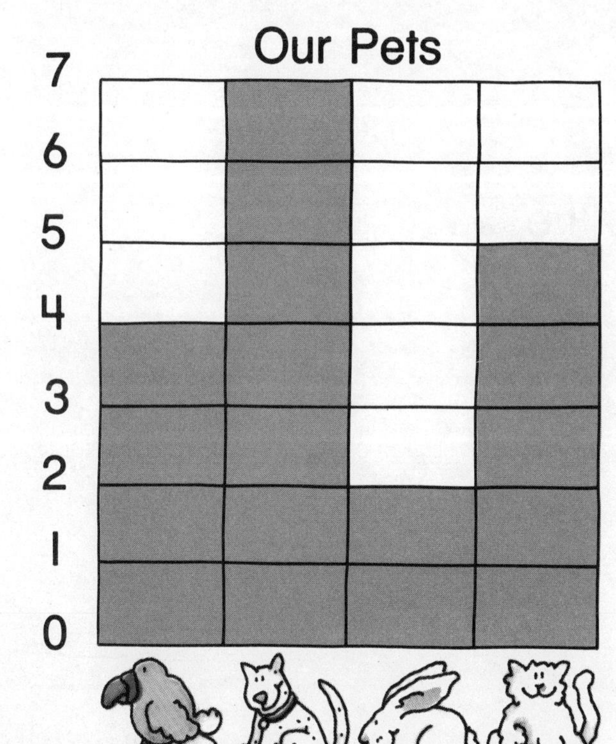

How many children have a bird? ____

How many children have a dog? ____

How many children have a rabbit? ____

How many children have a cat? ____

How many children have pets? ____